'BLEEDING HEART

STORY BY: HARRY HECKEL

ART BY: BRIAN LEBLANC

GABRIELLE?! NO! I DIDN'T MEAN . . .

CONALL? MY OWN ONE?

GABRIELLE . . . NO!!

SHE'S DEAD. BEING KINFOLK DIDN'T SAVE HER FROM MY CLAWS. THIS HAS TO END.

I KNOW WHAT I NEED TO DO. I'VE GOT TO STOP THEM.

THERE'S A LOT OF LOYALIST KINFOLK THERE TONIGHT. THEY'RE PLANNING SOMETHING.

GOOD. THEY WON'T BE DOING ANYTHING MUCH LONGER. REMEMBER THE MOTTO: TWO EYES FOR AN EYE.

AYE. DO YOU WANT TO WAIT FOR CONALL?

YOU DON'T HAVE TO WAIT, BRIGIT . .

. . ALTHOUGH YOU MIGHT WISH YOU HADN'T.

WHY NOT? WE ALLOW BLOODSHED BETWEEN TRIBEMATES EVERY NIGHT.

ARE YOU FEY-STRUCK? THEY'RE NOT REAL FIANNA! NEITHER ARE THEIR KIN.

WE'RE MURDERERS, EAMON, JUST LIKE THEY ARE. WE CAN'T KEEP FIGHTING FOREVER. THEY DON'T BLEED ORANGE, AND WE DON'T BLEED GREEN. ALL THE DAMN BLOOD'S RED . . .

WE HAVE THE COURAGE TO FIGHT, BUT DO WE HAVE THE COURAGE TO STOP? YOU'RE NOT BREAKING THE PEACE UNLESS YOU'RE STARTING WITH ME.

FINE, CONALL. WE WON'T ATTACK TONIGHT.

EVERYONE HEAR THAT? CLEAR OUT, AND GET BACK TO THE CAERN.

THE END

Fire in the Head and Heart

By Harry Heckel

Credits

Written by: Harry Heckel

Additional material and research by: Fallon Doherty, John "Mad Sweeny" Bridges

Developed by: Bill Bridges

Editing: Heather Bryden

Art Director: Richard Thomas

Comic book art: Brian LeBlanc

Art: Tony Diterlizzi, Richard Kane Ferguson

Front and Back Cover: Aileen E. Miles

Back Cover Art: Joshua Gabriel Timbrook

Special Thanks

Richard "Lost in time" Thomas for being obsessed with Doctor Eon.

Joshua "Pharoah's scepter" Gabriel Timbrook for what his mummy Halloween costume was missing.

Chris "Pitt-iful" McDonough for thinking Tom Cruise outdid Brad Pitt.

Rob "Santiago" Dixon for seconding Chris's sorry opinion.

Aileen "Armand" Miles for defending Louis.

Kathy "Grand Inquisitor" Ryan for asking too many questions for the '95 calendar.

Larry "Aaarg!" Snelly for having too many words in his pictures.

Michelle "Heavy Metal" Prahler for letting us trash her apartment — party down, dudes!

735 PARK NORTH BLVD.
SUITE 128
CLARKSTON, GA 30021
USA

WHITE WOLF
GAME STUDIO

Thanks and Dedication

Special thanks to Heather Curatola, Alan Fisher, Robert Kaminsky, everyone at Dream Wizards, the First Pack of RhyDin, and Gray

Dedicated to Daniel Greenberg for getting me started, and my father for everything.

Contents

Introduction: Slainte!   **12**

Chapter One: The Song of Our Tribe   **14**

The history of the Fianna

Chapter Two: The Ways of Our People   **28**

The culture of the Fianna

Chapter Three: Across the Waters   **40**

The Fianna around the world

Appendix One: Powers   **46**

New Gifts, rites, fetishes, and totems

Appendix Two: Lads & Lasses   **54**

Five ready-to-play characters

Appendix Three: The Dreamers   **65**

Famous Fianna of the past and present

Introduction: Slainte!

'Frail crescent Moon, seven times I bow my head,
Since of the night you are the mystic queen:
May your sweet influence in her dews be shed!'
So ran by heart the rune in secret said:
Relic of heathen forebears centuries dead?
Or just a child's, in play with the Unseen?
— Walter de la Mare, "Benighted"

Greetings and welcome!

Sit your arse down here and relax. Get a drink if you'd like. I've got a long story to tell you. It's the story of our tribe, the epic of the Fianna. But before I begin, I want you to do something. Close your eyes and listen. Listen carefully.

What do you hear? Silence?

If that's all, then you aren't listening. There's always something to hear, if you young cubs would stop talking long enough to listen for it. That's what my uncle used to tell me.

The damn rumble of traffic and the buzz of streetlights are the sounds of the Weaver. The background noise humans spend their lives ignoring… that's the Song of Gaia. The sounds of the land. The buzz of the insects, the soft burbling of water, these are the sounds of life, the sounds of Gaia. When the cold rhythms of the Weaver drown out the Song of Gaia, then you know the land's hurting.

Most Garou, even members of our tribe, don't understand our tribal name: Fianna. A few think it has to do with faerie,

but fewer still know that it was the name of the followers of Fionn mac Cumhail. You see, Fionn mac Cumhail, besides being a great hero and Kinfolk, was the protector of the land.

Now, the Irish Garou will tell you that's the whole story. They say our tribe exists to protect the Emerald Isle, and there you are. However, not all Fianna are Irish. We're more than the protectors of Erin. We're the guardians of Gaia. We take care of the lakes and streams. We watch over the ancient sites and the hollow hills. We not only protect the physical land, but the spirit of the world as well. That's why even the Brotherhood of Herne are Fianna.

Back to the tale I'll weave for you this evening… It's the story of our tribe, who we are and where we're going. But I'm only going to tell you part of it. The rest you'll have to discover for yourself. Our history is everywhere, even in the legends, moots and songs of all the other tribes. Half of their stories are just versions of ours. Don't worry, you'll have an uncle to help you sort it all out.

So, get a drink and listen well. All too soon this will be your story to tell…

Chapter One: The Song of Our Tribe

Time is a train
Makes the future the past
Leaves you standing in the station
Your face pressed up against the glass
— U2, "Zoo Station"

et's start with who you are and how you got here. They're really the same thing. If you know who you are, then you know how you got here. And if you know how you got here, then you know who you are. It's a matter of history and family. Any Garou — or human for that matter — who doesn't know her family or her history can never completely know herself. Since you're a Fianna, there's a lot of history behind you, and most of it you'll never know as well as you should. But don't get upset, that's just the way things are.

We keep the most complete histories of all the tribes. Some Fianna Galliards can take one look at you and recite your lineage back to the days of the Romans. Our Songkeepers know enough poems and stories to fill all the libraries in the world. Even the other tribes respect our knowledge. If the Silver Fangs have a question about breeding or lineage, they come to one of our caerns for an answer. We've resolved many disputes about bloodlines and past lives at Grand Moots, although not always for the best. The truth can hurt.

I'll start this off by letting you in on a secret: we aren't half as good as we say we are. I mean, how could we really remember as much as we say we do? Do you want to know how? Of course you do. I'll tell you: the songs are alive. That's right, they've transformed over the years of their own accord.

How's this? you ask. How can a song change on its own without the singer changing it? Because the singer don't create the song, the song creates itself, and a good singer knows that. The best singers know that they don't tell the stories, they find them. Aye, changing songs for the Changing Breed.

Surely you've heard many famous authors and poets say the same thing, that they don't write the story, it writes itself. That's Awen, the Muse. She's the one that doles out our inspiration and keeps the songs alive. Aye, there are some among us who say that songs are spirits, although these are the mad ones and don't get much listened to.

You see, all our stories about history and such, they're true. Truer than any facts you can find in some damn encyclopedia. That's 'cause our tales get to the core, the real truth behind the story. History is scraped away to reveal the truth beneath. History's an accident; truth is for real.

Oh, sure, our Galliards have been fighting for years over a few lines in a story, arguing over who's right and who's wrong. But it don't matter. It's the story that's right, and if you listen with your heart, you'll know when you hear it talking to you.

We're not the tellers of tales, we're their vessels, the mouths through which they are given life and form. This is our great secret and our strength.

For instance, you've heard of King Arthur and the Knights of the Round Table? Well, you won't find any two septs of Fianna who tell the story the same way. The knights' names are changed, the parts about which of Arthur's warriors were Kinfolk and which were Garou and which were mere humans are changed. The characters change from heroes to villains, and the entire story is almost completely different coming from every different Galliard. It's truly amazing.

Some Fianna tell the story that Arthur and his knights were members of the Brotherhood of Herne. You may have heard some bad things about the Brotherhood, and I may tell you a bit worse, but that's mostly out of jealousy. Of all the branches of our tribe, they're the most successful, and all the evidence from our ancestor spirits shows that some of the Knights of the Round Table were indeed part of the Brotherhood.

But, you see, it doesn't matter so much which words you choose to tell a tale. Oh, there's a few elders would skin me for telling you this, but the important part of any story isn't the words. The important part is the inspiration that you feel when you hear the tale. It's what's at the heart of the story that really counts. Remember that as I start, because my words aren't the best, but the tales I share with you are…

The Early Times

reeting to you, gem of the night!
Beauty of the skies, gem of the night!
Mother of the stars, gem of the night!
Foster-child of the sun, gem of the night!
Majesty of the stars, gem of the night!

—Scottish Gaelic traditional folk prayer, "To the Moon"

We were the second tribe. I'll say it proudly and thrash any Garou who says otherwise. We descend from the first wolf who was so enthralled with the majesty of life that she threw her head back and gave a song to her passions. Yeah, the Silver Fangs came first, but it was an ancestor of the Fianna who let loose the first howl. That's why, unlike some of the other tribes, all of our oldest tales and legends use the wolf-tongue.

Our ancestor taught her wolf-brothers and sisters to sing. Many joined in, kenning the joy of life up to Luna, Gaia's sister. Our part in the chorus of the Song of Gaia echoed across the land and through the heavens.

And our voices were heard…

The Fey, the spirits of the land and the dream, heard our cries of joy, of love, of the hunt. We awakened them, drawing them out with our emotions. They came to us in a glimmer of moonbeams, from the shadows of the deep woods, in the sparkle of moonshine, from the magic inside mushrooms. They danced to our songs, and they joined their voices with our own, inspiring us to greater harmonies. Can you imagine such times?

But the Fey were being pushed back by the migrations of humans. They beckoned us to join them, and we did. We left the other Garou and traveled with our Kinfolk to the lands of the Fey, far to the West. The Fey drew us away from the primal fires of our People, so dazzled were we by their beauty. We knew we had to go. Once we'd seen the Fey, our world grew too small. We had to follow.

But our departure was also sad. We sang for the other Garou for the last time, and they listened. A few responded with songs of their own, songs of loss and leave-taking. We took our pick of the flocks of Kinfolk, those with the strength of mind to face the Change, the strength of body to defeat our opponents, and the strength of spirit to help enforce the Impergium and protect Gaia. Faerie guides led us through the darkling woods and toward our destiny as a tribe.

How did we stray from our fellow Garou? Well, let your imagination carry you back to that primal time… Dream of the songs, the call of the Wyld, the dancing, the moonlight, the whirling bodies, the cries of passion… Imagine one of the sons of the moonlight, a Fey Prince, and a daughter of Gaia meeting eyes… each wondering what joys and secrets the other held. Ah, it must have been quite an age to be alive!

We are more than allies to the faeries; their blood courses through our veins. It's slight, and mixed with our own potent Garou blood, but it's there nonetheless. Some will tell you that we are the disinherited princes of Arcadia, the Kingdom of the Fey, while others deny our faerie heritage entirely. As my uncle always told me, when you hear two different sides to a tale, then the truth is probably somewhere in between. We are cousins to the Fey. You can see the touch of magic in the eyes of every Fianna, in the sparkle of blue or the flash of green.

You may have heard the tale of Brutus, the Trojan warrior who discovered Britain. That story symbolizes our journey across Europe, following the Fey as they were pushed further back by humans. As with most odysseys, not all our tribe completed the journey. Many settled with their Kinfolk in Brittany. Others decided to explore an ancient wood, far to the east. The descendants of these Fianna became the Wandering Rovers, the Celts of Europe.

After generations of wandering, our weary tribe finally splintered in Albion, or Britain. Many of our Kinfolk wished to stay in Britain, instead of traveling further. The Fianna who remained with them became the ancestors of the Brotherhood of Herne and the Dryn a drowd yn flaidd, the Welsh Garou.

But we weren't the first Garou to reach Albion. A strange tribe, the White Howlers, were there before us. At first, we fought, and fought hard, pushing them and their Kin to the north, into the highlands. But later, we made our peace and became fast friends, even interbreeding with them. We still mourn their passing.

If you have one duty as a Fianna, it is this: eradicate all Black Spiral Dancers. Every damn one of them! No parley and no mercy! Damn twisted black dogs! They disgrace the

memory of the White Howlers with every foul breath they take! There is no greater glory than covering your claws with their accursed blood!

Wait, I need another drink. Ah! A word of warning to you: we're a moody lot. Our passions burn hotter than those of other tribes. Be careful of them, or else they'll govern you and strip you of your senses. You can feel more love and joy than others can imagine, but you can also know pain and sadness that push the limits of the heart and anger and rage that know no end.

Sorry about the aside. The thought of Black Spirals raises my ire.

Erín

We finally reached Erin at the edge of the world. Ah, so beautiful a land it was — and still is, mind you. There we rejoiced to meet the Fey again, the Tuatha de Danaan, the tribe of Dana. There we found days of blessings and beauty.

As the Fey folk listened to our wolf-songs, we listened to their words. The faeries taught us of the power of names. When a thing gains a name, its spiritual strength grows. A place or object with a name becomes a source of inspiration. To protect things, places and people, from the Wyrm, we set about giving them names. When our warriors today call by name each ancient tree that witnessed the passions of our fathers and mothers, when they know each rock and stream as a brother, they fight to protect the land with all their hearts, and they are invincible.

We sing songs to remember these places, to strengthen Gaia. These are the Dindsenchas, the place name stories. They preserve the ancient song lines of the land.

Names hold the keys to power; that's why every Fianna has three names. The first is the name she is born with, the second is the name she receives from her sept as part of her Rite of Passage, and the third is a secret name, which she learns from Stag after her Rite of Passage. This last name you keep to yourself and tell no one except those you trust or love the most. For that name has power over you, and some will abuse it.

The Time of the Impergium

When your hand is in the dog's mouth, draw it out gently.
— Irish proverb

The swell of our people was a burden to Erin. There wasn't enough food to feed the humans and all the animals. We increased our enforcement of the Impergium to maintain control of the population. We also promoted battles between tribes of our Kinfolk. These wars made them strong. When other Garou learned of our wisdom, they did the same with their flocks to help protect the Mother.

Many werewolves will tell you the Impergium was cruel, especially the Children of Gaia. That may be so, but looking at the world now, all the damage that the Weaver's children — humans — have done, all the lives they've taken and the land they've claimed, perhaps the Impergium was a lesser cruelty. Just something to think about.

Ogham

Just like a name, a written word holds great power. When we first learned about the magic of writing, we used Ogham, a set of runes created by Druids. Those Druids were said to be mages. But we know they had help from the Fey in creating the runes. On the rare occasions when we write something down, even today, we still use the ancient Ogham. Warnings and secrets found at ruins and abandoned caerns are written in this secret language.

All Fianna who master our rites learn Ogham as part of their studies. When you get a chance to learn the runes, pay attention, because we rarely write something down unless it's too dangerous to say it.

The Secret Language of the Dindsenchas

We have a secret language we use from ancient times to describe our lands. It's not a language of its own, but a poetic tongue of kennings.

I'll give you an example from an old favorite of mine, the Irish poem, "The Wooing of Emer." Here Cuchulainn describes a travel route: "From the cover of the sea, over the great Secret of the Tuatha de Danann, and the Foam of the Two Steeds of Emain Macha; over the Morrigu's Garden…," etc., etc.

Now, someone versed in the Dindsenchas' poet language would be able to follow the itenarary. If you learn your rites well, and pay attention to the land, you can learn this language. And let me tell you, you can't get anywhere among the elders if you don't know it. I mean, how can you ward a caern if you can't find it when an elder says to you: "Travel over the Breasts of Deirdre, past the Great Deed of Aengus and over the Shaming of Mac Og"?

Unlike other Garou, we did not hide ourselves from our Kinfolk. We told them the truth, hiding only dangerous knowledge of the Wyrm from them. Our Kin knew of our shapechanging.

We founded our caerns in sacred groves, where we worshipped Gaia. Many of the legends attributed to Druids are based on the sacrifices we made to enforce the Impergium. A few humans learned the lessons of nature even better than we did. These witchy men and women called themselves Verbena. We knew they were thinking right, and so we allowed them to conduct the Impergium with us. Gaia blessed us and our people. Blood was spilled to maintain the Impergium, renew the land and give magick to the Verbena.

We met other shapechangers, the Corax, the children of the raven, and they became our allies. Many of our Kin were theirs as well, and many heroes would choose between the blood of the wolf and the blood of the raven. These were the Blessed Times. We were all allies, the Fey, the raven and the wolf, bound by the strongest tie of all, the tie of blood.

Of all Garou, the Wyrm feared us most, and to this day, it still does. Only the Children of Gaia have more friends than our tribe, and only the Bone Gnawers have suffered more than we. The Beast-of-War attacked our strongholds with its monsters, but we easily repelled them from the land. The Eater-of-Souls tried to crush our spirits, but we prevailed. We protected the body and the soul of the land.

The Fomori Wars

As the other faces of the Wyrm met us on the field of battle, the Defiler Wyrm, with its twisted cunning, watched us and our alliances. It plotted and waited. Then, it concocted a terrible scheme. The Defiler knew that no force could defeat our people, except ourselves. So the despicable monster turned our own Kinfolk and their tribes against us.

The Defiler created the fomori. Some legends say that the fomori dwelled on Erin before we arrived, but those stories are tales made to hide the truth. Some of our septs refuse to admit that our own Kinfolk could have turned against us, but the fomori were among us. They were Kin to faerie and Garou. In the legends, the veins of many heroes run with the blood of both the fomor and the Tuatha de Danaan. These warriors had to struggle to resist the song of the Wyrm. When they could resist and chose the path of Gaia, they stood as an inspiration to all.

Some of our best Kinfolk warriors succumbed to the promises of the Defiler. My uncle always said that the path to corruption starts with the desire to do good, and he'd feed me the line about the road to Hell. A few humans were jealous of our prowess against the spawn of the Beast-of-War and wished to have the Change. Others were imperfect in some way; they had a weakness which separated them from the beauty of the land. These were easy prey for the Wyrm.

A few Garou, not least the Children of Gaia, will say that if we had treated the infirm as equals, the Defiler could not have corrupted them. I doubt it. If the body is corrupt, it reflects a weakness in the soul. This is why we treat our metis cubs so badly, because we know the weak body of the metis hides a weak heart, easily preyed upon by the Wyrm. The Wyrm whispered to the weak ones in the darkness, haunting their dreams. The Wyrm even afflicted the Fey, twisting some of their number. Some faeries tried to resist the Wyrm by plunging deeper into the Wyld, perhaps past the point of no return.

The Fomori Wars were the greatest struggle our tribe has ever fought. We almost lost. Our Ahrouns perished, our warrior Kin littered the land with their broken bodies, and we soaked the earth with our blood. The fomori had a powerful leader, a monster named Balor, with such great magic that he could kill with his gaze. Time and again peace was made as both sides tried to recover from the devastation. The fomori made us many promises, but broke every one.

We could defeat their magics with our spirit, and we could trade blows with their best. But we could not overcome our own hearts. It was horrible to battle members of our own family who had fallen under the spell of the Wyrm. And even death could not stop our enemies. The Wyrm's forces would gather bodies from the field, both fomor and fallen Garou, and animate them to return to fight again and again.

If there's a lesson to be learned from these wars, it's this: Show no mercy to the Wyrm. Don't let the Defiler use your love or pity against you. If you love someone who's tainted, then kill her, for Gaia's sake, so that whatever part of her soul remains pure can return to the Mother before she's lost entirely.

The Celtic leaders learned to distrust outsiders during the Fomori Wars. Even an unknown kinsman had to prove himself before he could attend the war councils. The Celts started to test their leaders to make certain that they had no blemishes or marks of corruption. We did the same, ever ready with our claws if a member of our sept showed the signs of Wyrm-taint. Slowly, the traitorous fomori in our camps vanished. The same was not true of the Tuatha de Danaan, who struggled with treason throughout the wars.

We struck the heads from the bodies of our dead enemies, so that they would return to the land, instead of rising from the bogs to attack us again and again. We buried our own fallen in mounds or hid their bodies deep in the bogs where the spirits of the land could protect them. We continue these practices even today.

Our greatest allies in the Fomori Wars were the Corax. The ravens warned us of the fomori armies' movements. They spied on the camps of the enemy. In raging tempest, in darkest night, they always flew before us, warning us of evil. We remember their courage.

Nuada of the Silver Arm and Lugh of the Long Arm

Still, the days grew dark for us. Nuada, king of the land and leader of the de Danaan, lost his arm in battle, and the people would no longer follow him. Instead, Breas the Beautiful, son of a fomor, became king. Breas submitted to Balor's demands for tribute, and he would have given up the land if it weren't for the words of the renowned bard Cairbre, a Galliard of our tribe, who continually spoke out against Breas. Finally, after a dream (some say sent by our Galliards), Nuada had a silver arm forged to replace his lost one.

Aye, a silver arm. Sounds pretty dangerous, huh? A Garou at least would think twice about doubting the potency of a guy with a silver arm.

Nuada resumed the throne, but Balor had taken Breas' reign as an opportunity to strengthen his armies. Balor planned to attack and sweep our people from the land. What's more, the Beast-of-War sent a creature spawned in the depths of Malfeas to Balor's side. This was the Cromh-Cruach, one of the foulest monsters to ever sully the breast of Gaia. Were it not for the hero Lugh, all might have been lost…

Lugh was the grandson of Balor, but unlike his grandfather, he was untainted by the Wyrm's evil. He had to pass many tests to enter the halls of Nuada, so great was the fear of our people. Yet, after undergoing such testing, none could doubt his skills. Lugh was learned in many disciplines and a warrior without par. Nuada had the young hero lead his men in the final battle of the Fomori Wars, the Second Battle of Moy Tura.

The Second Battle of Moy Tura

There has never been another battle to equal the Second Battle of Moy Tura, save possibly the legendary Battle of Camlann. Nuada himself faced the dread Cromh-Cruach in single combat. Although Nuada slew the monster, he himself was slain by the Wyrm-beast. But the Cromh-Cruach did not triumph, for Nuada died in glory, untainted by the Wyrm's touch.

And then Lugh faced Balor, with the fate of Erin hanging in the balance. As the fomor turned to cast his gaze of death on Lugh, the hero took spear, the Lightning Spear, and hurled it with all his might at Balor's eye. The spear pierced Balor's eye, and down he went. Dead for good.

Then Lugh took out Balor's evil eye and claimed it as his own. But no more would it serve the Wyrm, for Lugh bathed it in the pure waters of Gaia and tamed it. Its power is ours now, thanks to him, and the Wyrm cringes whenever we deliver Balor's Gaze unto his minions.

With Balor vanquished and the Cromh-Cruach destroyed, the day went to the Tuatha de Danaan and our people. The wars against the fomori were over. We hunted them to the edge of the land and cast their remnants into the sea. Good riddance to them, the whole sorry lot of them.

The Promise

After the Fomori Wars, the land was safe from the Wyrm. However, while we had fought with all our strength against the great foe, the Weaver kept spinning her web, unchecked. Our victory was short-lived. We could feel the land tear, as her webs separated the spirit from the world.

The Fey and the Tuatha de Danaan sadly departed Gaia. They said that the time of the human was upon the world. While fighting the fomori, we had failed to uphold the Impergium, because we needed warriors for our armies, and the ranks of the humans had swelled. As the Tuatha de Danaan left, they swore a promise to us under the light of the Crescent Moon. Listen well:

"Though we are both spirits of the Wyld, the Changelings and the Changing Breed, our alliance, our friendship, will never change. We will ever regard you as our cousins and never treat you differently. The bond of blood between us will remain as eternal and constant as the land, so long as our stories are told."

That is the Promise. To this day, the faerie folk may be fickle in how they appear to others and how they treat other beings, even other Garou, but with us, they remain the same.

They hold to the oldest traditions, and we treat them the same. And we keep their stories alive.

If you wish to show respect to our cousins, learn the Silver Record and the ancient ways. Never forget our heritage. We are like the Fey. Our bodies are ever-changing, but our spirit remains ever constant.

The White Howlers

The White Howlers followed different ways, but we lived mostly in peace. When their songs joined with ours, there was never a sound more beautiful. We still warred with them at times, but it was for just and noble reasons.

Now, the Howlers, although they had a magic of their own, were afraid of the Fey and the Umbra, even though they wouldn't admit it. But in all other ways, they were a bold and confident tribe; they were our brothers and sisters.

Because we had destroyed the fomori in Erin, the Wyrm had but few shadows left in Britannia. We defeated them with the help of the White Howlers, and the Howlers grew confident in their abilities to best the Wyrm. But we grew worried when those of us who stayed on the continent, the Rovers, sent word of a new threat from the Wyrm, a greater threat than even the fomori. But the White Howlers remained confident, unfazed. Bloody cocky bastards, weren't they?

The Lion of the White Howlers

The Lion was the most powerful totem of the White Howlers. Did you know that there were once lions across Europe? There were. But the Romans hunted them to extinction, just as evil swallowed the Howlers. Still, some of our packs take the Howlers' Lion as their totem, for Lion is the totem of Lugh, the sleeping hero, who will rise again when the Apocalypse comes.

Rome

The Romans came to Albion, bearing the standard of the Wyrm. Vampiric centurions, fomori legionnaires and the war tactics of the Weaver decimated all who stood before them.

The old magics failed to stop the Romans from corrupting and changing the land. The Wyrm's legions left their roads like scars across the face of the Mother. They built fortresses to ward off the spirits of Gaia. We drove them away once, back across the sea, but they returned in greater numbers

with darker powers. Much to our shame, we failed to stem their foul tide.

Although our tribe never fell in battle, our people, our families could not hold against the Roman might. We retreated with our wounded and dying Kinfolk to our hidden caerns, determined to carry on the struggle from the forests and the fells. But the war was lost for us.

Many of the Fianna who lived in Albion refused to leave their homes and caerns, as did the wolves of Wales. Instead, the British wolves hid themselves and dedicated themselves to the great huntsman, Herne, to hide them in the night and keep them eternally vigilant against the Wyrm. They became the Brotherhood of Herne and dedicated themselves to hunting the Wyrm and defending the interests of Britain from its taint.

Most Fianna kept ready to protect the Emerald Isle. Our tribal leaders wanted to defend the land entrusted to us by the Fey, the land that was our home. The Brotherhood practiced guerrilla tactics, but could not stop Rome's legions. We could only pray to Gaia that the White Howlers had the strength to protect their peoples and homelands.

Up from the Pit

The Howlers fought long and hard alongside the Picts, and our songs give them their due, but they did not have the strength to stop the Romans. The arms and machines of the Weaver were too much for their spirit allies and mystical runes. But they did not give up or retreat and hide, as we did. They entered the darkness of the Wyrm itself to continue the battle. And from that darkness none of them returned.

The White Howlers were consumed by their Rage and anger, by their hate for the Romans and their hate for the Wyrm and all that it meant. All was as the Wyrm desired. Those who returned from the pits beneath the hills were no longer singers of Gaia. They were the Black Spiral Dancers, a foul corruption of what they once had been. Even the thought of these creatures sickens me.

The Resistance

The Brotherhood of Herne and the Welsh Fianna continued the struggle against the Roman invaders. The Scottish Fianna managed to hold the highlands against the Romans, even as they fought against the Black Spirals. We developed our first guerrilla tactics in this war — little must our ancestors have realized how much we would have to use those methods in the future. Time and again, we raised the banner of rebellion, only to be crushed beneath the legions and their dark allies. We paid in blood for our lessons in that war.

The Romans won many victories. They massacred our Kinfolk and raped the land. They tore roads through our forests, and built the cankers they called cities. They constructed walls from one side of the isle to the other to divide the conquered people from the free. We might have lost, but as in the Fomori Wars, we had allies.

Boudicca

When the King of the Iceni tribe died, he left his kingdom to the Romans. The legions stole everything they could from the Iceni. They tortured the land, driving out the old nobility who had cherished it. Boudicca, widow to the king, was stripped of her lands and goods, flogged and forced to watch as a cohort of legionnaires raped her daughters. As her daughters were raped before her eyes, the queen experienced her First Change — she was Fianna.

Boudicca raised an army and captured the Roman city of Camulodonum, now called Colchester. When a Roman legion faced her forces in battle, she destroyed them. She marched on Londinium, now London, and she massacred seventy thousand Romans in righteous anger. A massive Roman army, supported by the Wyrm, finally came to Albion and crushed Boudicca's forces. Boudicca took her own life after the defeat, but she remained an inspiration to the Brotherhood of Herne in their fight against the Romans. Even today, she is revered by the Black Furies.

Two Garou tribes joined us in the battle against the Roman invaders: the Black Furies and the Get of Fenris. Now let me tell you, the Furies and the Get don't like each other much. The Get think the Furies are a pack of uppity bitches who don't know their place, and the ladies have never taken well to that sort of attitude. So, if they can agree to fight together against a common foe, you know the enemy has to be dangerous. The leaders of the Brotherhood of Herne made alliances with these tribes.

Now, while the Romans were dealing with all three groups, the Scottish Fianna up north had help from the Get of Fenris, whose Kinfolk had moved into the Orkneys. Together, they walloped the Black Spiral Dancers. Not that the Scottish Fianna needed the Get's help, mind you. No one who values his hide ever says a Scot isn't tough. But they won that war together, driving the Spirals out of the land or into hiding beneath the Roman cities.

Slowly, the raiders of Herne, along with the Get and Furies, took back Britannia. The Roman eagle never tasted Irish soil. Soon, barbarian Kinfolk led by the Get joined with some of our Kin to sweep down and bring the battle to the Romans.

The empire built on the ways of the Wyrm could not stand. The Romans finally fell apart. The Get of Fenris, along their Kinfolk armies and their flocks, spread south to destroy the empire. We praised the Get in our songs, little knowing that we would soon wage war against them.

The Coming of the Get

As the Roman influence faded in Britain, our tribe retook the West and North. When the Saxons came to eastern Britannia, we were content to live in peace with them and with the Get of Fenris who came with them. We welcomed the Get to our caerns as our sisters and brothers.

But those bastards — the Get and their Saxon Kin — took our hospitality and spat in our faces! The leaders of the Get called us weak for falling to the Romans, unworthy to protect the land. They pointed to the defilement of the White Howlers and blamed us for the coming of the dark dancers. They called us cowards and said we welcomed them to our feasts out of fear and weakness.

Why, if one of them were here right now, I'd show him some hospitality! I'd introduce him to my fist! And if he didn't have the courtesy to thank me for it, he'd meet my claws next! Damn bloody Get bastards, don't know their arses from their own heads! I'd say they were always thinking with their balls if they had any!

The bards say that no song can convey the rage of the Righs and the Councils of Song at the Get. Even worse, the Get were insulting members of the Brotherhood of Herne, the children and grandchildren of those who had stayed in Albion to wage war against the Romans through the long centuries. They were strong and proud, with ideals and inspiration, the descendants of those who had survived the occupation.

We fought the Saxon dogs and their Viking Kin for centuries. I'll give the Get this: They're too stupid to stop fighting. Of course, we weren't about to let them walk all over us. The problem we had wasn't the Get — although, let me tell you the Get can fight, even if we taught them a few lessons on the way — it was that our people and Kinfolk spent too much of their time fighting among themselves. Different tribes of humans warred with each other while we tried to unite them against the Get menace. A few times we arranged for a High King to rise up to unite the people, and more than a few times, the people found a High King all their own. But it wasn't enough to hold the heart of Britain.

We kept Wales in the south and west of Albion, and the Scottish highlands, and, of course, the Emerald Isle. But the tribes of men called the Angles and the Saxons, with their Get allies, took Britain from us, defeating the Brotherhood of Herne.

But they didn't have time to get cocky over their victory. After our struggles, we were both beaten down like two wolves chasing after the same hare in a blizzard, fighting with each other the entire time. The Get heard that there was some trouble back on the continent, and a few of our Whispering Rovers also said big things were about to happen…

The Reign of the Silver Fangs

The Get and their flock, who had called us too weak to deserve the land, got their arses handed to them by the Silver Fangs and William the Conqueror. Though their flocks didn't leave, after the Norman Conquest, you couldn't have found one of the Get on the Isles if you lifted every stone. They'd keep raiding in their damned dragonships, but they'd never get another chance to rule. It was the Roman invasion all over again, except there were Silver Fangs instead of Spirals and French-speaking Normans instead of Latin-speaking Romans.

The Silver Fangs wanted the best breeding stock for their Kinfolk and felt they had the right to claim the Isles. The Fangs say Gaia gave them the right to rule, and rule they will, regardless of what the other tribes want. And I think we believed it, almost as much as they did. I mean, they were the most pure of the Garou, weren't they?

No matter what the Fangs are today, they had their act together then. They were lean and hungry to rule — not lazy, overconfident and at least half-mad. We fought them, but the struggle with the Get had drained us. The Brotherhood of Herne made a deal with the Silver Fangs and offered to share breeding stock if they'd help us expel the Get. The Fangs were smart as well as tough, and they agreed.

Oh, I've got some good jokes about the Silver Fangs, I do. But I can't repeat them here, not in this company. Look me up later, at the board, and maybe I'll tell 'em.

Where was I? Oh, yeah. Although the Fangs were ascendant in England, they couldn't take the Scottish highlands from our Kin. The Dryn a drowd yn flaidd, the wolves of Wales, held lands in the West and the South against the Norman forces, although they paid tribute to the Fangs to keep their power. Eventually, the Welsh Garou started to let their Kinfolk mix with the English. In later years, the Kin of the Welsh Fianna would ascend to the throne of England, breaking a string of Fang Kinfolk rulers. One of the most famous of these would be known as Henry V.

Meanwhile, the Irish Fianna had spent their time fighting to hold Erin. The Get and their Viking Kinfolk had attacked her shores relentlessly. But in 1014, at the Battle of Clontarf, they settled the score with the Get and showed them whose land Erin really was. Our Irish packs grew confident in their battle prowess and that of their Kinfolk. A few of them mocked the Welsh and British Fianna for losing their lands to the Silver Fangs. Maybe they hoped to goad them into overthrowing the Fangs. Instead, it just made them angry.

The Taking of Ireland

When the deposed Irish king Diarmaid Macmurchada asked King Henry II of England to help him regain his kingdom of Leinster, the eastern Fianna saw a chance to regain some pride. They recruited some Silver Fangs, who, unlike the Get, enjoyed good story and drink. In 1169, two years before Henry officially invaded, they went over with their Kinfolk and did what no one had ever done before… they conquered Erin.

The English nobles seized sections of the island and declared them fiefs of the crown. When Henry arrived in 1171, victory was all but complete. Of course, it helped that our Kinfolk didn't resist but so much, since the church had made Henry "Lord of Ireland" in 1155.

Despite the loss, it wasn't a tragedy from the Fianna perspective. If you have to lose, it's best to lose to your own tribe. The eastern Fianna treated their Irish cousins with respect and honor. Even the Silver Fangs were decent victors, and British Kinfolk of all tribes intermarried with Irish. Within a few years, the invaders were more Irish than anything, and even the English weren't so bad in those times. The Welsh even started the Eisteddfod festival for bards, a damn good talespinning event.

But while England certainly couldn't dictate the affairs of the nobles in Ireland, our Righs couldn't know how much pain and suffering would come of this conquest. Many songmasters will tell you that some few Fianna had visions of tragedy when they built Belfast, only six years after the invasion, but I don't believe them. Our tribe is full of visionaries who don't understand the difference between hindsight and foresight.

The Middle Ages

Things got messy in the Isles for a few centuries. There were so many rebellions and wars that it would take a lifetime to sort them all out. The same things happened over and over again. The English conquered Scotland. The Scots rebelled and asserted their independence. Wales fell to England, but a king of Welsh blood took the English throne. Ireland rebelled, parts of the island became independent, and then fell back under the English yoke.

Throughout it all, England battled constantly with the French, and the people slowly lost their Celtic culture. I guess the Magna Carta is the most important thing that happened, but let me tell you, it depended on the king as to whether it was just a piece of paper or the law of the land.

The Fangs started inbreeding with the European nobility and went a bit crazy — along with most European leaders. We Fianna defended our lands and traditions as best we could, but the real threats that we faced had less to do with politics than religion.

Religious Turmoil

uring the reign of Henry VIII, the English separated from the Catholic Church and established the Church of England. The Irish parliament, which got its orders from England, severed the Church of Ireland from Rome and declared the King of England the ultimate religious authority, right up there next to God himself. If you became Protestant, you were loyal to the English, and if you stayed Catholic, you were an Irish nationalist.

Catholics were robbed and persecuted, and Protestants and English Loyalists reaped the benefits. We're still living with the results of this today, over four hundred and fifty years later. Henry VIII and his bastard daughter Elizabeth I did their best to stamp out Catholicism on the Emerald Isle, which just made the people cling to the Church all the harder. After all, we Fianna and our Kin have always had a reputation for being stubborn.

James I of England decided to settle the matter by sending English and Scottish Protestants to Ulster. With them came more than a few British Fianna. Things didn't go well. All it took was a few words, a few drinks, and emotions boiled over into violence. Thousands of Protestants were slaughtered, and the Catholics rebelled against England.

Cromwell

A curse upon you Oliver Cromwell
Who raped our mother land
I hope you're rotting down in hell for the horrors that you sent
On our misfortune forefathers whom you robbed of their birthright
To Hell or Connaught!
May you burn in Hell tonight!
     — The Pogues, "Ned of the Hill"

Oliver Cromwell was one of the most Wyrm-ridden men in history. Some may jump to defend him, but none of our tribe. We know the truth. He overthrew a weak monarchy, and he used Protestant religious fervor to inspire his Wyrm-tainted followers. After assuming power in place of the king in England, the Lord Protector turned his attention to Ireland.

He had no mercy for Catholics. His attacks on the Irish people were unimaginable. He spitted infants on pikes. He massacred thousands. He let the people starve. He burned their homes. He stole their money and locked them in prison. Everywhere, he sowed the seeds of anger and pain, tempting people with the Wyrm. I won't describe the details of all of his atrocities, but let's just say that Malfeas can't be much worse than Ireland under Cromwell. When that man died, Gaia wept in relief.

Yeah, he's another one I'd like to get my hands on. I hear there are rumors that his ghost don't rest easy, and that it's wandering about haunting some places. And I've known Fianna that've waited up all night at the Parliament House just waiting for his restless spirit to show its face. God help him if we ever find a way to track him down in the lands of the dead...

The Webs of the Weaver

and without rent to you.

— Irish toast

Though religion tore our people apart, it was nothing compared to the suffering we endured during the Industrial Revolution, when the Weaver tore our world itself asunder. In Britain, they started destroying the forests. Now, we knew that we had been losing forest, but it vanished overnight when industry came. In Ireland too, all the hardwood forests were decimated. Our howls of mourning echoed across the Isles. We had failed as caretakers of Gaia.

The Fangs couldn't do anything, although they claimed to have influence. We were all powerless before the masses of humanity. Railroad tracks, like badly stitched wounds, were laid through the remains of ancient groves where we had enforced the Impergium. The face of Britain changed.

When Scotland officially joined England in 1707, the British Empire blossomed. Explorers traveled around the world, trading and conquering, adding colonies to the British crown. Many of our Kin went to work in factories and textile mills. We labored next to the Kin of the Bone Gnawers, while the Silver Fangs and the Glass Walkers took advantage of it all. As industry advanced in Britain, life grew immeasurably worse in Ireland.

Our Kinfolk in Ireland didn't fall so deeply under the spell of the Weaver. Instead, they tried to keep the spider's webs away, but the people suffered all the same. The Wyrm made an insidious attempt to destroy us. By the end of the 1700s, rich British citizens had bought almost all the land in Ireland. The Irish were renters who build peat moss huts and grew potatoes to survive. Out of desperation for extra hands and a desire for happiness, people married early and had many children. The population boomed, just as power was concentrated in the hands of fewer and fewer people.

The British landlords brutally exploited our Kin to feed the growing British Empire. The Brotherhood of Herne supported the growth of the Empire, as did the Dryn a drowd yn flaidd. The Brotherhood believed they had a duty to hunt the ends of the earth to drive out the Wyrm and felt that the situation in Ireland was the fault of the Irish Fianna.

Bastards! I've not yet forgiven them for that, and that's why you'll hear me spill a few unkind words for the Brotherhood of Herne. Some Irish Fianna appealed to the Silver Fangs, but they pled in vain. Neither they nor their Kin cared to help Ireland. They were far too concerned with their twisted dreams of empire and the sweet taste of their own power. Bloody pogues!

But the Silver Fangs were at a loss when it came to the early Glass Walkers and their Kin. The Walkers took advantage of the great merchant houses and trading companies.

The Silver Fangs were desperate to retain any control they could, so they boosted their egos by helping the Walkers. As for the Glass Walkers, they cared about nothing save their profits. To this day, we have little respect for those servants of the Weaver who call themselves Garou.

The Great Flight

he poverty of the Irish peasantry is on the extreme verge of human misery; their cottages would scarce serve for pig sties even in Scotland; and their rags seem the very refuse of a sheep, and are spread over their bodies with such an ingenious variety of wretchedness that you would think nothing but some sort of perverted taste could have assembled so many shreds together.

— Sir Walter Scott

God put the blight on the potato, but England put the hunger upon Ireland

— Irish saying

Life in Ireland was terrible for our Kin — we couldn't blame them for wanting to leave. They fled in droves to America and Australia. Many traveled to England and Scotland in search of work. Nothing did much good. A few were successful in America and Australia, but most ended up working under conditions that were only marginally better than those they had found at home.

Many urban workers in Scotland were Irish. They suffered terribly as our councils debated the plight of our Kin, not realizing that the worst tragedy was yet to come. It was a shameful time, let me tell you.

We had thought things couldn't get much worse for ourselves and our Kinfolk. But then, the Eater-of-Souls lashed out. You see, all of our people in Ireland lived off of one plant: the potato. The Wyrm let the land swell with the masses of humanity — then it took the potato away. In 1845 and 1846, we suffered the first of the blights. Then, there was another in 1848, and yet another in 1851.

Unless you experienced the blight in the Irish countryside in a past life, you can't imagine the horror that ensued. Thousands starved to death. Disease spread through communities. The Eater-of-Souls opened the peoples' heart to corruption. There were incidents of cannibalism. Villages fed off the rotting carcasses of starved animals. Bodies lay on the hills with grass stuffed in their mouths, a testament to their desperation. One person in four died during the famine.

Oh, it was terrible! Breaks my heart even now to talk of it! Ah, and you can believe we suffered with every one of them. But many of us turned to the Wyrm. Fianna fought Fianna for food. Caerns withered away because we no longer had the numbers to care for them. The Wyrm tormented us relentlessly. The Silver Fangs and Glass Walkers turned a blind eye to our plight. While our people died of want, they grew yet fatter on the fruits of our labor. So, we did the only thing we could. We fled the Emerald Isle with our Kinfolk. Most who left knew they would never see her shores again.

It makes me shake with rage to this day, thinking back on it all. Curse the damn Wyrm and all its works! Oh, if I could travel back in time, I would be splitting the heads of many a money-grubbing landowner!

Ah, but what's past is past, right? Wrong! Don't ever forget our past. Ever. Even if there's no revenge to be had, there are souls who died that deserve to be remembered.

Like all the attempts before to destroy us, the blight only strengthened our spirit. The Wyrm forced many of us from our homes, but it couldn't take our homes out of our hearts.

America

Thousands are sailing
Across the western ocean
To a land of opportunity
That some of them will never see
— The Pogues, "Thousands are Sailing"

America opened its doors to us. We swelled the ranks of the urban poor, but we found the paws of the Bone Gnawers open to us. They helped us survive in the cities. The Children of Gaia gave us aid wherever they could. The Black Furies took care of our mothers and daughters, even if they dealt harshly with a few of our merrier lads in the process. We were survivors, and we slowly clawed our way out of the pit of despair that the Wyrm had dug for us.

A toast to all them that helped us! May you never lack for a song on a cold night. Just call us, we'll be there for you.

We found ourselves fighting in America, on both sides of the law. Ever hear about Irish gangsters? Well, the Glass Walkers learned about them the hard way.

The Struggles Begin

ou can only kick a dog so long before it bites back. And wolves take to being kicked far less than dogs. The Irish Fianna did what they could to cure the country's ills. People stopped harvesting potatoes and started turning land into pasture. Early marriage stopped, and the population slowly came under control. But the British taxes and rents never stopped. When a countryman couldn't pay his taxes, his family was evicted and his house burned to the ground. We and our Kin couldn't take it; we lashed out. The Grandchildren of Fionn led the way, and guerrilla warfare started in Ireland.

The British Fianna and their Kin weren't happy about our little war, though even the Brotherhood of Herne admitted that things were bad in the Emerald Isle. They blamed us, blamed our Irish patriotism and stubbornness. They wanted the Irish to hail the Union Jack. They claimed the flag represented all Fianna and our Celtic Kinfolk. As the humans fought, so did we.

The elders tried to bring peace, but our packs just developed fiercer and fiercer rivalries. The best efforts to make peace within our tribe came from an alliance of the Silver Fangs and the Children of Gaia. The Fangs were tired of dealing with us, I guess. They wanted the fighting to stop so they could devote more time to the rest of their crumbling empire. The Children just wanted peace for its own sake. Unfortunately, they made the situation worse before they made it better.

A movement started in England to give Ireland home rule. But the Loyalists and Protestants in Ulster refused to submit to the rule of the mostly Catholic majority. They started to arm themselves. By December of 1913, the Ulsterites had an army of volunteers that may have numbered as many as 100,000.

The Parliament in London passed the Irish Home Rule bill in 1914. The Protestants refused to accept Catholic rule. Full civil war might have broken out right then and there, except for one thing. World War I broke out in Europe, and the British suspended the Irish Home Rule Bill.

The Great War

any Garou believed the Great War heralded the Apocalypse. The Wyrm-inspired gas weapons, the trench warfare, it all reeked of corruption. The seeds the Wyrm had sown across Europe finally sprouted. Many members of our tribe fought in the war, one or two flew biplanes. We even had a few heroes. I don't know if you've heard of T.E. Lawrence, but we claim him as our Kin.

Many of our elders were thankful for the war. Bad as it was, it got our packs' minds off killing each other and back to killing members of the Get and whoever else was fighting on the other side. I'm not saying we should be proud of killing the Get. A lot of Fianna died in the war, and the Silver Fangs lost their European hegemony. On the other hand, we did win…

Easter Revolution

Then, on Easter 1916, a group of Irish nationalists rose up in Dublin. They thought the time to strike was right, believing that the U.K. was too busy with the Great War to bother with Erin. The rising started in the Dublin General Post Office.

After British gunboats shelled Dublin for a week, our elders gave up on hopes that things would settle down at the end of the war. The British executed all the leaders of the Easter revolution; it's said that their ghosts still haunt the Post Office. My packmate swears she saw one of them once.

After the Great War, the British ignored the question of Irish home rule. Instead, they left our Irish kin to settle things, which they started to do in a bloody guerrilla war. A few years later, in 1922, the British Parliament finally granted southern Ireland home rule, dividing the Emerald Isle into a Catholic Ireland and a mostly Protestant Northern Ireland.

The War to End Empires

After the resolution of the Irish question — as unsatisfactory as it was — and the end of the Great War, our tribe was bone-weary of armed conflict. The questions of the day became questions of money and living conditions. Working conditions were still horrible for many of our Kin, both in Europe and America. We hailed Bone Gnawer efforts to improve working conditions and did our best to improve things.

Times were rough. And then the Great Depression hit. Strangely, it didn't bother us as much as some other tribes. I mean, some Glass Walkers even leapt out of buildings at the thought of poverty. As bad as the Depression was, it wasn't any worse than what we had endured over the last century. Our Kin were tough as nails.

Then, we heard a stirring in the protectorates of the Get. Rumors spread of visions of a coming darkness seen by the Theurges. A Grand Council of Song came together to debate these premonitions, but no one could convince the Sept of Tara of the danger.

We didn't want war. We were tired of fighting. Our tribe didn't want to see it coming, so we ignored most of the signs. A few screamed Apocalypse. But you know what? I think at least half of our tribe had decided that if it was the Apoca-lypse, then damn it, we were ready. If the Apocalypse was coming, then let it come so we can finish fighting and get around to the "Goodbye, Wyrm!" party! It's not a good attitude, but it's very Fianna.

Hitler came to power in Germany, and Stalin held the reins of the Soviet Union. Evil rose like a storm in the east. We started to prepare for war, because we knew that war wasn't far off. No Fianna, Irish, Scots, Welsh, English, or American thought Hitler wasn't evil. Some of our Kin were fooled, but not us. Even the Silver Fangs warned other Garou about the short madman with the mustache. But little did anyone know how many Get would fall into line behind the swastika.

Now, even though the Nazis wooed us Irish and told us how we could break British rule, we stood on the side of the British in World War II. Oh, it was bloody hard for some of the Grandchildren of Fionn to take, all right. Nonetheless, the Irish Fianna didn't fight enthusiastically until late in the war, when they could no longer ignore the stench of the Wyrm.

However, by then, most Fianna didn't live in Ireland. More Fianna lived in the U.K. than the Emerald Isle, and nearly as many lived in America. And that's not counting the Fianna in Australia and South Africa who were itching for a fight. The descendants of the transported Fianna are rough customers, and even a Shadow Lord'll think twice before shouting orders around one.

Our tribe operated in the Underground, sabotaging Nazi supplies behind the lines, supporting the Resistance in France and the Netherlands, even going over to help matters in Eastern Europe and Russia. At times, even the Silver Fangs appreciated our aid in defending their protectorates. They say the best way to talk to a Fang is in a foxhole when neither of you thinks you'll get out alive. Those in-bred aristocrats even knew how to drink then.

The worst part of the war was the Blitz. How terrified do you think the average British citizen would have been if he could have seen what was lurking in the Umbra in those bomb shelters? On the homefront, we fought claw-to-claw against the Black Spirals, who had developed a nasty tendency to prey on unsuspecting humans hiding in the tunnels beneath London. Wyrm-spawn sought out fear and hate in our Kin, and fomori again walked the isles. Many caerns were destroyed, especially those in the cities.

Finally, the Blitzkrieg stalled. The tide of war turned. The Get turned on their Nazi masters as the other tribes redoubled their efforts against the foe.

When the war finally ended, Gaia had paid a terrible cost. Many Garou were dead, and of those few left, most had lost their caerns. Unexploded shells covered the land. The British Empire had collapsed during the war, but except for the most ardent members of the Brotherhood of Herne, we didn't care. We realized that in our own way, we had been as arrogant as the Get, claiming protectorates that belonged to the Bone Gnawers, the Silent Striders or the Stargazers. After the war we realized that we, just like our cousins across the empire, had been used by the Silver Fangs to realize their dreams of wealth and power.

The Shadow of the Wyrm

he most terrifying legacy of the Second World War is the nuclear bomb. A few Old Ones have told me they think the whole reason the Wyrm started World War II was so humanity would create the bomb. I personally don't believe it. I think Hitler started World War II for his own mad reasons. The Wyrm doesn't cause all of the wrongs in the world. Nonetheless, nuclear terror was the order of the day in the Cold War.

Now, we come to Jack Kennedy. JFK. Most Garou will tell you that President Kennedy was just a man, not Kinfolk in the slightest. Well, no matter what the others say, the American Fianna claim him as their own, and if you dare suggest otherwise, you will get tossed from any Fianna caern

in the U.S. Of course, they don't always like to claim the rest of the Kennedy clan, and they certainly don't count "Ahnold" among their own.

But the Wyrm's minions killed President Kennedy. I don't know how, but they did. There are a lot of theories, but I haven't heard any that contain enough truth for my taste.

The Troubles

very man has to die
But it's written in the starlight
And every line in your palm
We're fools to make war
On our brothers in arms
— Dire Straits, "Brother in Arms"

During the Cold War, Ireland seceded from the British Commonwealth. On April 18, 1949, the Republic of Ireland was established. After a few bitter decades, the Republic chose to recognize British rule in Northern Ireland, on the condition that the majority agreed.

In the 1970s, the Troubles, as we call the conflict between Catholics and Protestants, got worse in Northern Ireland. The Irish Republican Army and Protestant paramilitaries were at each other's throats. The Grandchildren of Fionn and the Brotherhood of Herne were fools enough to let themselves be drawn into the conflict. It's been a long, bloody fight that's torn all Fianna down. I don't care if your blood comes from a Welsh, Scottish, or English line and you've lived all your life in America, Australia, or somewhere else a world away. The Troubles have hurt our entire tribe. Brother fighting sister, pack against pack, it's hard to understand and even harder to bear.

Finally, today, there may be a chance for peace. I just hope, no matter how many times they fail to make peace in Northern Ireland, that they keep trying. And they will.

If you learn only one thing from the long and muddled history of our tribe, it's this: We're tied to the land and the people who live there. We are the caretakers of Gaia. If we fail ourselves, we fail Gaia, and the Wyrm wins. But if we stay true to ourselves, it'll all work out for the best. Never give up your love or your hope.

Encumbered forever by desire and ambition
There's a hunger still unsatisfied
Our weary eyes still stray to the horizon
Though down this road we've been so many times
— Pink Floyd, "High Hopes"

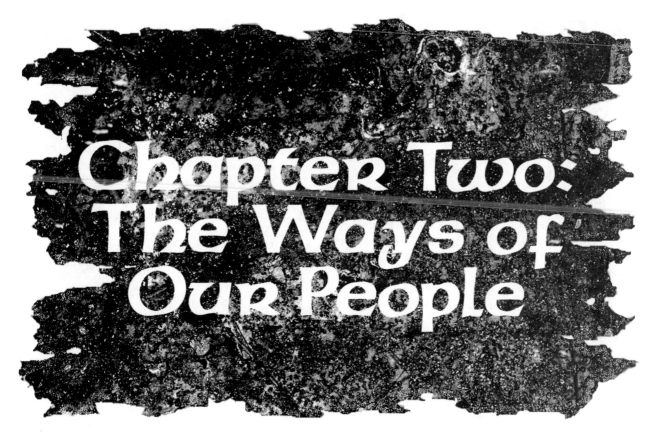

Chapter Two: The Ways of Our People

May you have the hindsight to know where you've been, the foresight to know where you're going, and the insight to know when you're going too far.
— Irish toast

e have the oldest culture of any Garou, except for maybe the Stargazers and of course, the Red Talons. We all trace back to the Celts. Some of us are Welsh, others Scottish. We're English, and we're Irish. Most of us are Americans or Aussies. A few are even Spanish, German and Czech. But we're all Fianna. We all trace our culture back to the first Celtic peoples, the Fey and a few wolves howling at the moon. We argue over bits of our history, but we remember our roots.

Kinfolk Ties

oving each other like sister and brother,
Sister and brother, sister and brother,
Loving each other like sister and brother,
About the merry-ma-tanzie.
— Anonymous folk song, "The Merry-ma-Tanzie"

We Fianna have a special relationship with our Kinfolk. We are much more open with our Kin than most tribes. Our Kin are our family. Our parents are Kinfolk, so are our brothers and sisters. We take lovers and mates from our Kin. They're part of our tribe. We defend them as part of our septs, and a few Kin have even joined packs. You can't break the Veil by talking to your Kinfolk, at least if you're Fianna. We need Kin we can trust, and we invite Kin to our moots.

Now, having said that, we do exercise a bit of discretion. We don't invite our crazy aunts to visit caerns, or change into Crinos in front of small children. We also know we have a problem controlling our emotions. Don't stay around Kin if you're upset. Letting loose the Beast and ripping open your relatives is a good way to ruin a fine party. Treasure your family, and protect them, from yourself and anything else that comes along.

Values

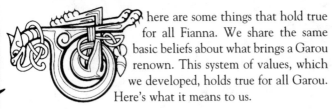

There are some things that hold true for all Fianna. We share the same basic beliefs about what brings a Garou renown. This system of values, which we developed, holds true for all Garou. Here's what it means to us.

Honor

The most important part of any Fianna's renown is Honor. A Fianna without Honor is nothing. Honor reflects not only on the individual, but on her pack, her sept, and her Kin, including her uncle. There are two ways to gain Honor in our society. First, obey the Litany. Second, do good for others, and if someone does good for you, return that good twofold. By the same token, we've long believed that if someone does you wrong, you return that wrong twice over. That last part is changing, though. If the Troubles have taught us anything, it's that sometimes it's better to return good for ill.

Give all that you can to the land, to your Kin, to your pack, and your Righ or packleader, and make sure that when you die, all your debts are paid. If your packmate dishonors another, then it's your responsibility to make it right, just as much as it is his; you are tied to your pack.

Glory

Our idea of Glory is simple. Destroy your enemies, and you will win renown. Despite the Litany, it's a tradition among our tribe to give the first part of the kill to the slayer in recognition of his victory. However, it's also honorable for the slayer to offer the first part back to his Righ or pack leader. Sometimes, making the offer to one's love is acceptable as well.

Wisdom

As loremasters to all Garou, we Fianna prize wisdom. For a cub, wisdom is memorizing the tales of the ancient heroes, learning the Silver Record, knowing your lineage and that of your packmates, and exploring the mysteries of the Umbra. We particularly honor those who discover new knowledge about the Fey, or those who uncover the truths about ancient legends.

Humor

As I've said, we have a problem with our passions. When we feel something, it consumes us. I don't know if you've heard about the Galliards who act out past events and get so caught up in their roles that when it's time for opponents to fight in the play, they start ripping into each other? No? Well, it happens, and I hope you never have to see it, but if you live long enough, you will.

We can't control our passions, and frankly, we don't want to. If you start shutting off your feelings, then you lose a bit of yourself and the wonder of life. You can't experience the good things if you close yourself off from the bad. On the other hand, we sure as hell can't go berserk when we see a movie we don't like or listen to a speaker we disagree with. If you live life like that, it'll be violent — and short. Just try going up to an Ahroun who ticks you off and tell her what you really think of her. You'll get the message real quick.

Instead, we use humor to express ourselves without bloodshed. There's nothing sharper than a good wit. If you don't like something or someone, make fun of it or him. Get a good laugh, and maybe the jerk will see the absurdity of his position. We laugh in the face of danger, and joke in the grip of fear. We make fun of ourselves when we're depressed and sinking into Harano. And when most of us lack the patience or will to use humor, thank the Mother for Ragabash!

I've seen more fights between Ahrouns stopped by a quick Ragabash than anything else. Learn to laugh out your feelings, it's the best way to go. Black humor, sarcasm, riddles, puns, light jokes — it all has its place. Don't feel self-conscious either. A bad joke's better than none at all, and you'll never tell good jokes until you've told your share of stinkers.

Humor puts a damper on our wild tempers and wakes us up when we're about to do something stupid. Of course, it sometimes makes us do stupid things, when jokes are taken too far. But that's the price you pay, I suppose.

Camps

Divisions in our tribe go back to ancient days, when clans fought each other, counties warred against each other, and our tribe split to watch over different flocks of Kinfolk. Time may have helped bring our Kinfolk together — though you can't tell with the Troubles sometimes — but it's done nothing but break our tribe apart.

We Fianna always find something to cleave to, and when we make up our minds, there's no way to change them. If there were naught but two

---

The Song

I'm going to get a bit sappy for a moment, so brace yourself.

We are tied, body and spirit, to the Song of Life. Gaia sings out Her joy to all of existence, and Her singing gives us life. In these days, the Weaver tries to control Her Song and weaken its intensity. The Wyrm wants naught but silence — or worse yet, discord.

The Song of Life is in our passions. We hear it in our lover's voice, taste it in our brews, and see the Song in the morning sunrise. It's our Song, because we are all part of Gaia, and each one of us has a voice to add to the chorus.

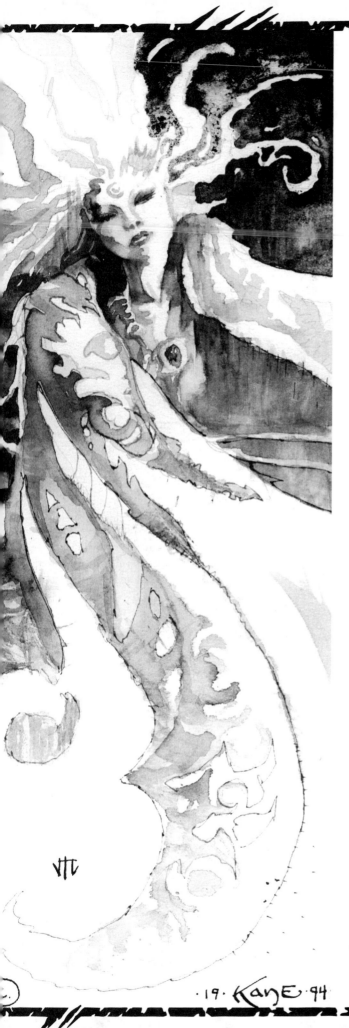

Fianna left in the world, one of them would take one position, and the other would take the opposite out of sheer perversity. That's the way we are.

Let me tell you a bit about some of the bigger camps, so you don't fall in with the wrong crowd.

Grandchildren of Fionn

You'll hear the legends of Fionn Mac Cumhail, the ancient hero of Erin, if you haven't already. Well, some of us aren't content just to listen to legends. They hear the story of the Fianna, the warrior band of Fionn, and want to live the myth. So, they sign up with the Grandchildren of Fionn.

You won't meet many more rugged lads and lasses than the Grandchildren. They travel around looking for a cause and a good scrap. They don't care about politics, they just like the fight. You can see it in their eyes. Sometimes they work for favors or funds, but half the time, they're simply looking for trouble to rear its ugly head so they can take turns trying to tear it off. I don't know what's more frightening, watching those blokes in action, with their guns and Klaives, or watching the sparkle in the eyes of a Grandchild Galliard when she sings about their latest victory.

Lucky for us, between the British army and the paras, the Grandchildren don't have to go far for a good fight. There are a couple of Grandchildren who've gotten a bit rabid about the whole thing. And to make matters more entertaining, a few of our other camps — like the Brotherhood of Herne— have their own political beliefs.

The Voice of a Grandchild of Fionn

You have a problem, friend? Well, me and my mates here, we'll handle whatever it is… We've been a bit bored of late. Got some drink? Good stuff? Well, maybe we can make this a freebie. After all, it's been a week or two since we saw any real action. We're getting a bit restless. And we have a rep to protect. It's all part of tradition. Except for the machine guns, of course.

Eire Fundamentalists

Tell your Kinfolk to lock their doors at night if you ever cross a member of the Eire Fundamentalists. They're more than a bit crazed. They believe the world should go back to the Impergium, starting with Ireland. They want to control the human population. They say human babies are screaming loud enough to drown out the Song of Gaia. So, the first thing they think needs to be done is to cull the human population to prehistorical levels. In their minds, there's a lot of killing to be done.

Don't get it stuck in your head that you can talk them out of what they're planning to do. They're all too mad for that. They let their hate for humanity eat them up inside. And I'll

·19· KANE ·94·

let you in on a little secret. Quite a few of them end up going down the same road the Howlers followed.

The biggest headache for the rest of us is that the Fundamentalists don't believe in keeping the Veil. You know, if it weren't for this camp of ours, a good third of all so-called terrorist attack reports would vanish.

If you're wondering why we put up with them, the answer is we usually don't. However, at big moots with other tribes, they love to crawl out of the woodwork, to the cheers of the Get of Fenris and the Red Talons, who agree with them just for the pleasure of starting a fight.

Words with an Eire Fundamentalist

Can't you feel it? They're everywhere. You look at the sky at night — you can't see the stars because of their cities. You take a breath of air and their pollutants choke you. I'm not saying that all humans have to die. Just 90% or so of them. It's past time to take Ireland and Gaia back. And I'm going to do it… or die trying. Let the humans fear. When will you join us… and rage?

Children of Dire

Now, despite the fact that there aren't any Fianna who can't fight, some few of us can really get down and dirty. The Children of Dire are the most vicious warriors you'll ever meet. They're all lupus, and not many wolves live in Ireland and the United Kingdom these days. Even in the U.S., wolves are scarce. But they've survived. Aye, and the survivors are tougher than spit.

The Children of Dire prefer to hunt in Hispo form. But don't underestimate them. Dires have tremendous cunning. They'll get their enemies, one way or the other. No mercy, no cowardice. They'll do or die. Never irritate one or let any friend of yours annoy a Child of Dire, even a Ragabash. They only understand violence. They're what becomes of a humorless Fianna. A warning to you — always keep a laugh at your side.

The other thing that the Children of Dire do well is howl. They make some of the best songs — rich and pure as only a song in the wolf-tongue can be. Their cries for the lost wolves of Europe will shatter your heart.

The Howl of A Child of Dire

Gaia, give our pack strength. Make our enemies weak, and send fear into their hearts. Weaken their flesh, and protect the throats of our packmates. We will not fail you, Mother. Tonight, the fallen wolves are avenged!

Whispering Rovers

These Fianna are descended primarily from Celts in ancient Gaul, otherwise known as France. They claim no land as their own and travel eastern and central Europe in bands they call bundles. They depend greatly on one another for survival. Like gypsies, these Garou are forever mobile, never staying in one place for more than a week or so.

The Rovers maintain an intimate knowledge of the European continent and are sought when such knowledge is need by other Fianna or even other tribes. They are also employed as scouts in Fianna war parties, due to their innate understanding of both woodland and urban environments.

A Chat with a Whispering Rover

What do you want to know? I can draw up a quick map of all the caerns between here and the Polish border if you need them. Look, no matter what it is, I've been there and done that. If it's a scouting job against the Get you want… well, I've only got one question. What are we waiting for?

Brotherhood of Herne

The Brotherhood of Herne consists almost entirely of Garou of British descent. It's really more a bloodline than a camp. However, these Garou stand as allies to the Provincial Army and are thus enemy to many Irish Fianna, especially members of the Grandchildren of Fionn. In fact, the war between the Brotherhood of Herne and the Grandchildren of Fionn has been the greatest threat to Fianna security for over a hundred years, despite the Council of Song pleading for peace and unity within the tribe.

The Brotherhood of Herne tends to be very loyal to the British ideals of imperialism, no matter how outdated and absurd they might be. Most of them are ready to see the Troubles in Northern Ireland get a bit worse, so they can step in and take over in the name of peace.

However, there's much more to the Brotherhood than the conflict with the Irish Fianna. They believe in protecting Britain and hunting the Wyrm wherever it lives and breeds. British imperialism let the Brotherhood destroy Wyrm strongholds all over the world. Although few admit it, many former colonies are better off after British rule than they were before.

Like other Fianna, the Brotherhood of Herne consider their land sacred. They were the first guerrilla warfare experts in the tribe, waging war against the Romans. Many heroes of English history were members of the Brotherhood or their Kin. Several members of this camp are Welsh and Scottish as well as English.

The Speech of a Brother of Herne

If the Grandchildren of Fionn would stop fighting with us and work together a bit, we could get on with the real problems of our tribe, like fighting the Wyrm. If we give the Wyrm a chance to take hold anywhere in the world, then one day we'll face yet another Reich, another Roman Empire. I don't think that's such a good idea in this nuclear age.

The Tuatha de Fionn (The Children of Finn)

The Tuatha de Fionn consider themselves distant relatives of the faeries. They make pilgrimages to the Arcadia Gateway in the Umbra every seven years, where they meet with representatives of the lords and ladies of the Fey. The Tuatha de Fionn are the best-loved of all the Fianna by the faerie court. They know many secrets of the Changelings, and some Garou say they have the power to use faerie magic. This camp also holds to some of the oldest Celtic traditions, including many long forgotten by most Fianna.

The Words of a Tuatha de Fionn

If we wish to remain strong, we must revere our faerie heritage. We are cousins of the Fey, and together, with their magics and our strength, neither Weaver machine nor Wyrm monster can stand against us. Respect the old ways; they will serve you best.

The Songkeepers

Dedicated to music in all its forms, the Songkeepers are a loose-knit camp made up mostly of Fianna Galliards, but all tribes and auspices are invited to join them. The Songkeepers travel between caerns in the fashion of ancient bards and add to the Silver Record with songs about what they see. They are universally respected, and no one refuses them hospitality, especially in exchange for a good drinking song.

The Tale of a Songkeeper

Well, this is a nice caern you have, steeped in tradition. It reminds me of a story first told by the legendary Amergin. Eh? You haven't heard any of Amergin's poetry? I'd tell you some, if I just had something to wet my throat. You have few brews here? Wonderful. Ah, well, you're in for quite a treat tonight…

The Totem: Stag

ur totem is Stag. He is the strength of the land, master of fertility, lord of the cycle of life and the mate of Gaia. The secrets of the Stag are many, and his powers are great. When he dies, his blood fertilizes the land, and a new stag rises up to take his place. Although he lives and dies, he is reborn anew in each passing generation, and possesses an eternal spirit.

Stag most often appears to us in the form of the Wild Huntsman, who leads us against the minions of the Wyrm. When the Wild Hunt calls, we gladly answer with howls to rend the night as we race to keep up with the Huntsman.

Stag guides us to wisdom as well. As the white hart, he is elusive; none can catch him save the wind. We give chase, and he always escapes, but he leads us to the miracles. Sometimes we discover a lost cub, other times a forgotten caern. We know that when the white stag appears to us, we must give chase.

Stag is our own inner strength. He is the passion which hides within our hearts, the part of us that remains unknowable until it is tested. Stag has ties to the Fey; our bards claim that the faeries revered Stag as their totem before he chose us as his children.

Breeds

o much of our view of Gaia depends on our breed. Blood means much to our people. Those of lupus stock are cherished for their rare wolf blood, the homids govern our tribe, and the metis… they do their part as best they can. We make certain that the metis cubs contribute as much as they are able.

Lupus

Unlike many tribes, we do not suffer a rift between homid and lupus. Lupus members of our tribe are precious, and we try to protect wolves whenever we can. The lupus have much to teach their homid brethren, and many of our most ancient songs and rites are in the wolf-tongue.

Homid

Like most other tribes, Garou of homid stock dominate. Homids are the best known among the Fianna, the ones most likely to have their tales told in our songs simply because there are so many of them. However, the homid Fianna also create the most strife for the tribe. If we were all lupus, would the Troubles have affected us at all? It is the duty of the homids to atone for the crimes of humanity against Gaia.

Metis

Our tribe takes a dim view of metis. If a body is corrupt or twisted, then the same is true of the spirit. Many tribes go soft on their metis cubs, especially in this day and age. They don't understand that they weaken themselves by doing this. Better to have a fit Kin in a pack than a metis.

A metis may never become a Righ or serve on a Council of Song. A Righ may never appoint a metis as Tanaiste, heir and second, because the metis doesn't have the physical purity to serve. Many of our septs let the young cubs tease their metis brothers and sisters in order to strengthen the spirits of the misshapen Garou. One thing's for certain: If a cub can survive being a metis of our tribe, he'll be able to endure the worst temptations of the Wyrm.

Moots

*ejoice in the sunrise
Dance to the moonlight
Dance to the storm*

— Hothouse Flowers, "Dance to the Storm"

We Fianna are at our best during our moots. Ah, the dances, the songs, the companionship, and of course, the drink. Makes me thirsty just thinking about it.

Some tribes don't know how to hold a good moot, but we've mastered the practice over the ages. We hold moots often, gathering our packs together and even bringing our Kinfolk with us. We're more open than most tribes and allow our Kinfolk to attend our moots often. It's the job of the Council of Song, the attendants to our Righs, to organize the moots.

Every sept of Fianna holds moots differently. It depends on the camp and the tradition they follow. A moot held by Fianna in Wales is different from one held in Australia. But there are three basic aspects to our moots.

First, a moot is a time for our people to gather and choose leaders. The moot provides an opportunity for grievances to be settled and for renown to be measured. It serves as a time for us to retell the old stories and share new ones. It keeps the tribe together.

Second, the moot gives us a time to pay our respects to Gaia and the spirits that guide us. It gives us time to commune with our cousins, the Fey. It helps us renew our spirit.

Finally, and most importantly, the moot lets us relax and enjoy life. We are a passionate tribe. We need our parties! Life is tough. Struggling against the Wyrm is hard enough, if you don't remember why life's worth living, then you can't fight to defend it. We love to drink, fight and love (that's why we invite our Kinfolk along).

It is at moot that we compete for the highest positions of honor in our tribe, the Chair of Poetry, the Chair of Song and the Chair of Stories. It's one thing to be a famous Righ and all, but to hold one of the Chairs — now that's an honor. Every year, at the Grand Moot at Tara, the Chairs go up for contest. Now, most of the time, the previous winner is good enough to keep his chair for a few years going, although the greatest keep it for life. But when a young rival wins the Chair — now that's an occasion for a party!

Other tribes always try to get into our moots. We have a certain rep. I think the worst of the lot, when it comes to getting in without an invite, are the Bone Gnawers. But, hey, if they enjoy themselves, the more the merrier. It's rare we have a moot with anything so secret that none can see. On those few occasions that we do, we protect our caerns well enough to keep visitors away. The Fey have an amazing talent for getting potential intruders lost in the woods.

© Kane '94

Fionn Mac Cumhail's Tests of the Fianna

We've long had an initiation test which we used in ancient times to discover early on which of our Kin was born true and would become Garou. These tests assured that an applicant to the Fianna fighting band of Fionn Mac Cumhail would live up to Garou heritage, whether he was Garou or Kinfolk. We often use these tests today as part of a cub's Rite of Passage.

• The applicant must be versed in the 12 Books of Poetry. Yep, that's right, book learning! You can't just be a warrior — you got to carry the wisdom of the people with you.

• The applicant is buried to her mid-section in the earth. She must then defend herself with but a shield and a hazel stick against nine warriors who cast spears at her. If she is wounded, she fails.

• The applicant's hair is woven into braids, and he is then chased through the woods. If he is caught, a braid of his hair is disturbed, or a stick snaps underfoot, he fails.

• The applicant must be able to pull a thorn from her foot while running without slackening her pace.

• And many more nigh-impossible feats at the choice of the ritemaster. Their severity depends, of course, on whether he likes you or not.

Fianna Calendar

These are the days of the endless summer
These are the days, the time is now
There's no past, there's only future
There's only here, there's only now
            — Van the Man, "These are the Days"

Our Councils of Song set the dates of our great moots according to the changing seasons of the ancient Celtic calendar. Solstice moots occur on the longest and shortest nights of the year. Equinox moots take place whenever the length of the night equals the length of the day before it.

Other, more festive moots are called whenever a Council of Song feels the sept needs spiritual and physical renewal. All our moots occur between sundown and sunrise. All septs have their own variations on moots, and I'd advise you to visit as many as you can.

Our moots all require special rites to get things going. If you want to be a ritemaster someday, I recommend you pay attention and learn them when you're at moot.

The Changing Seasons

Everything within my dwelling or in my possession,
All kine and crops, all flocks and corn,
From Hallow Eve to Beltane Eve,
With goodly progress and gentle blessing,
From sea to sea, and every river mouth,
            — Anonymous folk song, "The Beltane Blessing"

These are the four greatest moots of the Fianna calendar. Of them, Imbolc is considered the most important. All Fianna are expected to show up at their local seasonal moot and participate.

Imbolc (Feb 1 - Feb 2): The most widely and rigidly practiced of the Fianna moots, we use this ceremony to drink faerie brew and travel to the Umbra, where the Fey show us signs and clues about the year to come. Imbolc marks the change from Winter to Spring.

Beltane (May 1 - May 2): Still widely celebrated in different forms throughout Europe as May Day, Beltane is a fertility rite. Great fires are lit at night, and the Fianna salute Gaia and all Her glory. The Fey come and dance with the Garou around the Beltane fires, and it is a time for lovers to meet. More violations of the Litany occur on this night than any other, so the elders maintain a constant eye on the cubs. Many Fianna bring their Kinfolk to Beltane celebrations. Beltane marks the transition from Spring to Summer.

Lughnassa (August 1-2): This night celebrates Lugh and his victory over the first fomori. It is a night for telling tales of glory and a time to recover from the wounds of the year. It marks the end of Summer and the beginning of Fall.

Samhain (Oct 31-Nov 1): This marks the end of the Fianna calendar. During the night of Samhain, we believe that it becomes easier for spirits to enter the material world. We spend this moot reciting the Silver Record and paying homage to the spirits of our ancestors. Usually we hold a great feast on this night to celebrate life as well.

Solstice Ceremonies

Winter Solstice: At Winter Solstice, the Fianna gather and have a festival of light, sometimes with candles, other times with bonfires. This is a time for poetry and song. Many septs follow the tradition of calling the Wild Hunt on the first Full Moon after the Winter Solstice to drive the Wyrm from the land.

Summer Solstice: The Summer Solstice marks the peak of faerie magic during the year. This moot is often a solemn affair (compared to most Fianna moots) where great rites are performed to aid the septs and packs. Many elders create fetishes at Summer Solstice.

Equinox Ceremonies

Spring Equinox: In spring, we celebrate the reawakening of the land. For most Fianna, it is a time of feasting as the influence of the Wyrm wanes. Spring Equinox is a victory party in honor of the defeat of winter and the return of life.

Autumn Equinox: The Autumn Equinox is a time of rest after the harvests of the land. Like the Spring equinox, it tends to be a glorious party.

The Litany
Garou Shall Not Mate With Garou

Ahem. This part of the Litany has gotten more of us in trouble than any other. The body is sacred. Gaia creates us to be perfect. We test our bodies and our minds, and strive to take care of ourselves. And a metis can't ever achieve that natural perfection of the body.

Now, it's natural for two young pups who play together, fight together, drink together, and dance together to feel desire, passion, even love for one another. But it is wrong to bring a metis into the world. That's the way it is. Look, when you must slake your passions, then find one of our Kinfolk, stare into his eyes for a while, and just do what comes naturally.

Combat the Wyrm Wherever It Dwells And Whenever It Breeds

We were the first tribe the Wyrm tried to destroy, and we'll be the loudest at his wake when the Apocalypse comes. The Wyrm declared war on us, and we don't run from a fight. The fomori aren't gone; they live in every person the Wyrm corrupts. The Defiler made our Kinfolk suffer so it could break their spirits and enter their hearts. The Wyrm twisted the White Howlers, our brothers, into the Black Spiral Dancers. But did we let that get to us? Hell, yes!

Destroy the Wyrm wherever you find it and show no mercy to the tainted.

Respect the Territory of Another

Land is important to us. The body of our Mother gives us strength and nourishment, and she takes us back when we die. All Garou should respect the territory of others. We take this part of the Litany even further. Not only must you respect the territory of another, but you must respect your own territory. We are caretakers of Gaia. We must care for the land, just as she cares for us. Remain ever vigilant against the predations of the Weaver or Wyrm.

Languages

We use our own languages when we hold moots. We also speak in our own tongues to protect our secrets from outsiders. But we Fianna use many different languages. After all, most tales are best told in a tongue that suits their mood.

Irish Gaelic: We consider this our most traditional language, and many Fianna like to hold their moots in Irish. Even American-born Fianna often take the time to learn Irish Gaelic so they can drop a few words and impress others.

Scots Gaelic: The Fianna of Scotland and their descendants use this language. They take as much pride in using Scots Gaelic as the Irish do in using their language. Speakers of Scots and Irish Gaelic can sometimes understand bits of the other language, but they are almost two separate tongues.

Welsh: The Fianna of Wales have always been a little distant from their cousins. The Welsh spoken by the Dryn a drowd yn flaidd is very different from the Gaelic tongues, though it springs from the same Celtic mother-tongue.

English: Virtually all Fianna speak at least a little English. Although common English ruins some of the mystery and atmosphere of a rite, at least all our young cubs can understand it. English is commonly used for moots in England and her former colonies. We also use English to communicate with Fianna around the world.

Fianna elders sometimes cultivate an archaic style of Anglo-Irish with Gaelic syntax. For instance, you might say, "I've got a bad feeling about this," while an elder might instead say, "It is a bad feelin that is on me now." Or you'd say, "You piss me off," and the elder would say, "It is anger that you have on me." Instead of, "Do you speak Irish?" an elder might ask, "Do you have the Gaelic?" Yeah, it's weird to hear 'em talk like that at first, but it's natural after a while, and you might start picking it up yourself.

Garou: The Garou tongue is used in many caerns as a common tongue. More septs have started holding moots using the Garou tongue as so many caerns are now shared by members of several tribes.

The Fianna gave the Garou many of the words in the Garou tongue, such as airt and caern. We call the Garou tongue *Amharm* (pronounced ah-run), which is Irish Gaelic for "song." Some other Garou have adopted this term, but most use the traditional name, which is more wolf howl than word, and means "speak."

Wolf: The most ancient songs of the Fianna are sung in the wolf tongue. A few older septs use the wolf tongue for traditional reasons, claiming it's the purest all languages.

Accept an Honorable Surrender

There are too few Garou left, and each one we lose is another the Wyrm doesn't have to fight. This part of the Litany is especially important to us, because we have so long made a habit fighting amongst ourselves. It's an ancient Celtic tradition. To compensate, not only do we accept surrender, but we treat our vanquished foe as honored guests. We tell many stories of lasting friendships that came from fights. Also remember, there is no shame in surrender. Fight the good fight, but if you lose, do it with dignity, and buy the victor a round at the board.

Submission to Those of Higher Station

We've always respected our leaders. If you won't give the other members of your sept — your leaders and peers alike — the respect they're due, then you don't deserve their respect. It's that simple. But remember, nobody's above a good jibe now and then.

The First Share of the Kill for the Greatest in Station

Now, I know I said earlier that we Fianna have a tradition of giving the first part of the kill to the slayer. But you can expect a good beating if you tear in to your kill without waiting for your elders to offer it to you. Pups who don't show proper respect for their elders grow up with tattered ears.

Ye Shall Not Eat the Flesh of Humans

We are human and wolf. Both are our Kinfolk. We don't eat our own flesh, and we don't eat theirs, either. To eat the flesh of a human or a wolf is a sign of madness and Wyrm taint, and it tastes lousy besides — at least, that's what I've heard.

Respect for Those Beneath Ye – All are of Gaia

Everything is part of a cycle. Spring turns to summer, and summer turns to winter. We grow old. We die. All that matters are our deeds and how others remember us. If you spend your time cuffing cubs and puffing yourself up, then when those cubs meet in a Council of Song, and you're a pile of moldering bones, you won't be remembered well. And who'll toast you at your wake?

The Veil Shall Not be Lifted

Unlike many tribes, we're fairly open with our Kinfolk. Nonetheless, we've seen too many caerns destroyed or desecrated by archaeologists and historians. If anyone finds out about werewolves, then it's over for us. Just as the wolf was hunted from the Isles, so will humans hunt us across the globe. And then Gaia will have no defenders. If you violate this part of the Litany, your own packmates will tear out your throat.

Do Not Suffer Thy People to Tend Thy Sickness

There's a time for everything, and when a warrior's too old to serve his tribe, then it's time for him to return to the Well of Life. It's better to die in battle, fighting for something you believe in, than to rot slowly into a shameful grave. Most of our heroes head into the Umbra when their time comes. Perhaps you will as well.

The Leader May Be Challenged at Any Time During Peace

We believe that strong leaders make a strong tribe. No one can become leader without winning a challenge. In peacetime, any member of the tribe may challenge the leader. But I'll warn you right now: Garou who spend their time making challenges instead of winning renown don't stay leaders for long, even if they do manage to win a challenge or two.

The Leader May Not Be Challenged During Wartime

In time of war, no pack may stand divided and yet triumph over the Wyrm. This part of the Litany is critical. We don't have time to settle affairs among ourselves when we're busy settling them with our enemies. If something happens to our Righ, then the Tanaiste takes over, so that in wartime at least, our prowess is not hampered by the loss of our leader

Ye Shall Take No Action That Causes a Caern to Be Violated

It is the sacred duty of every Fianna to protect the land. Caerns are the most hallowed places of Gaia, and we must be willing to give our lives to protect them. Never allow a caern to be violated, through action or inaction. You'd just as soon piss in your beer. Again, should you betray a caern, your brothers and sisters will slay you as you stand.

Leadership

ur system of leadership is based on ancient traditions. A Righ, or warleader, commands each sept. Each Righ has a Council of Song made up of Philodox and Galliards who speak to her of the ancient legends and advise her on important matters. Members of the Council of Song serve as the officers of a sept, and the Council organizes rites and moots.

Righs lead their septs, but the Righs in turn recognize the warleaders of more powerful septs as their betters. This spiral of leadership continues up to the most important sept at Tara, which is led by the Ar-Righ, nominally the leader of the entire tribe. However, his claim doesn't carry much weight outside Ireland anymore.

All Righs, with the approval of their Council of Song, select a Taniaste. If the Righ falls, then the Taniaste serves as her successor, if she can pass the tests of the Council of Song. This prevents conflicts within a sept during time of war. Sometimes, the Taniaste of one sept is Righ of a smaller sept.

A new Righ must pass a number of arduous tests, both mental and physical. He must prove himself to be in the peak of physical health. He must know the Silver Record and the legends of our tribe. He must be quick-witted to jest and answer riddles. He must endure pain and show strength and speed enough to defeat the mightiest enemies. We test our leaders to make sure that they are the best among us — strong, quick and wise — and capable of protecting the sept.

Fostering

hen a young cub comes to the attention of the sept, he is fostered to an older Garou. In ancient times, fostering occurred between different septs. While this is still the case in some areas, this still the case in some areas, most fostering today happens within a single sept. The fostered cub refers to her surrogate parent as aunt or uncle.

Fostering is an ancient Celtic practice, and it lives on in the Fianna traditions of the uncle. The uncle has a responsibility to the tribe to make certain that the young Garou grows up well and honors his pack and sept. The behavior of the young Garou reflects on her uncle — her Honor affects his renown. For all practical purposes, the tribe sees the young Garou as the child of her uncle.

The uncle must do his best to strengthen and teach the young Fianna, so that the young one will become an asset to the tribe. But the young Garou is not required or expected to return the good done to her by her uncle; instead, she is expected to give of herself to the next generation.

A fosterling's uncle is usually the cub's closest blood relative at the sept. If a cub has no blood relatives, then the Council of Song chooses an uncle. Most Fianna consider it an honor to be asked to foster a cub. Elders who have never fostered a cub are not as respected as those who have.

Metis cubs are rarely fostered. Instead, they are solely the responsibility of their blood parents. If a metis' parents fail to care for their child, we send the cub to a caern of the Children of Gaia.

The Apocalypse

hese are the last days. It is the Time of the Wyrm. With each day that passes, the Apocalypse draws closer. Unlike many tribes, we don't look on the Apocalypse as the end of the world or even the end of the Garou.

In all of our legends and myths there are cycles; cycles of life and cycles of death. The Apocalypse is just the end of one cycle and the beginning of another. Gaia will not die as long as one Garou can raise a claw in her defense. It is like the death of the Stag. When the Stag dies, he gives up his blood to renew the world. So, then, the blood of the Garou who fall in the Final Days will renew the spirit of the world.

The Wyrm cannot destroy us as long as we have hope in our hearts. The key to surviving the Apocalypse is to prepare ourselves and believe in our hearts that we will triumph. This is why we celebrate life — in revels, in dance and in song — because we know that we must keep our spirits strong. As our spirits stay strong, so do we strengthen the spirit of Gaia.

When the final hour draws nigh, our fallen ancestors — Garou and Kinfolk — will rise from the land. Lugh, who slew Balor, will return. The banner of King Arthur will fly again. The warriors of legend will join with us at the last battle against the Wyrm. With our ancestors at our side, we cannot fail. We'll all sing and dance over the corpse of the Wyrm. For Auld Lang Synge.

Do not fear the Apocalypse. Prepare yourself, and live every moment to the fullest. When the end comes, with it comes a new beginning.

May you have warm words on a cold evening, a full moon on a dark night, and a smooth road all the way to your door.

— Irish toast

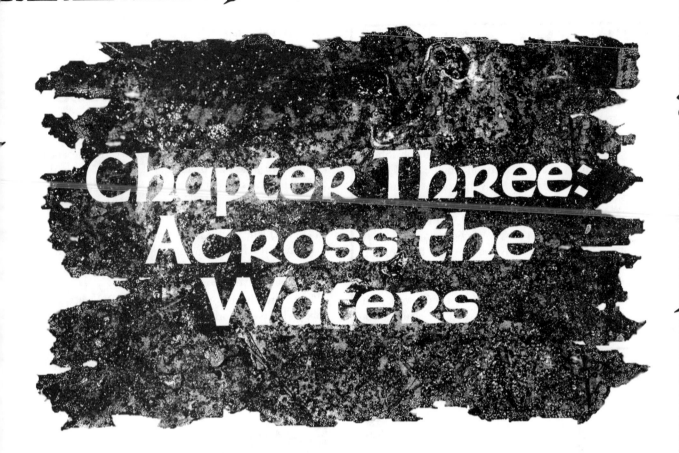

Chapter Three: Across the Waters

My Lord, this is our first offense but not our last. If you will be easy with us this once, we promise, on our word, as gentlemen, to try to do better next time, and next time — sure we won't be fools to get caught.

— attributed to the Irish prisoner Thomas Meagher, future governor of Montana, before he was sentenced to transportation for treason against the British crown

Where are the Fianna?
Ireland

The Celtic people have traveled since the beginning of time. We wandered across Europe from Greece — maybe even India, some say — before we got to Britannia and Erin. Some of our people kept traveling. We've spread across the globe with the British Empire. We've gone for different reasons. Some went for glory, others to serve our sentences, others because of wanderlust, but most for the hopes and dreams of a better life. Everywhere our Kin have traveled, we've followed.

In a land so beautiful
You just can't ever leave
Like a lover, she's so wonderful
But she only makes you grieve
— Grayson Hughes, "Hard Life"

Most Fianna consider Ireland their true home. The history and magic of the land is in every tree and every river. Fianna around the world know that when they set foot on Irish soil, they've come home. There's not a hill or plain or bog in Ireland that isn't part of a Fianna bawn.

The Dying Times

In the past, forests blanketed the British Isles. As the number of humans on the islands increased, they cut the forests down to build houses, roads and ships. These forests were the homes of many creatures, including the great Irish deer and the wolves.

As the woods vanished, so did the animals. Shepherds, farmers and noblemen alike hunted and killed the wolves. They used the Irish wolfhound to help exterminate our wolf brothers. We protected our human flocks, but could not save the wolf packs.

To this day, we aid wolves wherever possible. A number of Fianna have traveled to Alaska to try to stop the shooting of wolves from the air. Other members of our tribe work with the Red Talons to guard wolf populations around the world. Many Fianna work with environmental organizations to stop the slaughter of wolves and defend Gaia through peaceful means.

Wales

The wolves of Wales, the Dryn a drowd yn flaidd, are a strange branch of the Fianna. Descended from Cymric Kinfolk, they keep to themselves, fighting their own battles against the Black Spiral Dancers and the Weaver. Some say the Welsh Garou have a bit too much faerie blood in their veins for their own good.

The Dryn a drowd yn flaidd have strong ties to the Brotherhood of Herne, and they tend to side with the British Fianna against the Irish in most disputes. Many Welsh Galliards feel the Irish abandoned them during the Roman invasion, and they haven't forgiven them yet.

Scotland

The Scottish Fianna are some of the toughest Garou who have ever lived. Descended from the wolves and Irish Fianna who took the Pictlands from the Black Spirals, with a heavy mix of Irish workers who came to work in the mills, the Scottish Fianna have potent blood and powerful traditions. Rivalries between Scottish Garou tend to form along a line north and south of the Firth.

Scottish Fianna are renowned for their swordsmanship and fetish smithing. One of the greatest heroes of the Scottish Fianna is William Wallace, who, with Robert the Bruce, rebelled against the English crown and liberated Scotland.

They're a very clannish folk, and get along better with the Get of Fenris than the rest of us. The Get found out early on that you just don't piss a Scot off.

England

The English Fianna are the wealthiest and most influential members of our tribe. They all have relations to old families, and many have bred with Silver Fang Kin. They also are some of the most fervent hunters of the Wyrm. Members of the Brotherhood of Herne, the dominant English Fianna camp, have tracked the Wyrm to the far edges of the earth.

The United States

There may be as many Fianna in the United States as in the United Kingdom. Since the 1800s, many Kin have migrated to the United States in hope of a better life, and the Fianna have gone with them. Most European Fianna think of the Americans as poor cousins who don't understand their own history and legends. However, the American Fianna have shown strengths of their own.

They actually have a more romantic view of our history than many Irish Fianna, and have taught them a thing or two when it comes to songs about longing for Erin. Not a dry eye in the house, if you know what I mean.

Few Garou have gotten along so well with their fellow tribes as the New World Fianna. The American Fianna have strong alliances with the Bone Gnawers. They usually celebrate Super Bowl Sunday — the biggest American feast day of the year — together, and share the general American love of sport. Oh, yeah, we've gotten into scraps with them over it — I mean, who hasn't tumbled for their team? But we've come out pals in the end.

Boston, Massachusetts

This city in the northeastern United States has become a center for Fianna activity. It's no accident that some of the best microbreweries on the continent started in the area. Several Boston pubs are fronts for Fianna meeting sites. It's rumored that one even stands above a caern where everyone knows your name. Most of the Fianna around Boston are proud of their Irish descent. They tend to support the Grandchildren of Fionn and more than a few have done their part to aid in the Troubles. Very little goes on in Boston that doesn't come to the attention of the Fianna. In fact, one tale suggests that the vampire lords of Boston were Feystruck and driven mad when they tried to attack the Garou.

Australia

The Australian Fianna have little liking for the Silver Fangs and their English cousins, who they feel condemned their ancestors. They've adapted well to the land down under, and the Dreamtime has shown their Galliards and Theurges many mysteries.

The Continent

If a werewolf travels to all the caerns in Europe, he'll discover a number of Fianna who seem very different from their relatives in the United Kingdom and Ireland. These are the descendants of the Whispering Rovers and earlier Celtic peoples. Some of them are so different that they can barely be considered Fianna, but instead belong to their own unique cultures.

The Rest of the World

Wherever there was a British colony, there are Fianna today. Cyprus, India, Canada, South Africa, Zimbabwe, Belize and many, many other countries are inhabited by Fianna. These Fianna have very different perspectives from those who live on the Isles, but they still share the Fianna heritage and remember their past lives.

Beyond the World

Many Fianna travel to our Umbral homeland, a repository of Celtic spirit, where they find renewal. A pack of Tuatha de Fionn have even established a permanent caern there. But the most important part of the Umbra for the Fianna is the Arcadia Gateway.

Arcadia Gateway

Protected by strange twisting Moon Paths, the Arcadia Gateway is an Umbral Realm that contains the gate to the land of the Fey. The faeries hold two ancient castles in their realm, the bright castle of Lord Lysander of the Seelie Court, and a dark castle rumored to be controlled by an exiled faerie princess of the Unseelie court. Most of the realm is a thick forest, where pixies and brownies play tricks on any who enter. We believe the Gateway holds many secrets about the Fey and our own Fey-natures.

Attitudes Toward Other Tribes

 ell, we aren't the only Garou in the world, thank Gaia. We get along better than most with the other tribes. If only we could get along as well amongst ourselves. Generally, if you meet someone, give her the benefit of the doubt. If she does well by you, do well by her. And if she screws you over, make sure she can't do it again.

Black Furies

The Furies have a lot of the right attitudes about things, but there are more than a few messed-up lassies in that bunch. They're tough — that you have to admire — and they keep the worship of the Mother alive, but it doesn't take much to know that men and women both have their own types of magic, and one without the other can't do half as much as they can together.

Fellas who want to dance with a Fury — and many get that thought in their head — ought to do so with caution, or else they're liable to go missing their manhood.

Bone Gnawers

Let me tell you something: these blokes have a bad rap they just don't deserve. They understand loyalty and friendship as well as we do, and somehow — I don't pretend to understand it — they manage to find Gaia even in the heart of the Weaver.

Let me tell you this: you know what the best thing is about cities? You can almost always find a Gnawer around when you need one. Make friends with the Bone Gnawers, and you'll never need fear entering even the worst urban wasteland.

Children of Gaia

Peace-loving, wonderful mates, they understand what love is about, although they can take it a bit too far. Their problem is that they're a bit too nice. I mean, if it smells like a snake, looks like a snake, and sounds like a snake, you don't reach down to pet it — you bash its head in right good. Then you bloody well can look at it.

The Children of Gaia aren't willing to fight with fire, unless you can get them riled up. Still, we try and look out for them, 'cause we'd rather drink with them than with the damn Get. But they don't always get a good ethnic joke.

Get of Fenris

Speaking of the Get, did you know they once called themselves the Cubs of Fenris? We named them the Get cause they weren't worthy of anything else. 'Course, they liked that better, sick sado-masochistic macho Nazi lot. I mean, there just isn't much worse than the Get.

We have a lot of history with them, and you can sometimes find one or two worth sitting down and drinking with, for they do know how to drink, and some few can even tell a good story. One Get by himself may be okay, but together they're a nasty lot. And they think the harp is a sissy instrument — screw 'em. They can't grasp beauty.

One of the Get once told me that the best way to die is to leap down the throat of the enemy and choke the Wyrm-beastie. Well, if any of them want to volunteer, I'll be glad to help stuff 'em in. That way we can be rid of the Wyrm and the Get at once, and the world'll be a much nicer place.

Glass Walkers

Here's another that we're better off without. Most Glass Walkers are into crime or anything else that makes a profit. Big business never did us any favors, and the Glass Walkers' sense of capitalism and love of cities is something I don't think we'll ever understand...

As far as crime goes, well, some may not be proud of it, but our Kin and more than a few Fianna packs have set up their own criminal organizations.

Red Talons

These wolves need to lighten up. Killing people won't solve anything, it'll just stain the soil with more innocent blood. Gaia knows all our claws have more than enough blood on them. You have to feel sorry for the Talons, though. They've lost everything they believed in. If we lost all our Kin, well, we don't have to look any farther than the Eire Fundamentalists to see what could happen. For the Talons, the Apocalypse has already come.

Shadow Lords

These tight-arses tried to take over Europe during the Dark Ages. And you know what? They fell flat on their faces. The Shadow Lords are no more than a bunch of irritating whelps. If the Silver Fangs or anyone else ever ask us to help put them in their place, we'll be more than happy to oblige.

Silent Striders

A strange lot, the Striders… The Rovers like them, and I've been to a few parties where they dropped in all mysterious and unannounced. Some of 'em are like the gypsies, and they're worth sharing a good drink with. Keep an eye on your things, though. Some Striders are just weird. It's hard to explain. They ask a lot of questions and keep trying to look into old burial mounds. The secret to the Striders is keep on their good side — and keep your good eye on them.

Silver Fangs

The poor Silver Fangs, you've got to wonder how they managed to survive all these years. Some say they are all just prematurely gray. The Mother knows I'd go bald if I were one of them, what with the other tribes looking to me for help or resenting the hell out of me. Some are more than a bit mad, but I wonder sometimes… I've spoken to many who seemed a bit off, and it bothers me. I don't think it's just thin blood. Anyhow, they know their history, respect our knowledge of the Silver Record, and make wonderful drunks if you can get them to take off those pompous stuffed shirts of theirs.

Stargazers

The Stargazers are a funny set of blokes. They practice their asceticism and look for the world outside, when all the time life surrounds them, waiting for them to experience it. But they are reliable sorts, with unusual wisdom and experience. Like us and the Fangs, they are aware of history, although their view of the cycles of life doesn't always mesh with our own. Get them to loosen up, and pay attention to what they say.

Uktena

Creepy fellas, the Uktena. Constantly puttering around in magical things that any smart wolf should keep his snout clear of. They seem jealous of our relationship with the Fey, and you know they'd love to learn the secrets of our Gifts. We have a lot in common with them, though. Both our peoples have suffered oppression, and we've both lost a brother tribe. They could be strong allies against the Black Spiral Dancers.

Wendigo

Well, if they want to fight about the New World, they shouldn't start with us. It was conquered long before we started coming across the ocean. We understand how they feel — the Brits conquered Erin and have dominated her for 700 years! But, if they want to scrap, let's do it.

Other Shapeshifters

The Corax are our allies and our brethren. As for the rest, we keep our distance. The Moloké are the spitting image of the Wyrm. And no one can trust the Bastet, or anyone else so afraid of getting dirty, for that matter.

Vampires

Few things in this world are as vile and twisted as the Leeches. These creatures run the cities. They literally sap the life blood from their victims. Some are a pathetic, miserable lot, but they'll often as not tear your heart out if you open it to them. The best way to deal with a Leech is to shred him to pieces, and let Gaia sort out the mess.

Mages

We have strong ties to the Verbena. We shared our secrets of spirituality and Gaia with them, and they took that knowledge to levels beyond even the wisest Garou. They helped us practice the Impergium through human sacrifice, and sadly, they've gotten a poor rap for it. We consider the Verbena among our strongest allies.

As for other mages, be wary. There are some who worship the Weaver and its devices. Fear them. Others are pawns of the Wyrm itself. A few seem inspired by the Fey — they're called Marauders — but they do not care for the precious magicks of the land. Instead, they abuse them. Many mages covet caerns, so keep your eyes open when you're around them. Most of their ilk are best left alone.

Wraiths

Listen, as far as ghosts go… avoid them. There are some out there, and they have a nasty tendency to appear in front of our leaders during times of crisis — at least that's how the bards tell it. Be warned. Let the dead have their peace. And if you ever hear a thin wail echo across the night, beware. That's the call of the Banshee, and someone's going to die.

Faeries

The faeries are our distant cousins, and some of them, those with human blood, are trapped here. They are the Changelings, and they are in some ways like us. If you ever meet a faerie, remember you owe him, and he owes you. Stand by and protect them, but be warned, not all faeries are safe to be around. Beware the Unseelie courts and their dark minions.

riverrun, past Eve and Adam's, from swerve of shore to bend of bay, brings us by a commodius vicus of recirculation back to Howth Castle and Environs.

— James Joyce, *Finnegan's Wake*

Appendix One: Powers

Good they are at man-slaying,
Melodious in the ale house,
Masterly at making songs,
Skilled at playing fidchell.

— Anonymous folk rhyme, "The Hosts of Faery"

The Fianna have many secrets and special powers unknown to other tribes. Their long traditions and association with other supernatural beings, such as the Fey and the Verbena, have taught them much.

Tribal Weakness (Optional)

An optional rule was introduced in the first **Werewolf** Tribebook: tribal weaknesses. These are quirks each member of a particular tribe possesses, usually due to the social or even genetic nature of the tribe. Weaknesses should not always be enforced. There are some situations where a Bone Gnawer may not suffer a higher difficulty on Social rolls. These situations may be rare, but they can occur. For instance, Black Furies suffer from inborn anger against men, but a Black Fury may not feel anger toward a man whom she trusts.

It is up to the Storyteller to enforce these rules when an appropriate situation occurs in the game. After all, a player may be unwilling to remind the Storyteller that her Uktena's curiosity will get her into trouble.

Fianna Weakness

Low Self-Control: +1 difficulty for Willpower rolls

The Fianna often find it hard to rule their passions. They ride the emotional waves of anger, joy and melancholia. Most find it hard to govern themselves enough to shake off their moods.

Fianna players may roleplay this tribal weakness by having their characters feel everything intensely, turning the character into a frothing, boiling cauldron of emotion.

Merits and Flaws

Voice of the Songbird (3 point Merit)

Fianna with this Merit possesses a beautiful voice that haunts his listeners. On any Social rolls involving speaking or singing, he gains one automatic success. Wildlife also respond to his voice, and his songs will inspire most animals to join the singing.

Pain of the Past (4 point Flaw)

You suffered terribly in a Past Life. Flashbacks haunt you continually, especially when you are in pain. Whenever a Fianna with this Flaw takes damage, he must make a Willpower roll (difficulty 6) to avoid collapsing from Past Life flashbacks of starvation or torture. This collapse only lasts for a turn, but on a botch, it may last much longer. The Fianna must have the Past Life Background to purchase this Flaw.

Geas (1-7 point Flaw)

A Fianna may take a Geas, or prohibition, as a Flaw. If she violates this prohibition, she loses the ability to shift forms or suffers some other penalty, such as -1 to all combat Dice Pools for a story. The level of the Flaw depends on how common the Geas is and the nature of the penalty. The players and Storyteller should feel free to create their own Geases.

- May not enter a city (2-3 pts, depending on the chronicle).
- May not slay a fellow Garou, save for Black Spirals (2 pt.).
- May not harm a fellow Garou, save for Black Spirals (3-4 pt.).

Abilities

Faerie Lore (Knowledge)

You possess information pertaining to faeries. You know something about the Seelie and Unseelie courts and the great kingdom of Arcadia. You also have a good chance of identifying faerie spirits.

- • **Novice:** Your knowledge is largely speculation and hearsay.
- •• **Practiced:** You know some facts.
- ••• **Competent:** You possess a general knowledge of faerie ways.
- •••• **Expert:** You possess extensive knowledge of the Fey.
- ••••• **Master:** You truly understand how little you know of these creatures.

Possessed by: Faeries, Fianna, Occultists, Vampires, Mages, Witch-Hunters

Specialties: Enchanting Music, Faerie Food, Spirit Allies, Arcadia, Arcadia Gateway, Changelings

Poet's Language

The Fianna language of kennings is used in almost all their great songs and their Dindsechas, or place name songs. These kennings can be used in any language, but there are accepted conventions for using them. The Rituals Knowledge is useful for composing songs using accepted kennings, but it is Expression or Performance that determines how well they are used.

New Fianna Gifts

Faerie Light (Level One) — With this Gift, a Fianna can create a wisp of ghostly light, usually white, green, or faint blue in color. She can direct the glow to move, but the light isn't strong enough to illuminate more than three feet around the Garou. Some Fianna like to use this Gift to make their eyes flash green or blue. Ragabash love to create tricks with Faerie Light. This Gift is taught by marsh spirits and faeries.

System: The Garou rolls Wits + Enigmas against a difficulty of 6. The light appears anywhere the Fianna chooses, as long as it is within line of sight. It may float slowly at about 10 yards per turn. The Gift lasts for one turn per success, unless a Gnosis point is spent, in which case, the Faerie Light remains in effect for an entire scene.

- • **Ceridwen's Blood (Level Two)** — Blood has a power within it. With this Gift, a Fianna can tap the life-force within her own blood to restore a fallen ally. However, by doing so, she must suffer the wounds she heals. This Gift is taught by spirits allied to Stag.

System: The Garou can heal an injured target by spilling her own blood (a small cut will do) and rolling Stamina + Medicine against a difficulty of 8. One wound level is healed per success. However, the Gift-user suffers a number of wounds equal to the amount healed — she cannot soak this damage. The Fianna can heal aggravated wounds by spending a Gnosis point, although she will only take non-aggravated wounds in exchange.

- • **Howl of the Unseen (Level Two)** — The Fianna have strong ties to the Umbra. A member of the tribe with this Gift may howl in the Umbra or in the Realm and have her kenning echo on the other side of the Gauntlet. This Gift is taught by the spirits of animals that make loud noises but remain unseen, such as crickets and frogs.

System: The Garou must spend a Gnosis point to activate this Gift. He may speak or howl for a full turn, and his voice will be heard on both sides of the Gauntlet. The Storyteller is free to determine how much the Garou can say in one turn. Consider timing the player as he speaks for five seconds (if he speaks too fast and you can't understand what he says, then neither can anyone listening).

- • **Luck of the Irish (Level Two)** — This Gift gives the Fianna a supernatural streak of luck. Mundane effects include finding four leaf clovers, bills lying on the sidewalk, plump sleeping rabbits waiting to be caught for supper and minor fortunate coincidences. This Gift is taught by a faerie spirit.

System: The Garou spends one Gnosis point. She may then reroll any failed or botched roll. This Gift is usable only once per scene. Other minimal, although beneficial, effects may occur at the Storyteller's whim.

- • **Warp Spasm (Level Four)** — Many tales of Cuchulain state he would glow in combat, radiating a great heat. At the end of a battle, women would dump water over his body to cool him down. This Gift causes the user to radiate a tremendous heat, igniting nearby flammable items and melting metal. The aura only works while the Fianna is in a berserk frenzy. At the end of the frenzy, the Fianna cools off. This Gift is taught by Fianna ancestor spirits.

System: The Garou spends one point of Rage to activate this Gift, after which she will automatically go into a Berserk Frenzy. All flammable material she touches bursts into flame. Her hand to hand attacks do two aggravated wounds of damage in addition to regular attack damage.

• **Sleep of the Hero (Level Six)** — This powerful Gift has been invoked many times in Fianna history. When a great hero (Rank 5 or higher) dies in battle, the Fianna take the body and dedicate it to the land. This Gift forms a bond between the Fianna and the land and the spirit of the hero. The champion's life returns, but he remains in a deep sleep, not to awaken until the Apocalypse. The target must be placed somewhere in the earth, such as a cave, or within a burial mound. During this sleep, the hero is unaffected by the elements and does not need to breathe. This Gift is taught by Fianna ancestor spirits.

System: The Garou spends two points of Gnosis and rolls Intelligence + Rituals against a difficulty of 9. If she succeeds, the life comes back into the hero and he falls into a deep sleep, usually after having a chance to say a few last words. If the wielder of this Gift receives five or more successes, then the hero may awaken and return to the caern at any time of great crisis, at the Storyteller's option.

Tuatha de Fionn Gift

• **Sense the Unnatural (Level Three)** — As the Lupus level two Gift in **Werewolf: The Apocalypse**. The Tuatha de Fionn have long delved into magic and have gained the ability to sense its presence.

Songkeeper Gift

• **Cairbre's Tongue (Level Three)** — This Gift was used by the ancient songmaster Galliard Cairbre to show his people the corruption of Breas the Beautiful. By speaking out harshly against or satirize someone who is Wyrm-tainted, the possessor of this Gift will cause the Wyrm-taint to appear as splotches on his target's face, lowering the target's Appearance. This Gift is taught by faeries and Fianna ancestor spirits.

System: The Garou using this Gift must spend a Gnosis point, then roll Manipulation + Performance against a difficulty of the opponent's Willpower. If the roll succeeds, and the target is Wyrm-tainted, then she loses a point of Appearance for every success as incriminating blotches spread across her face and body. These marks last for a scene. If the roll fails, or the target is not Wyrm corrupted, nothing happens.

Rites

Rite of Inspiration, or "Awen's Blessing" (Level One Mystical)

This rite is used by a Fianna who is seeking inspiration for a poem, song, story or any artistic endeavor. The Garou must eat boiled pork while lying down in a dark room with his eyes covered and a stone on his stomach. If successful, he will be granted an idea or some solution to a problem he was facing in his art.

Rite of the Solstice (Level One Caern Rite)

This moot rite must be learned to conduct a solstice rite (at the Winter or Summer solstice). More information on solstice moots can be found in Chapter Two.

Rite of the Equinox (Level One Caern Rite)

This must be learned to conduct an equinox rite (at the Spring or Autumn equinox). More information on these equinox moots can be found in Chapter Two.

Rites of the Changing Seasons (each Level Three Caern Rite)

Each major moot on the Fianna calendar, is distinguished by a specialized rite. There is a Rite of Samhain, a Rite of Imbolc, etc. For more details on the moots, see Chapter Two of the **Fianna Tribebook** and the example of Imbolc in the **Werewolf Storytellers Handbook**.

Sacred Directions

The Fianna recognize five sacred directions in their rites. Each direction, besides having a quality associated with it, has a part of Ireland it governs also. Fianna caerns are often divided into representations of these areas. For example, when the Theurges gather, it is in the western part of the caern.

Direction	Qualities	Irish Province
West	Knowledge, Druidic wisdom (Theurge)	Connacht
North	War (Ahroun)	Ulster
East	Money, Wealth (Ragabash)	Leinster
South	Music, Song (Galliard)	Munster
Center	Sovereignty, Kingship (Philodox)	Tara

Fetishes

The Fianna have many legends about powerful magical items that transcended the limits of most fetishes. Fetishes like Excalibur, the Spear of Destiny and the Holy Grail (or Cauldron of Life) are artifacts and cannot be purchased by player characters; they must be found through adventure. It is up to the Storyteller to decide whether or not these items can be obtained and their powers within her chronicle.

Below are listed some more common, although still quite unusual, fetishes known to the Fianna.

The Lightning Spear

Level 5, Gnosis 6

This ancient spear transforms into a bolt of lightning when activated and thrown at an enemy. It does four dice of aggravated damage if it hits and automatically returns to the hand of its possessor, turning back into a solid spear.

Pipes of Terror

Level 4, Gnosis 6

This is a finely woven bag and set of well-crafted pipes. When the bagpipes are played and successfully activated (they do not have to played well), all Wyrm spirits within hearing range must check their Willpower (difficulty 6) or flee in terror.

Torc of Wisdom

Level 3, Gnosis 5

When activated, this torc increases a Garou's permanent Willpower, Rage or Gnosis (choose only one) by one point (one dot on the character sheet) until the end of the scene. Multiple torcs do not have cumulative effects.

Knotwork

The Fianna have created many types of knots for binding spirits. Each of these knots can hold a different type of spirit (for a look at the vast array of Celtic knotwork, visit a library or bookstore). If a Garou botches when activating the knotwork, the knot unravels and the spirit is freed.

Knot of Protection

Level 3, Gnosis 7

When activated, this knot automatically soaks the first wound level of damage taken by a Fianna in any given turn. This knot contains a turtle or stone spirit.

Tattoos

Much like Knotwork, Fianna may give themselves tattoos of woad and bind spirits within them.

Tattoo of Protection

Level 3, Gnosis 7

See Knot of Protection, above. If the Garou botches her activation roll, the tattoo flares and vanishes from her skin.

Talens

The Fianna have learned many lessons about magic and spirit. They can tap into the power of the land to create numerous talens.

Brews are the most common talens among the Fianna. Here are a few of the more popular Fianna draughts.

Gaia's Best

Gnosis 7

The absolute peak of Fianna brewing. Only a master brewer can make Gaia's Best. The ingredients are kept secret, and an apprentice brewer must pass many arduous tests before she learns the ancient methods of brewing. All that most Fianna know is that it takes years of work to make Gaia's Best.

The drinker must make a Stamina roll against the Gnosis of the brew. If he fails, he immediately falls into a deep sleep, filled with wonderful dreams of happy childhood memories and faeries.

If he botches, he stays asleep for a full day and doesn't rise under any circumstances.

If the drinker succeeds, he regains all his Willpower and Rage points, and becomes very happy. All his physical attributes rise by one for the next 24 hours. The effects of multiple draughts of Gaia's Best aren't cumulative. In any event, a few mouthfuls of this will send even the most hardy Ahroun reeling, regardless of her Stamina.

Unicorn's Milk

Gnosis 6

This drink is passed around during tense meetings to help the assembly relax. The drinker must make a Willpower roll against the Gnosis of the drink. If the drinker is successful, this elixir raises the difficulties of all Rage rolls by two.

If a drinker fails his roll, he loses a Rage point. If he botches, then he loses all but one of his Rage points, and he becomes a happy, philosophical drunk. The Fianna refer to this state as being comfortably numb.

In order to make Unicorn's Milk, the brewer must find a piece of hair from a unicorn's mane, usually gotten by traveling to the Children of Gaia homeland.

Faerie Fyre

Gnosis 7

This drink is especially favored by Fianna, because it gives a hot rush and makes the eyes of the drinker glow slightly.

A Garou who drinks Faerie Fyre must make a Willpower roll against the Gnosis of the draught. Failure means that all Willpower rolls increase in difficulty by one (+2 if the Storyteller is using the Fianna Tribal Weakness; see above). A botch means the drinker gets completely drunk and wild, acting on her basic passions, completely uninhibited. Faerie Fyre is called Wyld Wine by some Fianna.

War Whiskey

Gnosis 6

War whiskey is a harsh drink that explodes in the throat and burns all the way down. Some Fianna packs like to take a few shots before battle.

The imbiber rolls Willpower against the Gnosis of the drink. If successful, she can ignore the first wound level of damage she suffers in combat. If she fails the roll, then all Rage roll difficulties are reduced by one for the rest of the scene. If she botches, then she frenzies immediately.

Totems

Totem of Respect

Lion

(see also **Werewolf Player's Guide**, pg. 130)

Background Cost: 4

Proud and strong, Lion is the master of all he surveys, remaining ever vigilant of the Wyrm. He is the beast of Lugh, the slayer of Balor. Lion seeks vengeance on those who slew his children, and he saves a special anger for the Black Spirals who turned from him. Children of the Lion are especially hated by Black Spiral Dancers, but they are liked by the Bastet, most Fianna and Silver Fangs.

Traits: Lion's packs gain three points of Honor and Animal Ken 3. They also receive -1 to their difficulties when impressing elders.

Ban: Children of the Lion must protect helpless animals from danger.

Totems of War

Boar

Background Cost: 5

The savage and powerful boar is feared by many hunters. With its ferocity and anger, it will fight long after weaker warriors fall in battle. Many combative young packs chose Boar as their totem.

Traits: Boar gives his Children an extra point of Stamina and Brawl 2.

Ban: Children of Boar must never hunt or eat boars.

Herne the Hunter

Background Cost: 4

Herne is the horned master of the hunt. He stalks the Wyrm across the land and unleashes his packs to destroy it. Herne is the favored totem of many British Fianna, who see him as an aggressive version of Stag.

Traits: Herne gives his Children an extra point of Stealth and Survival and the Gift Sense Wyrm.

Ban: Herne's packs must always attack minions of the Wyrm, no matter what the odds.

Totems of Wisdom

The American Dream

Background Cost: 8

Only those born in the 1950s or 1960s can become Children of the American Dream. Prior to the '50s, the Dream was not strong enough to mark children as its own, and after the '60s, the American Dream lost much of its power . A child of the American Dream gains the following benefits: so long as he is in the United States of America, he never becomes lost. In addition, even if he is abroad, Americans make an extra effort to help him. The Storyteller may have Ma and Pa America show up just as the character is about to be thrown in jail, pay his bail, and give him money to buy a bus ticket back home. Difficulties involving interactions with public officials, government officials, or police — anyone who has sworn an oath to uphold and defend the Constitution of the United States of America — are decreased by three.

The downside to this totem is that devotees must make a Stamina + Survival roll (difficulty 7) each month to avoid becoming instantly addicted to something of the Storyteller's choosing (television, beer, cigarettes, etc.). They also begin to adopt a swaggering demeanor, tell other people what to do, and often cheat at cards, taxes and games. If a devotee ever leaves the U.S., this effect increases, and a Child of the American Dream living overseas only requires three successes to frenzy.

American Fianna, as well as Silver Fangs, Glass Walkers and Bone Gnawers receive five points of Honor renown when they ally with this totem. Non-American Garou, especially Silver Fangs, Black Furies and Shadow Lords, lose three points of Honor for making such an alliance, and will be marked by their own tribes as potential problems.

Many Fianna who came to the U.S. shared the Bone Gnawer tribe's vision of the American Dream. They believed in hope and opportunity, a chance to better themselves and their station. There are still a large number of American Fianna packs who still place their faith in the American Dream.

Merlin

Background Cost: 5

A merlin is a small bird of prey, a miniature hawk. Sharp-witted and dangerous, Merlin knows many secrets. Merlin understands magic, and, despite her small size, Merlin hunts the Wyrm with enormous ferocity and courage.

Traits: Merlin gives her children an extra point of Occult, Rituals, Enigmas and Primal-Urge.

Ban: Merlin commands her packs never to destroy knowledge.

Rooster

Background Cost: 3

The loud, echoing crow of the Rooster announces the sunrise and warns of the coming of the Wyrm. He watches for danger and uses his bright plumage to scare off threats.

Rooster is a proud totem, though his reputation suffers because most Garou only think of him as a barnyard animal. He is more popular among British and continental Fianna.

Gifts: Rooster gives all his Children the Gift Sense Wyrm.

Ban: None of his children may eat domesticated animals.

Fianna Renown Rules (Optional)

Honor

The Celts have long held that the status of the individual reflects on the status of the group. If a Fianna gains or loses 3 or more temporary points of Honor, then her Fianna packmates may also gain or lose a point of Honor. This gives Fianna characters lots of reasons to make sure every member of the group stays honorable.

Wisdom

Fianna who learn the Faerie Lore Knowledge (see above), or who discover something of significance to the Silver Record, may gain an extra point of Wisdom renown in addition to any other awards, at the Storyteller's discretion.

Legends of the Fianna

To learn more about the legends of the Fianna, go to your local library. There are several sources of Celtic legends which, with a little adaptation, can easily become true tales of the Fianna. Remember, each Fianna sept tells the stories a bit differently. Feel free to make your own interpretations. The history presented in this book takes liberties with Celtic myth to work it into the World of Darkness. Here are some of the oldest sources for Celtic myths:

Irish Sources

There are three main Irish cycles of legends. The first is the epic of the Tuatha De Danaan (the people of the goddess Dana), which is part of the *Book of Invasions* or the *Book of Conquests*. It describes the invasions of Ireland by different peoples and includes a different version of the Fomori Wars than that presented in this book.

The second cycle focuses on Cuchulain. It describes his life, including his tutelage by the warrior woman Scathatch and his love for Emer. His legend provides a great deal of useful material for **Werewolf** chronicles. Part of this cycle is covered in the *Tain Bo Cuailnge*, or the *Cattle-Raid of Cooley*.

To the Fianna, the most important cycle of legends is the Fenian cycle, which details the life of Fionn mac Cumhail. In this legend, Fionn, an Irish king, gathers together a band of warriors known as the Fianna.

Welsh Sources

The *Mabinogion* contains many stories from Welsh legend and myth. This includes some early tales of King Arthur. It is the best source of Welsh mythology, although it was written in the Middle Ages, although some of the tales can be traced to Roman times or earlier.

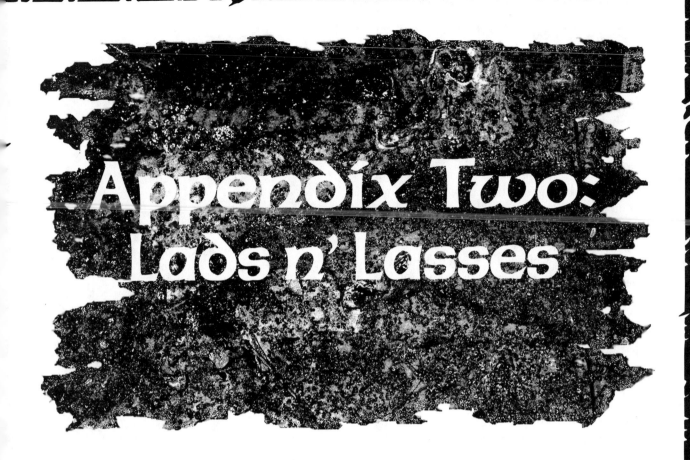

Appendix Two: Lads n' Lasses

O warlike man, rise that you might be great.
— "The Wasting Sickness of Cuchulain"

he Fianna share a common Celtic heritage, whether they are Irish, Scottish or Welsh. But they have split into all types of camps and individuals: modern Druids, street punks, aristocrats, vagabonds and gangsters. Here are five ready-to-play character templates.

Roving Ragabash

Quote: *If I haven't been there, it ain't there.*

Prelude: Both your parents died when you were young. After you went through a series of guardians and finally got access to your trust fund, life was going nowhere. You traveled around the world, looking for excitement, adventure, spontaneity, but nothing kept your attention. You had passions, but no goals. Then you had your First Change. You stopped exploring and started running. Luckily, you met a young man with bright green eyes who explained the Fianna to you. Overnight, you changed from a little girl with too much money to a woman with goals and a reason for living.

Concept: You still jetset and love to travel, and you enjoy bankrolling your pack's vacations. You leave the investments to the accountants; you dedicate yourself to whatever cause seems best at the time. You want desperately to explore all of creation, and you have a tendency to poke your nose where it doesn't belong. Some might consider your attitude toward life hedonistic, but you know that most people are afraid to really live. You've seen almost everything, and you still want to see more. Life is short, and there's too much time spent fighting the Wyrm not to have a good time while you can.

Roleplaying Hints: You are well-versed in all sorts of trivia. You know just enough to get yourself in trouble, but that's fun, isn't it? You love to spend money on people you care about, but not if it makes them feel uncomfortable. You've had lots of acquaintances, but few friends in your life. Your packmates are very dear to you, and you'd do almost anything for them.

Equipment: Cellular phone, yacht, credit cards galore, lots of clothes

FIANNA

Name: **Breed:** Homid   **Pack Name:**
Player: **Auspice:** Ragabash   **Pack Totem:**
Chronicle: **Camp:** Whispering Rover   **Concept:** Roving Ragabash

Attributes

Physical
Strength _____ ●●○○○
Dexterity _____ ●●●○○
Stamina _____ ●●●○○

Social
Charisma _____ ●●●○○
Manipulation _____ ●●●○○
Appearance _____ ●●○○○

Mental
Perception _____ ●●●○○
Intelligence _____ ●●●○○
Wits _____ ●●●●○

Abilities

Talents
Alertness _____ ●●●○○
Athletics _____ ●●○○○
Brawl _____ ●●●○○
Dodge _____ ●●●○○
Empathy _____ ●●○○○
Expression _____ ○○○○○
Intimidation _____ ●○○○○
Primal-Urge _____ ●○○○○
Streetwise _____ ●●○○○
Subterfuge _____ ○○○○○

Skills
Animal Ken _____ ○○○○○
Drive _____ ●○○○○
Etiquette _____ ●○○○○
Firearms _____ ○○○○○
Leadership _____ ○○○○○
Melee _____ ●○○○○
Performance _____ ○○○○○
Repair _____ ●○○○○
Stealth _____ ●●●○○
Survival _____ ●●○○○

Knowledges
Computer _____ ○○○○○
Enigmas _____ ●○○○○
Investigation _____ ○○○○○
Law _____ ○○○○○
Linguistics _____ ●●●○○
Medicine _____ ○○○○○
Occult _____ ○○○○○
Politics _____ ○○○○○
Rituals _____ ●○○○○
Science _____ ○○○○○

Advantages

Backgrounds
Resources _____ ●●●●●
_____ ○○○○○
_____ ○○○○○
_____ ○○○○○
_____ ○○○○○

Gifts
Smell of Man
Blur of the Milky Eye
Persuasion
Open Seal

Gifts

Renown

Glory
● ○ ○ ○ ○ ○ ○ ○ ○ ○
□□□□□□□□□□

Honor
● ○ ○ ○ ○ ○ ○ ○ ○ ○
□□□□□□□□□□

Wisdom
● ○ ○ ○ ○ ○ ○ ○ ○ ○
□□□□□□□□□□

Rank
[ ]

Rage
● ○ ○ ○ ○ ○ ○ ○ ○ ○
□□□□□□□□□□

Gnosis
●● ○ ○ ○ ○ ○ ○ ○ ○
□□□□□□□□□□

Willpower
●●●●● ○ ○ ○ ○ ○
□□□□□□□□□□

Health
Bruised		□
Hurt	-1	□
Injured	-1	□
Wounded	-2	□
Mauled	-2	□
Crippled	-5	□
Incapacitated		□

Weakness
LOW SELF-CONTROL:
+1 DIFFICULTY FOR
WILLPOWER ROLLS

Attributes: 7/5/3 **Abilities:** 13/9/5 **Gifts:** 1 Level One from breed, auspice and tribe; **Backgrounds:** 5; **Freebie Points:** 15 (7/5/2/1)

Fey-Struck Garou

Quote: *They are among us, my brothers and sisters. We must join their dances with our songs.*

Prelude: You still remember the first time you saw the lights bobbing in the forest. You were angry when everyone told you that you had a wonderful imagination, but didn't believe you, so one night, you snuck out on your own.

You discovered something wonderful: you saw the Fey. At least, you're sure you did. They were entrancing and frightening all at once. Somehow, you fell asleep in the woods. The next day, when your parents found you, they weren't amused. They didn't even notice the circle of mushrooms. You never saw the lights again as a child, except in your dreams. You always dreamed about them. You even dreamed about distant Arcadia, land of the Fey.

Still, you kept waiting for the magic to come back. Finally, as you entered your teenage years, you saw the lights again. You snuck out again, and unlike when you were little, you had a key to get back inside. Except this time, instead of faeries in the woods, there were huge wolves.

Concept: You are a perpetual dreamer. When you look around, you notice things others don't, like the shapes of sky between the leaves of the trees. You've been to the Arcadia Gateway once, and you long to go back again. You want to be Peter Pan and never ever grow up. However, you aren't completely impractical. The magic of the Fey will also give the land and your pack the power to defeat the Wyrm and the Weaver. At least, you believe it will.

Roleplaying Hints: You only pay attention about half the time when people talk to you. Usually something important is on your mind. You look for the magic hidden everywhere in the world, and you assume magical, faerie reasons for things a bit too often. You are spontaneous and outspoken.

Equipment: Four leaf clover (for luck), map of local ley lines, tattered copy of *A Midsummer Night's Dream*.

FIANNA

Name: **Breed:** Homid   **Pack Name:**
Player: **Auspice:** Theurge   **Pack Totem:**
Chronicle: **Camp:** Tuatha de Fionn   **Concept:** Fey-Struck Garou

Attributes

Physical
Strength ●●○○○
Dexterity ●●●○○
Stamina ●●○○○

Social
Charisma ●●●○○
Manipulation ●●○○○
Appearance ●●●●○

Mental
Perception ●●●○○
Intelligence ●●●○○
Wits ●●○○○

Abilities

Talents
Alertness ●●○○○
Athletics ●○○○○
Brawl ●○○○○
Dodge ●○○○○
Empathy ●●○○○
Expression ●●●○○
Intimidation ○○○○○
Primal-Urge ●○○○○
Streetwise ○○○○○
Subterfuge ○○○○○

Skills
Animal Ken ●○○○○
Drive ○○○○○
Etiquette ○○○○○
Firearms ○○○○○
Leadership ○○○○○
Melee ○○○○○
Performance ●○○○○
Repair ○○○○○
Stealth ●●○○○
Survival ●○○○○

Knowledges
Computer ○○○○○
Enigmas ●●●●○
Investigation ●○○○○
Law ○○○○○
Linguistics ●●●○○
Medicine ○○○○○
Occult ●●●○○
Politics ○○○○○
Rituals ●●●○○
Science ○○○○○

Advantages

Backgrounds
Past Life ●●●○○
Rite of the Questing Stone ●○○○○
Rite of Talisman Dedication ●○○○○
_____ ○○○○○
_____ ○○○○○

Gifts
Persuasion
Spirit Speech
Faerie Light
_____
_____

Gifts
_____
_____
_____
_____
_____

Renown

Glory
○○○○○○○○○○
☐☐☐☐☐☐☐☐☐☐

Honor
○○○○○○○○○○
☐☐☐☐☐☐☐☐☐☐

Wisdom
●●●○○○○○○○
☐☐☐☐☐☐☐☐☐☐

Rank
☐

Rage
●●○○○○○○○○
☐☐☐☐☐☐☐☐☐☐

Gnosis
●●●○○○○○○○
☐☐☐☐☐☐☐☐☐☐

Willpower
●●●○○○○○○○
☐☐☐☐☐☐☐☐☐☐

Health
Bruised		☐
Hurt	-1	☐
Injured	-1	☐
Wounded	-2	☐
Mauled	-2	☐
Crippled	-5	☐
Incapacitated		☐

Weakness
LOW SELF-CONTROL:
+1 DIFFICULTY FOR
WILLPOWER ROLLS

Attributes: 7/5/3   **Abilities:** 13/9/5   **Gifts:** 1 Level One from breed, auspice and tribe; **Backgrounds:** 5;   **Freebie Points:** 15 (7/5/2/1)

Black Rose

Quote: *Centuries of suffering make a tribe strong. Even the Wyrm cannot make us endure anything we have not already survived.*

Prelude: You are the child of a Fianna and another Garou. A few members of the sept tease you and say that your father was a Bone Gnawer. You don't really care. You know your mother and father loved each other, and your mother loves you. She taught you the Litany and the Silver Record. She taught you the names of things, and most importantly, she taught you how to sing and howl. Your deformity haunts you every day, although you've learned to compensate. You are blind.

Concept: You have a strong sense of who you are and where you come from, and powerful Past Lives. Your blindness makes a fun joke. This way, you can't see all the suffering in the world. You travel and sing like many Songkeepers, and you cling to the hope that one day, like your mother, you'll truly fall in love. Your favorite story is that of Cuchulain and Emer.

Roleplaying Hints: You carry yourself with confidence, probably to hide your insecurity about being a blind metis. You love being a Songkeeper. You find a beauty in songs and poetry that nothing can take away.

Special: Due to your blindness, you automatically fail all rolls involving vision. You often use your wolf senses to compensate, and the Storyteller may allow you to make smell rolls (Perception + Primal-Urge) even when you are in Homid form. Note: the character sheet lists the Blindness Flaw from the **Werewolf Players Guide**.

Equipment: Flute, rose-colored glasses

Fianna

Name: _____ **Breed:** Metis **Pack Name:** _____
Player: _____ **Auspice:** Philodox **Pack Totem:** _____
Chronicle: _____ **Camp:** Song Keeper **Concept:** Black Rose

Attributes

Physical
Strength _____ ●○○○○
Dexterity _____ ●●●○○
Stamina _____ ●●○○○

Social
Charisma _____ ●●●●○
Manipulation _____ ●●●○○
Appearance _____ ●●●○○

Mental
Perception _____ ●●●○○
Intelligence _____ ●●●○○
Wits _____ ●●●○○

Abilities

Talents
Alertness _____ ○○○○○
Athletics _____ ○○○○○
Brawl _____ ●○○○○
Dodge _____ ○○○○○
Empathy _____ ●○○○○
Expression _____ ●●○○○
Intimidation _____ ○○○○○
Primal-Urge _____ ●●●○○
Streetwise _____ ○○○○○
Subterfuge _____ ○○○○○

Skills
Animal Ken _____ ●○○○○
Drive _____ ○○○○○
Etiquette _____ ●○○○○
Firearms _____ ●○○○○
Leadership _____ ●○○○○
Melee _____ ○○○○○
Performance _____ ●●●○○
Repair _____ ○○○○○
Stealth _____ ●○○○○
Survival _____ ●○○○○

Knowledges
Computer _____ ○○○○○
Enigmas _____ ●●○○○
Investigation _____ ○○○○○
Law _____ ●●○○○
Linguistics _____ ●●●○○
Medicine _____ ○○○○○
Occult _____ ●●●○○
Politics _____ ○○○○○
Rituals _____ ●●●○○
Science _____ ○○○○○

Advantages

Backgrounds
Allies _____ ●●○○○
Mentor (Mother) _____ ●●●○○
_____ ○○○○○
_____ ○○○○○
_____ ○○○○○

Gifts
Sense Wyrm
Resist Pain
Persuasion
Truth of Gaia

Gifts
_____
_____
_____
_____
_____

Renown

Glory
○○○○○○○○○○
□□□□□□□□□□

Honor
●●●○○○○○○○
□□□□□□□□□□

Wisdom
○○○○○○○○○○
□□□□□□□□□□

Rank
□

Rage
●●●○○○○○○○
□□□□□□□□□□

Gnosis
●●●○○○○○○○
□□□□□□□□□□

Willpower
●●●●●○○○○○
□□□□□□□□□□

Health

Bruised		□
Hurt	-1	□
Injured	-1	□
Wounded	-2	□
Mauled	-2	□
Crippled	-5	□
Incapacitated		□

Weakness
LOW SELF-CONTROL:
+1 DIFFICULTY FOR
WILLPOWER ROLLS

Attributes: 7/5/3 **Abilities:** 13/9/5 **Gifts:** 1 Level One from breed, auspice and tribe; **Backgrounds:** 5; **Freebie Points:** 15 (7/5/2/1)

Warrior's Inspiration

Quote: *If you need to know why you fight, I've got plenty of answers.*

Prelude: You grew up in a rough neighborhood. The people around you were poor and disillusioned. You knew orphans, and you fell asleep to the sounds of gunfire. The world was a bleak, unforgiving place.

Then the Fianna kidnapped you. You were free. A new world opened up for you, although you resisted at first. Still, there was a magic in the world and something lasting. There were stories of battles and the eternal struggle against the Wyrm. You listened with open ears as the Galliards described ancient wars and love stories and recited epic poetry. You tried to hold everything in your memory, but you don't remember the details of most of the tales. However, you do remember the spirit of what you've been told. If you can recapture your brutalized childhood spirit, then those around you can find the strength to relive those legends. You don't just want to hear stories of honor and glory. You want to live them.

Concept: You see yourself as the emotional guardian of your pack. If spirits ever flag, you're responsible for raising them again. Your tongue can be sharp or soft, and you aren't afraid to speak up. Part of you wants to be an Ahroun, but you know that in your own way, the fighting you do to preserve the hearts of your packmates is just as important, especially since your packmates are Fianna. You love moots, where you get a chance to dance and sing to your heart's content. Your greatest triumphs come from inspiring others.

Roleplaying Hints: You are confident and friendly, always willing to work with others. You like your human form best and enjoy wearing sexy clothes, although you hardly want others to get the wrong impression.

Equipment: Leather jacket, ripped T-shirt, knife, small pistol

FIANNA

Name: _____
Player: _____
Chronicle: _____

Breed: Homid
Auspice: Galliard
Camp: Grandchildren of Fionn

Pack Name: _____
Pack Totem: _____
Concept: Warrior's Inspiration

Attributes

Physical
Strength ●●●●○
Dexterity ●●●○○
Stamina ●●○○○

Social
Charisma ●●●○○
Manipulation ●●●●○
Appearance ●●●●○

Mental
Perception ●●○○○
Intelligence ●●○○○
Wits ●●●○○

Abilities

Talents
Alertness ●●○○○
Athletics ●○○○○
Brawl ●●○○○
Dodge ●○○○○
Empathy ●○○○○
Expression ●○○○○
Intimidation ●○○○○
Primal-Urge ●○○○○
Streetwise ●●●○○
Subterfuge ●○○○○

Skills
Animal Ken ○○○○○
Drive ●○○○○
Etiquette ○○○○○
Firearms ●○○○○
Leadership ○○○○○
Melee ●●○○○
Performance ●●●○○
Repair ●○○○○
Stealth ●○○○○
Survival ○○○○○

Knowledges
Computer ○○○○○
Enigmas ○○○○○
Investigation ○○○○○
Law ○○○○○
Linguistics ●●○○○
Medicine ●○○○○
Occult ○○○○○
Politics ●○○○○
Rituals ●○○○○
Science ○○○○○

Advantages

Backgrounds
Contacts ●●○○○
Pure Breed ●●●○○
_____ ○○○○○
_____ ○○○○○
_____ ○○○○○

Gifts
Persuasion
Mindspeak
Resist Toxin
_____
_____

Gifts
_____
_____
_____
_____
_____

Renown

Glory
●●○○○○○○○○
□□□□□□□□□□

Honor
○○○○○○○○○○
□□□□□□□□□□

Wisdom
●○○○○○○○○○
□□□□□□□□□□

Rank
[_____]

Rage
●●●●○○○○○○
□□□□□□□□□□

Gnosis
●●○○○○○○○○
□□□□□□□□□□

Willpower
●●●●○○○○○○
□□□□□□□□□□

Health
Condition	Penalty	□
Bruised		□
Hurt	-1	□
Injured	-1	□
Wounded	-2	□
Mauled	-2	□
Crippled	-5	□
Incapacitated		□

Weakness
LOW SELF-CONTROL:
+1 DIFFICULTY FOR
WILLPOWER ROLLS

Attributes: 7/5/3 **Abilities:** 13/9/5 **Gifts:** 1 Level One from breed, auspice and tribe; **Backgrounds:** 5; **Freebie Points:** 15 (7/5/2/1)

Red Wolf

Quote: *All blood is red.*

Prelude: You were born behind bars in a zoo. You had an easy life; people fed you and made sure you got all your shots. You grew bigger than most of the other wolves, and although the Alpha put you in your place a few times, he knew his days as pack leader would soon end. The Alpha female was already afraid of you, although she tried to hide it. You knew that she would be your mate soon. You fought the Alpha, and he fell beneath your teeth. It was his time, he was old. Then, you felt a stinging pain in your side, then another and another. Soon, the world swam around you and you collapsed.

When you awoke, you were in a separate cage. You didn't understand. You had beaten the Alpha, the pack was yours. The humans shouldn't get involved. Then, a human unlocked the door to your cage. You snarled and lunged. If a human wanted your pack, he would have to earn it. The huge red-haired man caught you in mid-air, and you could tell by his scent that there was something different about him. He tossed you aside as though you were a cub. You were about to attack again, but he changed from a man to a large cross between man and wolf, and suddenly you wanted to be a cub again. You paused, and he cuffed you with a huge claw. You felt anger burn up in you, then something strange happened. Your bones cracked, and suddenly, your muscles felt more powerful. The huge wolf looked smaller, but there were more wolf-things. They swarmed you and brought you to the caern.

Concept: At the caern, you learned of your Fianna heritage. You also learned the truth about wolves and men. Man had all but exterminated the packs. You were kept alive to amuse humans, not out of fear. You want to end the shame and suffering of your fellow wolves and open all the cages. The day will come when the call of the wolf instills terror in humans again, when no one will mistake a wolf for a dog. But first, you must defeat the true enemies, the Wyrm and the Weaver. The hunting grounds are much wider now.

Roleplaying Hints: You tend to answer questions with grunts and growls and prefer your wolf forms over your human ones. You don't hate individual humans, but you despise humanity as a whole. You want to be pack Alpha, but you understand that the Alphas of Fianna packs aren't like the Alpha from the zoo. This frustrates you, and the songs and legends intimidate you, although you'd never admit it.

Equipment: You don't need anything

FIANNA

Name: **Breed:** Lupus   **Pack Name:**
Player: **Auspice:** Ahroun   **Pack Totem:**
Chronicle: **Camp:**   **Concept:** Red Wolf

Attributes

Physical
Strength ●●●●○
Dexterity ●●●●○
Stamina ●●●○○

Social
Charisma ●○○○○
Manipulation ●●○○○
Appearance ●●●○○

Mental
Perception ●●●○○
Intelligence ●●○○○
Wits ●●●○○

Abilities

Talents
Alertness ●●●○○
Athletics ●○○○○
Brawl ●●●○○
Dodge ●○○○○
Empathy ○○○○○
Expression ○○○○○
Intimidation ●●○○○
Primal-Urge ●●●●○
Streetwise ○○○○○
Subterfuge ○○○○○

Skills
Animal Ken ●●○○○
Drive ○○○○○
Etiquette ○○○○○
Firearms ○○○○○
Leadership ●●○○○
Melee ○○○○○
Performance ○○○○○
Repair ○○○○○
Stealth ●●●○○
Survival ●●○○○

Knowledges
Computer ○○○○○
Enigmas ●●●○○
Investigation ○○○○○
Law ○○○○○
Linguistics ○○○○○
Medicine ○○○○○
Occult ○○○○○
Politics ●●○○○
Rituals ○○○○○
Science ○○○○○

Advantages

Backgrounds
Allies ●○○○○
Past Life ●●○○○
Pure Breed ●●○○○
_____ ○○○○○
_____ ○○○○○

Gifts
Heightened Senses
Razor Claws
Resist Toxin
Leap of the Kangaroo

Gifts
_____
_____
_____
_____
_____

Renown

Glory
●●○○○○○○○○
□□□□□□□□□□

Honor
●○○○○○○○○○
□□□□□□□□□□

Wisdom
○○○○○○○○○○
□□□□□□□□□□

Rank
[ ]

Rage
●●●●●○○○○○
□□□□□□□□□□

Gnosis
●●●●●○○○○○
□□□□□□□□□□

Willpower
●●●●●○○○○○
□□□□□□□□□□

Health
Bruised   □
Hurt   -1   □
Injured   -1   □
Wounded   -2   □
Mauled   -2   □
Crippled   -5   □
Incapacitated   □

Weakness
LOW SELF-CONTROL:
+1 DIFFICULTY FOR
WILLPOWER ROLLS

Attributes: 7/5/3   **Abilities:** 13/9/5   **Gifts:** 1 Level One from breed, auspice and tribe; **Backgrounds:** 5;   **Freebie Points:** 15 (7/5/2/1)

Appendix Three: The Dreamers

The Legend of the Hound of Ulster

If you know no other legends of the Fianna, save of course the tales of Fionn mac Cumhail, then learn this one, and learn it well, young cub, because 'til this day, there's never been a man alive who could best the Hound of Ulster, Cuchulain.

It was a time long ago, when King Conchubar ruled Ulster from his court in the palace of Emain Macha. One night, after a great feast to celebrate the wedding of his sister Dectire to Saultim mac Roig, Dectire fell into an enchanted sleep. During the night as she slept, she was carried off by a Kami spirit who served Lugh.

A year later, during another feast, a flock of birds led by the Corax came to Emain Macha and devoured all the food, inciting the men of Ulster to anger. They pursued the birds across the land. Finally, night fell, and the men encountered a cottage, where a young man offered them his hospitality. He was the Kami of Lugh. During the night, the men heard the screams of a woman. In the morning, they discovered Dectire and her newborn son. She told them that she had sent the birds to call them so that they would return her and her child to Emain Macha. After they returned, King Conchubar decided that the child would remain with Dectire and her husband Saultim until he was of age. Dectire named her son Setanta.

One day, as Conchubar was setting out to attend the feast of the great smith, Culain, he saw a group of boys playing on the green of Emain Macha. One boy played against "three fifties of boys," and the boys could not stop him. Conchubar asked about this boy and discovered that the boy was Setanta, his nephew. The king asked the boy to come with him to the feast, but Setanta wanted to finish playing. Setanta told the king that he would follow the chariot tracks later. Conchubar laughed and set out for the house of Culain.

After the king arrived, Culain the smith asked him if any more were to follow. Conchubar answered no, forgetting Setanta. Culain let loose his great hound, one of the last dire wolves of Ireland, and renowned throughout the land for its savagery and cruelty.

Young Setanta finished playing and followed the chariot tracks to Culain's home. The wolf heard him approach, and rushed to attack the intruder, howling loudly. It leaped upon Setanta and tried to devour him.

According to the human stories, Setanta threw his game ball with enough force that it entered the wolf's mouth and passed through its body. What really happened was that Setanta underwent his First Change as the wolf leaped upon him. Suddenly, Setanta was a Crinos, filled with Rage. He tore into the wolf, splitting the beast open and smashing it to the ground.

Hearing the sounds of the savage combat, the feasters came running. King Conchubar and his men found the boy, seemingly unhurt, next to the bloody body of the wolf. The men asked Setanta what had happened, but he wasn't sure. He told the men that he only remembered throwing the ball at the beast. Luckily for Setanta, one of the guests, a druid named Cathbad, was a Fianna himself and quickly recognized the potential of the young Ahroun.

When Culain the smith saw his hound dead, he exploded with anger. He ordered Setanta to leave his house. Setanta quickly promised Culain that he would find a pup to replace the dead hound, and until he did, he would guard Culain's home himself.

Conchubar and his men agreed that the youth's promise was fair. Before anyone else could speak, Cathbad the Druid named the boy Cuchulain, the Hound of Culain. And that was how the great hero received his name.

Cathbad secretly took Cuchulain to his sept, and there taught the boy the ways of the Fianna. Cuchulain went on to become one of the greatest heroes ever seen by man or Garou, feared by all on the battlefield for his transformations and Rage. This is but the beginning of the tales of the hero of the Red Branch, the Hound of Ulster.

Cuin the Wanderer

hough I am old with wandering
Through hollow and hilly land,
I will find where she has gone,
And kiss her lips and take her hands.

—W.B. Yeats, "Song of Wandering Aengus"

The man who would take the name Cuin was always a strange one, even for a Garou. He was born in America, somewhere near Massachusetts. They say Cuin used to wander, exploring the deep woods, investigating the old houses and churches. Unlike most Garou, Cuin was never kidnapped by his own kind. The young lad just wandered one day into a caern, passing the warders, and asked where he belonged. The sept leader saw the sign of the Crescent Moon in the boy's eyes.

When Cuin first ventured into the Umbra, the lad found the Moon Paths to the Fianna Homeland without a guide. He traveled to the Arcadia Gateway, and may have ventured beyond to the courts of the Fey. A few believe the lad was part Changeling, part Garou, but I wouldn't say that.

He travels out in the Umbra, a wanderer without a caern to call home. Stories about Cuin have grown over the years. A few believe he saw the heart of the Wyld. Others claim he ventured beyond into the Lands of Death and returned. They say he searches for something, but what, no one knows. If you ever see him, you'll know Cuin. He has a wolf-coat of the darkest black and eyes that blaze with an emerald light, even in the deepest pits of the Wyrm.

Emira Ruith-an-Eas

ind the cost of freedom
Buried in the ground
Mother Earth will swallow you
Lay your body down

— Crosby, Stills, Nash, and Young, "Find the Cost of Freedom"

One of the most dangerous members of the Grandchildren of Fionn is Emira, a woman with flashing green eyes, beautiful red hair and possibly the best demolitions skills of any Garou. Emira has spent her entire life learning the art of terrorism. She could take apart a car before most people know how to drive.

After she was taken for her Rite of Passage, Emira was torn between her human lover and her Fianna pack. Then, soldiers killed her lover as he reached for his wallet, which they thought might be a gun. He died in her arms. Her Rage knew no bounds. She swore vengeance on the British and convinced her packmates to do the same. But the assaults her pack made in retaliation drew the attention of the Wyrm. Black Spiral Dancers and corrupt fomori attacked her caern. Her pack scattered to the four winds.

Now, Emira travels, working as a mercenary for any cause she believes in. Any time bombs go off outside a dictator's residence or a military target is mysteriously attacked, the Grandchildren know it's Emira, trying to make them pay for her lost love.

Patricia McKinnon

hen Patricia was young, her mother fled Northern Ireland to settle in Salisbury, England. Patricia always knew she was different from the other girls. She enjoyed visiting the White Horse and Stonehenge. She always heard voices and had dreams after she visited them.

After her Change, Patricia quickly gained renown as a Galliard. Her songs were among the most beautiful ever heard in England. When the Troubles in Northern Ireland escalated, Patricia felt the call of her home. She went back to try to stop the violence and bloodshed.

Patricia McKinnon wages a war in Northern Ireland to protect the innocent, Catholic and Protestant alike. Her songs have gathered werewolves from many tribes together, including members of the Children of Gaia, the Silver Fangs, and the Black Furies. Several terrorist attacks planned by loyalists and IRA members alike have ended on the tips of her claws. Both the Brotherhood of Herne and the Grandchildren of Fionn have tried to stop her, but to no avail.

One story about her claims that she was surrounded by members of the Grandchildren of Fionn, who planned to kill her. She made a last request for them to listen to her song. She sang about the atrocities of the Troubles, about the violence, and about the young children without fathers, the wives without husbands and the pain in all their hearts. Her voice moved even these hardened terrorists to weeping, and they left her in peace.

Fianna

Name: _____ Breed: _____ Pack Name: _____
Player: _____ Auspice: _____ Pack Totem: _____
Chronicle: _____ Camp: _____ Concept: _____

Attributes

Physical
Strength_____ ●0000
Dexterity_____ ●0000
Stamina_____ ●0000

Social
Charisma_____ ●0000
Manipulation_____ ●0000
Appearance_____ ●0000

Mental
Perception_____ ●0000
Intelligence_____ ●0000
Wits_____ ●0000

Abilities

Talents
Alertness_____ 00000
Athletics_____ 00000
Brawl_____ 00000
Dodge_____ 00000
Empathy_____ 00000
Expression_____ 00000
Intimidation_____ 00000
Primal-Urge_____ 00000
Streetwise_____ 00000
Subterfuge_____ 00000

Skills
Animal Ken_____ 00000
Drive_____ 00000
Etiquette_____ 00000
Firearms_____ 00000
Leadership_____ 00000
Melee_____ 00000
Performance_____ 00000
Repair_____ 00000
Stealth_____ 00000
Survival_____ 00000

Knowledges
Computer_____ 00000
Enigmas_____ 00000
Investigation_____ 00000
Law_____ 00000
Linguistics_____ 00000
Medicine_____ 00000
Occult_____ 00000
Politics_____ 00000
Rituals_____ 00000
Science_____ 00000

Advantages

Backgrounds
_____ 00000
_____ 00000
_____ 00000
_____ 00000
_____ 00000

Gifts
_____
_____
_____
_____
_____

Gifts
_____
_____
_____
_____
_____

Renown

Glory
0 0 0 0 0 0 0 0 0 0
□ □ □ □ □ □ □ □ □ □

Honor
0 0 0 0 0 0 0 0 0 0
□ □ □ □ □ □ □ □ □ □

Wisdom
0 0 0 0 0 0 0 0 0 0
□ □ □ □ □ □ □ □ □ □

Rank
[   ]

Rage
0 0 0 0 0 0 0 0 0 0
□ □ □ □ □ □ □ □ □ □

Gnosis
0 0 0 0 0 0 0 0 0 0
□ □ □ □ □ □ □ □ □ □

Willpower
0 0 0 0 0 0 0 0 0 0
□ □ □ □ □ □ □ □ □ □

Health
Bruised		□
Hurt	-1	□
Injured	-1	□
Wounded	-2	□
Mauled	-2	□
Crippled	-5	□
Incapacitated		□

Weakness
LOW SELF-CONTROL:
+1 DIFFICULTY FOR
WILLPOWER ROLLS

Attributes: 7/5/3 **Abilities:** 13/9/5 **Gifts:** 1 Level One from breed, auspice and tribe; **Backgrounds:** 5; **Freebie Points:** 15 (7/5/2/1)

FIANNA

Homid
No Change

Difficulty: 6

Glabro
Strength (+2)_____
Stamina (+2)_____
Appearance (-1)____
Manipulation (-1)__

Difficulty: 7

Crinos
Strength (+4)_____
Dexterity (+1)_____
Stamina (+3)_____
Appearance 0
Manipulation (-3)____

Difficulty: 6

INCITE DELIRIUM
IN HUMANS

Hispo
Strength (+3)_____
Dexterity (+2)____
Stamina (+3)_____
Manipulation (-3)___

Difficulty: 7

Lupus
Strength (+1)_____
Dexterity (+2)____
Stamina (+2)_____
Manipulation (-3)__

Difficulty: 6

Other Traits

_____OOOOO
_____OOOOO
_____OOOOO
_____OOOOO
_____OOOOO
_____OOOOO
_____OOOOO
_____OOOOO
_____OOOOO
_____OOOOO
_____OOOOO
_____OOOOO
_____OOOOO
_____OOOOO
_____OOOOO
_____OOOOO
_____OOOOO
_____OOOOO
_____OOOOO
_____OOOOO

Fetishes

Item: _____ ☐Dedicated Level _____ Gnosis _____
  Power_____

Item: _____ ☐Dedicated Level _____ Gnosis _____
  Power_____

Item: _____ ☐Dedicated Level _____ Gnosis _____
  Power_____

Item: _____ ☐Dedicated Level _____ Gnosis _____
  Power_____

Rites

_____
_____
_____
_____
_____
_____
_____
_____
_____
_____
_____
_____

Combat

Maneuver/Weapon	Roll	Difficulty	Damage	Range	Rate	Clip

Brawling Chart

Maneuver	Roll	Difficulty	Damage
Bite	Dex + Brawl	5	Strength + 1†
Body Slam	Dex + Brawl	7	Special
Claw	Dex + Brawl	6	Strength + 2†
Grapple	Dex + Brawl	6	Strength
Kick	Dex + Brawl	7	Strength + 1
Punch	Dex + Brawl	6	Strength

† These maneuvers do aggravated damage.

Armor: _____

FIANNA

Nature: _____   Demeanor: _____

Merits & Flaws

Merit	Type	Cost	Flaw	Type	Bonus
_____	_____	_____	_____	_____	_____
_____	_____	_____	_____	_____	_____
_____	_____	_____	_____	_____	_____
_____	_____	_____	_____	_____	_____
_____	_____	_____	_____	_____	_____

Expanded Background

Allies
_____
_____
_____
_____

Contacts
_____
_____
_____
_____

Kinfolk
_____
_____
_____
_____

Aunt/Uncle
_____
_____
_____
_____

Resources
_____
_____
_____
_____

Pure Breed
_____
_____
_____
_____

Past Life
_____
_____
_____
_____

Pack Totem
_____
_____
_____
_____

Possessions

Gear (Carried) _____
_____
Equipment (Owned) _____
_____

Sept

Name _____
Caern Location _____
Level _____ Type _____
Totem _____
Leader _____

Experience

TOTAL: [   ]

Gained From: _____
_____

TOTAL SPENT: _____
Spent On: _____
_____
_____

FIANNA

History

Prelude

_____
_____
_____
_____
_____
_____
_____
_____
_____
_____
_____
_____
_____

Description

Age_____   _____
Hair_____   _____
Eyes_____   _____
Race_____   _____
Nationality_____   _____
Sex_____   _____

	Height	Weight
Homid		
Glabro		
Crinos		
Hispo		
Lupus		

_Battle Scars_____
_____
_____

_Metis Deformity_____

Visuals

Pack Chart   _Character Sketch_

THUS CAINE — THE FIRST MAN BORN OF MAN —
SLEW HIS BROTHER, AND WAS CURSED WITH
IMMORTALITY AND A TERRIBLE LUST FOR BLOOD.

AND HIS CHILDREN AND HIS CHILDREN'S CHILDREN
BEAR THAT CURSE AND WILL RULE THE WORLD
FROM THE SHADOWS — UNTIL THE FINAL NIGHTS.

PREPARE FOR THE FINAL NIGHTS

In 1991, **Vampire: The Masquerade** changed the roleplaying world by introducing mature themes, avant-garde design, and an unprecedented emphasis on character. Since then, the story of the Kindred has grown through dozens of supplements, leaving the core rulebook behind.

THIS OCTOBER, **VAMPIRE: THE MASQUERADE** CATCHES UP WITH A VENGEANCE.

WORLD OF DARKNESS

WHITE
GAME S

www.white-wolf.c

SGT. RAGE AND HIS KILLING COMMANDOS IN:
THE FALL OF THE WAR WOLVES!
I MAY BE GET, YOU NAZI PIG. . . BUT I'M ALL AMERICAN!
STORY BY: JAMES MOORE
ART BY: RON SPENCER

SCRUNCH!!

THERE AREN'T ENOUGH STEEL DOORS IN THE *WORLD* TO HELP *HITLER'S CRONIES* NOW! *LET'S TAKE 'EM DOWN*, BOYS!

GE! HE'S GETTING *AWAY!*

NOT IF *I* CAN HELP IT!

SOMETHING *STINKS* DOWN HERE! SMELLS LIKE *WYRM* AND *FEAR!* LET'S GIVE 'EM REASON TO BE *AFRAID!*

SARGE! *LOOK OUT!* IT MAY BE A TRAP!

BLUT-KRIEG! SO *THIS* IS WHERE YOU'VE BEEN *HIDING!*

AMERIKANER SCHWEIN! YOU'VE *BETRAYED* THE GET OF FENRIS! IF YOU WOULD FIGHT FOR THE IMPURE ONES, YOU ARE NO BETTER THAN THEY ARE!

BETTER FIGHTING WITH THE JEWS THAN TRYING TO *KILL OFF* WHOLE RACES! HOW CAN YOU CALL YOURSELF GET. . .

WHEN YOU FIGHT ON THE SIDE OF *ADOLF* AND *HIS WYRM-PATROLS!?!* WHEN YOU USE *GAS CHAMBERS* TO DO YOUR FIGHTING?

YOU'RE ALL JUST *COWARDS!*

COWARDS?! NOW YOU WILL *DIE!!*

IT'LL TAKE *MORE* THAN A FEW *RATZIS* TO KILL US, BLUT-KRIEG!

GIVE US YOUR *BEST SHOT*, YOU TRAITOROUS FIEND! WE'LL SHOW YO WHAT IT *MEANS* TO BE *GET!*

KILL THE AMERICAN DOGS, MY *WAR WOLVES!* IN THE NAME OF HITLER, KILL THEM *ALL!* FENRIS UBER ALLES!!

4

SARGE! LOOK OUT!

THE DIRTY RAT'S STILL--

DIE, RAGE! DIE!

KA-BOOM!!

NOT SO *EASILY*, HERR RAGE.

SHOT CORPORAL! NAZI SCUM!

I'LL. . .

. . . SEE. . .

. . . YOU. . .

. . . BURN. . .

. . . IN. . .

. . . HELL!!!!!!

AAARRRGH!

CORPORAL? HOLD ON, KID!!

7

GET OF FENRIS
TRIBE BOOK

Of Axe and Claw

by James Moore

Credits

Written by: James Moore
Research assistance: Keith Winkler
Developed by: Bill Bridges
Editing: Laura Perkinson
Art Director: Richard Thomas
Comic book art: Ron Spencer
Art: SCAR Studios (Steve Carter and Antionette Ryder), Ron Spencer
Layout, Typesetting and Cover: Aileen E. Miles
Back Cover Art: Joshua Gabriel Timbrook

Special Thanks

Oh Soon "Red Nosed" **Shropshire** for guiding White Wolf's X-mas through the fog.

R. Christian "Not from aroundhere" **Naberhause** for his foreign ways.

Keith "Paducah Fats" **Winkler** for wielding his stick.

Danny "Toy boy" **Landers** for his growing collection.

Brad "Lost cause" **Butkovich** for all his Civil War books.

Rebecca "Flame on!" **Shaefer** for her human torch hair.

Diane "Dominatrix" **Zamojski** for being naughty, not nice.

Mike "Whipping boy" **Chaney** for being the X-mas present victimization poster child.

Louvie "UN peacekeeping force" **Locklear** for proudly bearing the flags of all nations at the X-mas party.

Jim "Designated driver" **Souter** for his remodeling skills.

Eric "The Red" **Turnbow** for being a Contender.

Sarah "Churchmouse" **Timbrook** as in "quiet as a…."

735 PARK NORTH BLVD.
SUITE 128
CLARKSTON, GA 30021
USA

Author's Dedication

The author would like to thank Keith Winkler for all of his assistance and enthusiasm, and Bill Bridges for making certain I didn't step on too many toes. Thanks also to my wife, Bonnie "The Black Furies are superior to the Get" Moore, for being a patient soul in an impatient world. Also to my entire family, for being fabulous Get of Fenris role models, though not quite as extreme.

This book is dedicated to the memory of Karl Edward Wagner. You died too soon, sir. Take Asgard by storm!

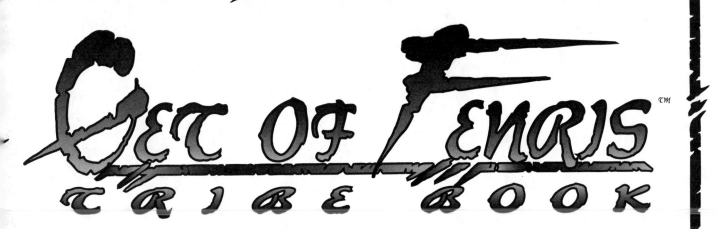

Contents

Introduction: Sturm und Dom (Storm and Doom)   12

Chapter One: Dreyrugr Spor (Bloody Pawprints)   14

The history of the Get of Fenris

Chapter Two: Krieg Lagern (War Camps)   24

The culture of the Get of Fenris

Chapter Three: Eine Welt für Nehman (A World for the Taking)   36

The Get of Fenris around the world

Appendix One: Seidar (Powers)   44

New Gifts, rites, fetishes, and totems

Appendix Two: Jung Fenrir (Young Fenrir)   51

Five ready-to-play characters

Appendix Three: Hamarar Fenrar (The Hammers of Fenris)   62

Famous Get of Fenris of the past and present

Introduction: Sturm und Dom (Storm and Doom)

A fighter is one who fights simply for the pleasure of fighting.
A warrior is one who fights because he must.
—Japanese saying

The Saga of the Get of Fenris, as told by Erik-Westfal-Wisetongue-Speaks-With-Truth, Thunder of Mjolnir, Skald of the Get of Fenris

Listen up, you morons! There's a lot to learn, and only a short time left to learn it. There are other tribes of Garou, and most of them think we're mad, that we fight simply for the pleasure of feeling a foe's bones crack beneath our fists. Don't listen to their foolish drivel! They don't understand the glory and honor of being a Get of Fenris, nor do they truly comprehend Ragnarok. There are a few who come close — the Black Furies, and even, Gaia help us all, the Children of Gaia — but most of them are mewling kittens, waiting for the Wyrm's teeth to come to them instead of reaching into Jormangundr's mouth to pluck away his fangs.

Let them believe as they will. Let them call us by any names they choose. They are weak. Their opinions are useless. They haven't realized that we are all going to die, that we are going to be buried in the stench of the Wyrm and suffer pains unlike anything we could ever hope to escape. Do not be afraid of death. Do not cower at the thought of pain. Revel in these things! Live for the moment when we can face the Wyrm in final combat and know that in our dying, we will destroy the Great Devourer. Only then can Gaia be at peace. Only then will the weaker Garou understand all that we have done for them.

Chapter One: Dreyrugr Spor (Bloody Pawprints)

That was early in the beginning times, when the gods had not yet created Midgard and built Valhalla.
    —The Edda of Snorri Sturluson (trans. by Keith Winkler)

The Fimbul Winter — the Final Winter — comes. The Fenris Winter is almost here. Learn your lessons well, know the faces of your enemies and know their weaknesses. Know the feel of fomori fangs in your flesh, and the touch of a Leech's fangs in your throat. Know the mages for what they are and how they can twist the world to do their bidding. Seek your enemies and fight them well, for only in facing your foes can you understand the truth about their lies.

Find combat where others would flee, and feel the Rage burn brightly, for the Fenris Winter will be cold, and you will need your Rage to warm you. Learn the soft spots of the Wyrmlings and be ready to use those secrets to your advantage, for the time of the Final Winter is near. Some have seen it in the Spirit World: their breath mists over in the coming cold. The prophecies will be fulfilled. Great Fenris will be free, and with him we will paint the world red with the blood of our enemies.

The Distant Past

Where do we come from? We come from Germany, from Scandinavia, from Iceland, and from a dozen other parts of the world. The history of our roving is as much a part of our heritage as anything the humans write about our Kinfolk in their history books.

We were not the first Garou, but we will be the last. Some say that we are merely a branch that evolved from the Silver Fangs. Few have said this to the face of any Get and lived to brag about the insult. We know better. Ages ago, Great Fenris created us as a favor to Gaia. Gaia was displeased by the humans who slaughtered her wolf children, wearing their skins for warmth and leaving the meat to rot or feed the carrion crows. The humans rarely slaughtered the wolves for food or survival. Instead, they killed for sport and to prove their paltry valor.

Fenris called us his Get, and demanded that we serve as Gaia's Claws, destroying the weak and feeding on the corrupt. In those days, Fenris still roamed free and often led his children in glorious bloody battles. From him, we learned how best to cull the weak from the flocks of humans. Humans fell before us, victims of the Impergium.

But we were both wolf and human. We learned many of the ways of the Nordic people, those who were the strongest and fiercest, those who resisted the Impergium well. We learned to live among them, to fight with them, and we chose from them the Kinfolk we deemed worthy. Does this sound arrogant to you? It should, for we are the Get of Fenris and our destiny is to kill Jormangundr in the time of Ragnarok.

From the first days, the Ahrouns have led us, for they are the strongest and the most savage. There are many who feel this is wrong, that others should be allowed to lead the tribe. I say to you what has always been said to the whiners: If you can take the leader down in honorable combat, than you can lead us.

The greatest heroes of Viking lore were actually Get of Fenris. We have tolerated the dilution of the truth among the humans only for the sake of the Concord. I can see it in your eyes… you feel that the Concord was a mistake. Many agree with you, but the decision was made before our time of power.

But I am getting ahead of myself. The Get of Fenris have been around longer even than the Vikings. The tales are a great deal older than you might imagine. They go much farther back than human archaeologists believe. They say the Norsemen were not really a cohesive people until 200 B.C., but this is wrong. We kept the Weaver from our Kinfolk longer than most tribes protected their flocks, and thus our people left no writing or proof of their ways until later. We are proud that we are thus able to hide the oldest secrets from the human scientists.

We walked the earth and roamed the barren wastes of the Northlands hundreds of years before the Iron Age. We have changed a lot along the way. In those times, we were simply called the Sons of the Wolf, or the Fenrir.

When our tribe arrived in the north, they discovered weak humans. If these humans were to be part of our flocks, they had to be hardened. Thus we began our lessons. We taught them to coat their hearts with ice, and let only the fires of their own hearths melt it. For dangers lurked everywhere, and a weak heart asked for death. Only among family and pack can one relax. All others are to be distrusted.

There were a few Garou in the area, but they were weak, like the humans, and we destroyed them. No one is certain, but many believe they were leftovers from the so called Pure Ones. Back in those days, when the Northlands were still in the grip of the Ice Age, the lands were harsh and food was hard to find. The Garou in the area had even given up on hunting properly, and kept their herds penned in, destroying the balance that Gaia had created. The Fenrir took the ways of the local Garou as signs of the Wyrm, and slaughtered many, driving others far from the lands we had claimed as our own. Some of the elders in the tribe say there were White Howlers among those we drove away. More likely, they were Fianna. If they were Howlers, then it is good we were rid of them before they could corrupt our chosen home.

The Demands of Fenris

Now you're messing with a son of a bitch.
— Nazareth, "Hair of the Dog"

Not long after we settled in the north, Fenris came to make a few demands. He called for weapons made of metal, and so we learned to smelt bronze. He demanded that we improve our fighting skills, and, to keep Fenris happy, we did just that. There was no one who could match us, but that did not matter. The Wyrm started playing dirty around the same time and, as Banes

and other creatures started creeping around in the woods, we got our first taste of the Wyrm's blood. Leeches lurked in the area, fleeing from other parts of Europe, and we taught them that they did not belong here.

The Bronze Age was hard on the Fenrir, but that was to be expected. Those who fell in battle were remembered in song and poem, and great moots were held in their honor. Those who died a coward's death were stricken from all of our records, the oral and the rare written ones as well. There is no place in the tribe for cowards. This much has not changed since those ancient times.

Our ancestors followed Gaia's plan as well, cultivating forests in areas that had been all but barren, making certain that the Wyld had a chance to grow strong again after the Ice Age — the punishment Gaia had to use to stave off the Wyrm's foul advances. In those days the Weaver was almost unknown.

The faeries grew strong in the area, and we became friends with some of them, and enemies with others. Around the same time, we were getting familiar with iron weapons, a trick that the Dvergar — the Dwarves — taught us well. We made bitter enemies among the Trolls and the Jotunn — the Giants. Both groups felt they were better than us, more qualified to watch over the land and willing to smash our Kinfolk in the process. Most of you already understand how important our Kinfolk are these days. They were just as important back then. So when the Jotunn came in raids to steal our women, we smashed them back down.

In the Iron Age, we perfected our ways as the true warriors of Gaia. Everything before that was just a game in comparison. The Wyrm's minions came in force, this time working in unison, often ruled by Leeches. They brought iron of their own, and silver as well. For a few centuries, it was uncertain who would hold the land. But in the end, we held out, and put the Wyrm in retreat. For a short time…

The Roman Invasions

The Romans tried to conquer our southern lands. We had a Rotagar — a Ragabash — who ran around from place to place, never staying where he belonged. He came to the aid of Arminius when the Romans started getting nasty. There was a tribe of humans, called the Cherusci, that the Rotagar watched over. While they were good Kinfolk, both savage and remorseless in combat, they had no Get with them at the time the Romans came. They lived in the nasty, rough terrain of the Teutoburg Forest.

Well, Publius Quinctillius Varus, a pompous general with a snotty name, came to the area with three full legions under his command, and got ready to march right over the people in the area. When the New Moon learned of the attack, he decided to give the people a little help.

He called on the leaders of the area septs and asked for any pups in need of the Rite of Passage. He found seven total. The pups were joined together in combat in order to help the Cherusci. That was the first time a Rite of Passage among the Get was a joint challenge instead of a solitary quest, but it wouldn't be the last. None of the legions survived.

Arminius pointed out to the seven rankless Garou a narrow canyon through which the Roman soldiers had to pass in order to reach his tribe's land: the perfect site for an ambush. The human tribesmen, lining the walls above the canyon, watched over the Get of Fenris as they met the approaching legions, prepared to pick off the survivors of the pups' fury. The legends say Arminius' tribe had only a few dozen to worry about.

The Fall

The Roman Empire fell hard because the Get of Fenris, along with the Black Furies and the Fianna, brought the Wyrm-ridden empire to its knees. A long series of battles against the Romans unified our tribes for the first time in centuries. We had found others who were enraged by the foul, crushing weight of the Wyrm's personal army.

I see I need to explain myself here; I can see the confusion in your eyes. We have always been aware of the other tribes, and we have been allied with some; but we seldom bothered with the others in those distant times. We were busy establishing ourselves as a power in the Northlands. There were Get in other parts of the world — in Russia and Gaul — but they were emissaries, not leaders.

The Fianna and the Black Furies fought well, and for a time we were close allies. But the relationship ended after we crushed the Wyrm's Empire, and the other tribes attempted to force their own beliefs upon us. We were too set in our ways, and they were too set in theirs. There could never have been a long-time alliance, for the other tribes refused to acknowledge our superiority. We had too many problems to settle in our own lands to teach them the error of their ways.

The End of the Mythic Age

Just when things seemed their worst, the first of our tribe to call himself a Get of Fenris came around to set things right. He was favored by Fenris, there is no doubt about that. When the Roman Legions were trying to force their way into our lands, along with the Leeches and the Wyrmlings, a brave Garou was chosen by Fenris to lead us in glorious bloody combat.

He came from Denmark, bringing with him everlasting honor and glory that are examples to us all. His full Garou name was Get-of-Fenris-Slays-Grendel. In the human legends, he is known simply as Beowulf.

No one can say for certain what Grendel was, but the nasty creature served the Wyrm and worked with the Leeches. It even worked with mages, and supposedly could call upon the dead to do its bidding. Some say Beowulf actually faced Grendel alone, after his entire pack was torn apart by the Wyrmling. Others say he was the only one to survive the battle against Grendel. No one knows for sure. But he did tear the monster apart, and killed the foul thing's mother, too. With Beowulf leading the way, there was no doubt that our time had come.

It was in this time that the Fey fled their homes all over the world. Only a few still remain. Do not harm them unless they stink of the Wyrm. They were our allies once, and the time will come when we shall join with them again.

The forces of Jormangundr were driven back, and the Get learned to fight together in those times, learned to understand the importance of military strategy and to appreciate the feel of a good weapon in a blood-stained paw. However, some Leeches still remained deep in the woods; they are still there today. That will change in time. They will soon know the fury of the Get, and learn the meaning of fear.

Get-of-Fenris-Slays-Grendel's most important accomplishment was to drive the mages out of the Black Forest. There was a place of mage power in the Schwarzwald, where they used the blood of Kinfolk and Garou alike to hide their secrets and to steal power from our kind. Beowulf learned of the Verbena witches. He traveled to Germany from his native home in Denmark. By that point, he was the leader of both his pack and the entire tribe. Beowulf ordered the witches to flee. They scoffed at his threats, casting fires from the sky with the aim to destroy him. He was grievously wounded, but this did not stop him from calling the Get to arms and leading the battle to drive the witches away from the Black Forest.

Many years later, Beowulf died a hero's death. The humans say he battled the Fire Dragon to save the Geats, his human tribe. They are right. Get-of-Fenris-Slays-Grendel died to save

the Fenrir from one of the Great Zmei, the Forgotten Dragon Who is Nameless. The Silver Fang of Russia claim it was but a baby that Beowulf killed, but we know it was the greatest of all the Zmei yet, more powerful than the Silver Fang can imagine. If Beowulf had not killed the monster, it would have carved its name across the world. But Beowulf was triumphant. The creature was destroyed and its name with it, as our Godi had bidden for reasons of their own.

To honor this greatest of heroes, the Fenrir changed the name of their tribe to the Get of Fenris. When Get-of-Fenris-Slays-Grendel died, the newly-named Get of Fenris found themselves without a leader, and so Great Fenris called upon the Ahrouns to do battle. Each pack, each sept, selected a champion from among their numbers. The combatants met beneath a harvest moon, and all fought as fiercely as any Get ever. When the struggle was finished, only one champion was left standing. He earned the right to lead us all, and was called Blood-Rage from that day forward. His Great-Grandson, Erik Thorvaldson, called Eric the Red, later discovered Greenland, and claimed it for the Get of Fenris.

The Viking Era (750–1050 AD)

When the Vikings came into power, we were there with them. The other tribes ignored the Get of Fenris up until that point, but no longer would we be treated as a lesser tribe. Once again, Fenris made himself known to us. He demanded that we begin culling the weak of other lands, for the other tribes had become lax in this purpose. By then, the Get were physically superior to most other Garou: we were stronger, and our life in the north had prepared us to survive even the harshest living conditions.

We moved into all parts of Europe, testing the strength of other Garou, slaying those too weak to hold their caerns, and celebrating with the ones who matched us in ferocity. We traveled with our Viking Kinfolk, using their raids to cover our own retributions. Meanwhile, we culled the weak from the lands we raided.

Leif Eriksson, son of Eric the Red, went as far as America in those times. Many claim he was lost, and landed there by mistake, but the Get know better. Leif knew where America was because a Kinfolk of his, Bjarni Herjolfsson, had actually gotten lost, and had come upon this land of the "Pure Ones." The Pure Ones took offense to the Kinfolk of the Get, and chased them away.

Leif took the insult personally, as all good Get are offended by attacks against their Kinfolk. Fenris had demanded that we cull the weak from all the lands, and so Leif took this opportunity to challenge the naive Native Americans. Leif and his pack swept into the Pure Lands. They remained there for three years, smashing down all attackers until they were certain their point had been made. You'll hear that the Vikings were driven away from America, fearing for their lives, but that is not the case. They stayed only long enough to track down and destroy all the fools who had assaulted their Kinfolk.

Other Vikings came to the Americas, but they left of their own volition when they realized the lands held nothing of great value. The Skraelings, the ones who called themselves the Pure Ones, were filthy little savages who had nothing better to offer than a few furs in trade. No Get or Viking ever needed to trade for a fur, so we left.

We made friends and enemies alike in Europe. We joined with those of our tribe who had never settled in the Northlands, and reaffirmed our alliance with the Silver Fangs, who by virtue of their pure breeding had traditionally been the leaders over even our tribe in intra-tribal matters. They were weaker than us by then, but they were also wise and noble, well prepared to lead the other tribes.

We reintroduced ourselves to the Romans — or what remained of them — and avenged ourselves against their earlier attempts to conquer our lands. We would have overwhelmed them completely, if not for the Black Furies. There was no love lost between our tribes, for they had grown proud and foolhardy since the fall of the Roman Empire. They deny it now, but it was only because we felt sorry for the bitch-wolves that we spared them the worst of our wrath. I've heard talk about how we supposedly helped the humans burn Black Furies as witches, and I can tell you matter-of-factly that those tales are nothing but lies; the Get of Fenris are warriors, and even the craftiest Rotagar would never stoop that low.

The Red Talons met our standards as warriors, but had to be forced to leave our Kinfolk alone. There were a few bloody battles between our tribes, but in the long run we came to an understanding. We have much in common with the Red Talons: we both know how to use our Rage as a tool for combat, and we both understand the need for slowing the humans' expansion.

Britain and the Get of Fenris

Eventually we made our way to the British Isles, and it was a damned good thing we arrived when we did. No sooner had we smashed down the human resistance in the area, claiming land as our own and rescuing several caerns, then the Wyrm made its presence known in the worst possible way. The Wyrm-corrupted Black Spiral Dancers were attempting to expand their Scottish stronghold, forcing the Fianna away from their own caerns and bringing every foul creature they could with them. If it had not been for our presence, the Fianna would have fallen before them.

Now, I need to explain a little here. The White Howlers were brave warriors, and they had done many great deeds in their time. They and the Fianna had much in common. We have always respected the Fianna as worthy enemies — weaker than us, certainly, but worthy enough opponents. They believe, as we do, that the only way to win a war is to actually fight the battles. They drink too much, and they spend too much time singing happy songs and sleeping with whatever will have them, but they are almost capable warriors when the need arises. And I say almost because they didn't manage to drive the Romans away, but instead were forced into subjugation.

Rather than suffer this fate, the Howlers sent their best forward to fight the Wyrm in a battle to the finish. They failed. All either died or surrendered to the Wyrm. The White Howlers were gone when we arrived in Britain, their Kinfolk stunted and warped by the Wyrm. They were weak. We remember the Howlers no longer. Their name is as dirt.

The Fianna proved themselves to us in those days. Despite their love of song and drink, they exchanged their harps for weapons when the time came to drive the Dancers back into the Wyrm pits from which they had come. Since then, however, the Fianna have repeatedly proven themselves to be drunkards and fools.

Many Get and Fianna died in those battles, but their deaths were necessary to stop the Black Spiral Dancers from destroying all of Britain. Most Get, and I, myself, included, believe that if we had not been sent by Fenris to cull the weaklings of other tribes, if we had not moved outward from Scandinavia, the Fianna would have been forced into the service of Jormangundr. They let themselves fall too often to the vices the Wyrm has set forth. They still need watching over.

The time of the Vikings was glorious, but all things, both good and bad alike, must eventually come to an end. The Vikings were not prepared for the world at large. They spread themselves too thin. In time, they lost control of many of the lands they had held so strongly, and so were forced to leave them. In some cases the Get left with them, returning to the Northlands, but in others, we stayed behind to maintain our vigil against the Wyrm. Many Get live in Britain even today. They are a deadly lot indeed. They must be, for the Wyrm is still strong in many parts of the British Isles.

There are still parts of Europe where people are primarily blond-haired and blue-eyed, and in those areas where our Kinfolk live we are still strong. Despite what many have said about us, we do not seek war with the other tribes. We simply make certain they are strong enough to face the final battle that lies ahead. Also, we do not tolerate insults from lesser tribes. There are too many who are willing to throw insults our way.

The Binding of Fenris

No one can give an exact date, but at some time during the reign of the Vikings, Great Fenris was barred from returning to the Gaia-Realm. He was forced to stay in the Umbra and guide us from afar. While he could send Avatars to our aid, he could no longer come himself to teach us.

Most agree that this was a result of the Wyrm's foul operations, a plan that worked too well. Few of the Incarna are free to walk here anymore; instead, they are forced to use us as their physical warriors. Do not view as a sign of weakness; instead, think of it as a sign of the Wyrm's power. Many claim that the mages had something to do with the division of the worlds, and with the imprisonment of Fenris and the other totems. I do not believe this. They are only humans, and most do not understand the mysteries of the separated worlds.

Fenris was bound through treachery. The legends say that when Great Fenris came and told us to cull the weak from other lands, one among us, called Tyr, stood and said that we had no right to do so. He claimed that the time for war was over, and threw down his sword. Fenris contemplated Tyr's words, and then asked him if he would prefer to live without his guidance. Tyr imagined how life without Great Fenris would be, and begged forgiveness for his actions. I should explain that he had help in his decision: many of the Get offered to make an example of him by way of apology to the Wolf-Father.

Fenris demanded a sacrifice, and Tyr offered to give his hand. Fenris then bit the hand off, and by that allowed that Tyr was forgiven. But Tyr went on whining about his paw long after, bearing resentment in his heart. For this reason, he was seduced to the Wyrm's ways. Later, begging to speak with Great Fenris, he led the Wyrm's minions into Fenris' lair, and they bound the Wolf-Father in chains, thus preventing him from entering Gaia's realm again.

The Delirium fear has caused the humans to warp the truth of this tale. To them, Great Fenris is a monster, righteously bound by the simpering, so-called gods. This act was led by Tyr, who is supposedly a hero for losing his hand in the process. It never ceases to surprise me how foolish humans are, how their fear leads them to create all sorts of false truths. Only weaklings could believe Fenris was a monster, rather than our great leader.

I have seen Garou torn to pieces for daring to call another of the Get by Tyr's name, and if you ever want to commit suicide, that's probably one of the best ways to do it. From that day forth, Fenris has demanded that those he chooses must continue to pay the price for Tyr's folly. The Hand of Tyr are the most savage of all Get of Fenris. They concentrate on fighting against the Wyrm in the foulest places. Never doubt that the Hand of Tyr is fearless; they must be to overcome the name they have chosen for themselves.

The Rifts

I heard screamin' and bullwhips
Cracking
How long? How Long?
　　　— Neil Young, "Southern Man"

The first split in relations between the Get of Fenris came when the settlers in America broke away from Great Britain. There were a good number of the Get in the Colonies, some from Germany and Scandinavia and some from Britain. We had little trouble recognizing each other. We settled in areas where we could live in the climates we were used to. The area that would later become the New England states was ideal for us, and despite a few arguments with the Wendigo tribe — we won, for they had grown soft over the centuries — we were happy.

But when our American Kinfolk decided they needed to war against Britain, we did as we have always done and stood ready to fight with them. This did not make the Get of Fenris in Britain happy, but there was little they could do from across the ocean. A few came with the reinforcement troops sent over by the humans, and attempted to explain their position to us in traditional Get fashion. You can still find the places where they are buried, but you have to look closely.

The arguments lasted sometime, and feelings were hurt. No surprise; the Get hate to lose more than just about anything. But eventually the rift was repaired and communications started again. Besides, we were still too damned busy dealing with the "Pure Ones" to hold grudges, and the British Get still had the Dancers to worry about.

As a result, when the Fangs of Garm arose to stop the more determined Get from wiping out the Native American tribes, we were divided once more. The Fangs of Garm were strongest in Michigan and the Midwest, and the camp would have been very short-lived had they not reminded us of the Croatan tribe's great sacrifice. Though for some Get the idea of listening to reason is almost foreign, we do understand the need to remember the valiant, even if they are from weaker tribes. For the sake of the Croatan, the Get permitted the Wendigo and Uktena to live. We did not, however, make their lives easier as a result of this decision. Great Fenris gave us a mission, and we will continue with that mission until Ragnarok is nothing but a distant memory.

The Get of Fenris also played their part in the shaping of the United States and Canada, though our involvement in Canadian affairs was rather limited. Canada suits the Get of Fenris. The land is often harsh and the winters are brutal, so much like the Northlands we came from. Also, the wolf population still permits us a fair number of wolf Kinfolk.

The second fracture in Get relations came after the Civil War. The war was primarily a human conflict; the Get joined in the conflict whenever their Kinfolk needed protection or as a cover in fighting the Wyrm.

It was after the war that yet another division occurred. After the abolition of slavery, a few Get decided they were tired of having to deal with the lesser races. They formed a camp called the Swords of Heimdall. Many of this camp bore the taint of the Wyrm in many cases, though others were simply confused, and willing to follow the fools who cried for blood.

Be sure of this: The Get of Fenris are warriors. We thrive on combat and live to crush our foes. But there are those among us who believe that combat is everything. They are the ones who give us a bad name. Certainly, we should not tolerate the cowardly, nor should we tolerate the minions of the Wyrm. But there are some who will find any excuse for combat, and if no valid excuses are available, they will invent tales to justify their actions.

I do not see this as a fault so much as a part of our nature. The blood of heroes runs in our veins, and as times change and the world becomes more civilized, with more conveniences and fewer direct threats, the Get of Fenris must start looking for fights. This mentality has faded some over the years, but there are still a few who would see battle simply for the sake of battle. At the time of the Civil War, there were simply not enough enemies in the south to make some Get happy. The Wyrm was learning new tricks, and hiding itself better: The Pure Ones had fled to the west to escape our attempts to make them stronger, and the humans slaves had been broken by chains and whips, fodder for the Wyrm's worst temptations. How can a man be made strong when he is broken? There was simply not enough violence to satisfy the Rage of some Get.

For a time, the Get were forced to fight one another, for many Get saw the taint of the Swords of Heimdall. It was the westward expansion, more than anything else, that halted this rivalry. There was simply too much else to do, too many other important tasks awaiting us. Many of the Get took to the west and fought against the Wendigo and Uktena again. The lands were harsh and suited well our need to struggle. Here, we could set up our holdings and raise strong families.

In time, the wounds of our inner division healed and again the Get spoke to one another with words instead of claws. But the scar caused by Heimdall's Sword remains, and is still in danger of infection from Jormangundr's poisons.

World War I

The American Get decided not to fight in this war. What's this, you say? A Get ignoring a war? But to the American Get, it was a human problem. Their Kinfolk were not involved — at least, not at first — and so there was no reason for them to be.

However, Scandinavia and Germany fought against each other, and the Get in both these lands believed their Kinfolk were right. They allowed themselves to be drawn into human affairs, and that is always a mistake.

The American Get chose not to make matters worse, even when our own Kinfolk were sent to fight in the war. There were matters to deal with here, especially toward the west, where Leeches were trying to swarm into the continent. In Mexico, the Uktena called for help and we gave what we could. The people in the United States were trying to decide too many things about themselves, and we opted to stay in the country and make certain that no one went too far down the trackless path of the Wyrm.

Besides, the war soon became an excuse to reinstitute the Impergium in Europe. The American Get knew this experiment would be short-lived. But another chance would come…

World War II

There's somethin' wrong with the world today
I don't know what it is
Something's wrong with our eyes
    — Aerosmith, "Livin' On The Edge"

A final rift broke the Get of Fenris into many camps during the Second World War. For the first time, the division between Get went beyond mere skirmishes and evolved into a full-scale conflict. Times had been very difficult for the Get in Germany before the war started. The Get of Europe were torn apart, for many believed the propaganda of Adolf Hitler, and joined his conquest to see an end to all races that were not pure.

Let's get this straight: The Get are not racial bigots; we just don't like to see our Kinfolk spread too thinly. We kept ourselves separated from others for a long time, for we wanted our Kinfolk to be strong as well. Perhaps too strong. Some Get do believe that genocide is a rational way to protect our Kinfolk, but they are only a small portion of our tribe. Genocide is cowardly and pathetic. Our duty is not to destroy the weak, but to make the weak stronger. Jormangundr is not picky; he will find allies anywhere, even among our own. We are superior because we strive for perfection, not for the skin color or the religious beliefs of our Kinfolk.

While a few Get fell to the Wyrm, sucked in by stupid human propaganda, none can argue that their methods were so cowardly as to fall below the likes of even the most conniving Shadow Lords. Great Fenris had long ago charged us to cull the weakest from all tribes, and hone the survivors to become as great as we are. What Hitler and the Get who joined him wanted was nothing less than the extermination of entire races, both Garou and human alike.

The Get of Germany who did not follow the little madman called to the American Get and even traveled by Moon Bridge to plead their case. I will note, however, that they did not call on the U.S. and British Get until they realized that they were losing the battle against Hitler's great army. We then joined with other tribes as seldom before, and marched upon our homelands with the weight of our Rage burning in our hearts.

Of course, there were practical reasons why we had to stop our own, for if we did not, the retribution of the other tribes would have been terrible. It is foolish to believe that we could have killed so many of their flock and not seen a reaction from them. The Silver Fangs were once more a paragon of their former glory, rallying the Garou about them to stop our German brethren. Even the Shadow Lords were to be feared, for they had lost more of their Kinfolk to Hitler's marches than any of us, and the desire for revenge seethed within them. And some of the tribes used the war to once again wage the Impergium. Woe to any troops caught in the no-man's land where the Red Talons hunted.

The Get who followed Hitler were many, but far more opposed him. The war was brutal, and the loss to both sides was almost too much for the tribe to handle, but in the end, we made most of the Get see their mistake. Once the German Get learned of the concentration camps and the terrors performed on Garou by the Nazi's scientists, they turned away from the mouth of Jormangundr and returned to the proper ways.

The Get Today

Brothers will fight and they will kill each other,
Cousins will commit incest,
The battles will be hard for heroes,
and great whoredom will abound.
Age of the battle axe, age of the sword,
Shields split by violence.
Age of the storm, age of the wolf
All of this shall come to pass before the world falls into ruin

      — The Edda of Snorri Sturluson (trans. by Keith Winkler)

The mission set before us by Great Fenris is not easy, nor should it be. We have made our lives into a conquest of any tribe too weak to stop us, and our brutal ways have made us strong. While other tribes ran and hid, we always stood ready to face the enemies of Gaia, and we have watched those enemies fall. We have challenged all of the other tribes, and we have seen the ones that are weak: the Wendigo, the Black Spiral Dancers, the Glass Walkers and Bone Gnawers. They fear us because we are strong. They accuse us of brutality because they are unprepared for the challenges we set before them, because we alone refuse to hide from combat when the time comes for bloodshed.

The other tribes claim that we are mindless killing machines, but they spend too much time scheming in dark rooms and trying to sneak past the Wyrm instead of simply tearing Jormangundr's putrid heart from his chest! The Warriors of Gaia must never be weak. Even as we long for peace we must call for war. Let the other tribes play their foolish political games, let them thrive like cockroaches in the hearts of the Scabs, growing soft because they no longer understand the need to hunt and to kill. Let them breed with weaker races and raise their young as "civilized people." In the end they will understand that we are right, that there can be no peace without sacrifice, that there can be no pleasure without pain.

We will lead them in battle and they will follow us as they always have, fearing the threats we know are commonplace because they have never sought the Wyrm in its own foul nest.

We will bring the war to them. We will call them forth for Ragnarok and show them the ways of combat. We will watch them run and hide, fearing for their worthless hides while we bathe in the blood of the Wyrm and feast on the entrails of Jormangundr's followers. Those few who are worthy will fight with us, and we will accept them as family. Those who die a coward's death shall lay unburied in the fields of battle, reviled and despised as weaklings.

Ragnarok is upon us, and the time for friendship is past. Those who would flee from us must be destroyed, for surely they would fall to Jormangundr's wiles. Those that would fight us must be taught the error of their ways, and those who ignore us must be made to remember that we are here, no matter the cost. Those who would be our leaders must prove themselves in honorable combat.

Have no fear of death, for beyond death there is Valhalla. Valhalla, where Fenris waits for us, calling to his Get and

sharpening the weapons that will help us in the final conflict. For each of us that falls, Ragnarok comes one moment closer. Do not fear Ragnarok. Instead, prepare for it. Know that Ragnarok is your destiny and the final time when Jormangundr will fall before our might.

The Get are divided; they fight among themselves as well as among the other Garou. Some demand the Impergium be brought back; some have even started enforcing it again. This is the first sign of Ragnarok. The metis population among Garou increases. Perhaps this increase is brought about by too long a time away from Kinfolk and too much time with packs of mixed heritage. This too is a sign of Ragnarok. The Garou must fight against greater odds than ever before, and they must fight Pentex, the greatest whore to capitalism that has ever existed. These too are signs. So far as the Get of Fenris is concerned, Ragnarok is coming.

It would be presumptuous to say that we are the only ones who have seen the signs, for most Garou openly admit that the Apocalypse is here. Are we simply following the majority in this case and drawing upon facts from our own beliefs to find support for our fears? I don't think so. I believe that the final times are indeed upon us. The human Vikings had many legends about Ragnarok, and in many ways they coincide with our own. Both agree that, in the final days, Great Fenris will be released from his bonds, although the Vikings considered this a bad thing. No one can honestly blame them for their fear: the genetic memory of the Impergium is still strong.

Ragnarok is when Great Fenris will finally be freed from the chains that hold him back, where the Wolf will again know the taste of raw meat and the feel of bones shattering beneath his awesome fangs. We are the Get of Fenris, the children of the Dire Wolf.

Fenris will be released, and as our own sayings tell, he will call forth the Fenris Winter, called the Fimbul Winter by the humans, and he will slay Wotan, the greatest of the Viking gods. But let us not forget that the Vikings, despite their many admirable qualities, were only human. Because they did not understand the meaning of Wotan, they could not understand the necessity for his destruction. He was the greatest of their gods, but he is also the bringer of death. Wotan is another name for Man. He is a god of the humans. The prophecies say simply that Fenris will destroy the humans. The most likely means for this destruction is, of course, the Get of Fenris.

In last few decades, almost all signs from the Rite of the Three Wells have revealed the same image again and again. This image scares some of the Get, but not all of us are frightened by it. The image shows Fenris consuming Wotan. Both comprise countless thousands of beings: Fenris is an amalgamation of our tribe, and Wotan contains the sum of humanity. The death of Wotan does not necessarily mean the literal death of all humans. It could just as well mean the end of the domination of the human race on Gaia. Only time will tell which interpretation is correct.

But enough of that. The Get are separated, and the time of Ragnarok is near. Some fools in the Get believe we will be reunited as one tribe after Ragnarok. This new tribe will allegedly lead us out of danger and into safety, destroying the Wyrm along the way.

These same dreamers claim that the Get as a whole have refused women the right to fight as Modi — Ahroun — for the tribe. I will make clear to you right now what has always been clear to the Get who follow their traditions properly: The females among our tribe have the same rights as the males. Just like the males, they must prove themselves worthy of any title they fight for. Auspice is auspice; if a woman is born under the full moon and is not called an Ahroun, that is her choice. It is not something that any self-respecting Get would force on her. Regardless of auspice, we are all warriors first. Even the Ragabash are warriors; they just don't always fight the same way.

There are rumors of a camp within our ranks, the Valkyria of Freya, which allegedly fights against us, working in secret with the Black Furies to gain equal rights. If they have joined together to oppose the perceived chauvinism of the Get, then they are fools. The only women among the Get who have anything to complain about are those will not fight for their rights. Life in our tribe is not meant to be pleasurable. It is meant to be harsh, in preparation for the Fenris Winter.

Ragnarok

The sun will grow black, the earth sinks into the sea.
High in the heavens, stars disappear,
Smoke and nourisher of life rage,
Tall flames lick against heaven itself.
Here it is said: At the field called Vigrithr, a battle takes place.
Surtur and Jormangundr battle against the gods,
Vigrithr is 600 miles on each side,
A field is set aside for this purpose.

       — The Edda of Snorri Sturluson (trans. by Keith Winkler)

Ragnarok is soon upon us — has already started. Know the following things to be true, and know that they are what the Get of Fenris have strived for all along: Valhalla is real. It waits for us in the Umbra. Also waiting for us is Vigrithr, the field where we shall fight and defeat the Midgard Serpent, Jormangundr, the Wyrm.

Vigrithr is a field of battle prepared by Fenris, a place in the Spirit World where we will fight our final battle against the Wyrm, and break the foul embrace it has upon Gaia. We are not likely to survive this greatest of battles, but Gaia will be saved. Many believe the Fimbul Winter will come as a result of nuclear war. The fires will indeed reach the heavens, and many stars will be extinguished. But that is not the end of Gaia. She will sleep, She will have a time of rest, a time to recover from Her great wounds, and She will come back again, as strong as ever, and freed from the Wyrm's poisons.

The time of the humans will end, and Gaia will again find a way to flourish and to grow. The Garou will have peace. We will all be born into the world again, for even in times of peace, Gaia will always need her defenders.

Ragnarok is not to be feared, but rather to be revered. Ragnarok is the end of the Wyrm's dominion, the time when balance will be restored and the Umbra and the Gaia Realm will once more be as one, as it was before the Wyrm went mad. The Weaver will be put right, and the Wyld shall again be strong and healthy.

I say this to you one more time: Do not fear death, for death is only the first step on the way to Valhalla and the great battle at Vigrithr, where all will be put right for Gaia. Do not fear combat, for we must train as few ever have to earn the right to serve Great Fenris and Gaia in the final war and to reap the rewards that will come thereafter. The time is soon. Be strong. Be brave. And know that we shall have peace when Ragnarok is ended.

Chapter Two: Krieg Lagern
(War Camps)

Be Aggressive,
B-E Aggressive
B-E-A-G-G-R-E-S-S-I-V-E!
— Faith No More, "Be Aggressive"

There is no such thing as peace. Peace is a fool's dream that serves no purpose but to lull us into false relaxation, so that the Wyrm can catch us napping. Throw any stupid ideas about a carefree life away before your Rite of Passage. Fenris did not create the Fenrir to live a soft life. He created us to fight for Gaia, and that is what we do. We have never had it easy.

Battle Scars

No Get of Fenris is considered worthy until he bears scars. Battle scars are a sign of prowess; you must earn them in the only way possible — by risking everything to prove your worth as a warrior against a true threat. Most of the Get receive their first battle scars during their Rite of Passage, for our rite is dangerous: it would kill members of lesser tribes. Get never back down from a fight, and as a result most Get manage to earn more scars than other tribes' warriors. Some even gain their scars during informal moots, playing the games. We do not play nicely.

Virtues

You've heard of the American Dream? Well forget about it! It's a load of crap! A wet dream for the weak. If you want something, then you work for it. That means if you want a new house, you build it with your own hands, because when that house is finished, it is something to be proud of. When you get a job, you don't sit behind a desk for eight hours a day groveling at the feet of your boss in the hopes of a promotion. You work the fields. You plant and tend your harvest, because when you are done no bread will ever taste as sweet as the bread made from wheat you planted and protected. If you can't own it outright, then you don't need it!

I know many Get who work in construction and raise skyscrapers for the humans. But even that is all right, because they own the companies, and you'd better goddamned well believe those buildings meet every possible requirement to keep Gaia as unscathed as possible. Better the Get than some pissant human out to make a quick buck and cutting corners whenever possible!

If the Get of Fenris uphold an American Dream — and you can believe this, you little whelps — it is the idea that people will actually take the time to do things right. We're not the corporate raiders or generals of the world, we're the ditch diggers and drill sergeants. We don't demand respect, we command it. When I'm taking you through your paces and teaching you the art of war, you'd best remember that, because I will gladly peel the fur off your worthless hides the first time you forget. We had a saying in the Army that still stands true today: "Don't call me 'Sir,' goddamit. I work for a living!"

No Get of Fenris ever took governmental kickbacks or robbed banks for a living. No Get ever battled the Wyrm and then checked in to work another shift at O'Tolley's. No self-respecting Get would think of dealing drugs, or taking them, either, because that leads to the Wyrm. No worthwhile Get ever started drinking and allowed himself to go beyond the point where he could fight — at least, not away from a moot. Dependency on anything, on anyone except your tribe and your pack, is a sign of weakness. And we don't like sissies in this neck of the woods!

Leave the nine-to-five jobs and the whining to the other tribes; we've got better things to do with our time. We're above that sort of sniveling. You'll meet the other tribes soon, the ones that call us psychopaths and wear peace signs around their necks. But we'll talk about them later; right now, it's time to let you know a few things about the camps, and to give you some warnings as well. In order to be fair about this, I'll tell you the facts, and then you can ask the Garou around you what they think of my opinion. All I can tell you is what they were willing to tell me.

The Valkyria of Freya

The Valkyria exist; I've met them. They are as fierce as any Get — don't even think of believing otherwise. The camp is made up of women. Ideally, the Valkyria have no reason to exist, but as I'm sure many of you know, the Get are a battle tribe, and that means that sometimes the bullshit level around here climbs a little too high. There are a few Jarls around who do not believe that women have any rights. Perhaps that is the way it used to be, but these days we need every warrior we can get.

The world isn't ideal. Now and then, the tempers of the Jarls are a bit intimidating. I don't believe the drivel about the Valkyria leaving to be with the Black Furies, and you shouldn't either. Just remember to treat your family, male and female alike, with a little respect. Sex doesn't make a difference; only physical prowess matters.

You might have trouble believing this, but there are two separate accounts of bitch-Jarls, Freya-Troll-Breaker and Brynhyld-Broken-Sword. I won't lie and tell you that either lasted long as Jarls; there were too many other Get willing to challenge them. But in both cases, they led for their spans because they formally challenged the Jarl and won. Never let

anyone tell you the crap about females being lesser warriors or lesser citizens, because it just isn't true. They can fight and they can challenge just like any other member of the Garou. In times long past, they could only be considered Modi if their families were killed, and then it was their duty to fight. But in America, at least, that's not the case. I've heard of a few hard-asses back in the Old Country who disagree with this philosophy, but only a few.

The Valkyria Speaks

Despite the words of a few males, the general belief is that the female Get of Fenris should have no duties save to serve as scullery maids. We must work twice as hard to prove ourselves, and we must constantly watch our backs. There are those males who feel they can attack a female without honor and suffer no consequences, because they say she was not acting with honor herself. I will not lie, the idea of joining with the Black Furies has arisen on several occasions. No decision has been made....

The Hand of Tyr

The Hand do not believe in surrender. They fight until they die, and they never accept the surrender of an enemy who has challenged them. They might let one of their challengers survive, but only if he was a truly worthy opponent. A Get of the Hand of Tyr is the closest thing you'll ever know to an executioner. They do not forgive or forget a sin committed in their sight. If they are afraid of anything, I've yet to hear about it.

The Hand have been known to hunt down enemies for decades, never resting until their prey is destroyed. There were a lot of Nazi leaders after the war who were never captured, whom even Mossad, Israel's elite special forces, could not find. I know of at least three cases in which there was nothing left to find after the Hand of Tyr had finished making the bastards pay.

You know those stories that go around from time to time about Bigfoot cruising into a campsite and tearing the hell out of some nice little camper? Well, often as not the "camper" was not a nice person but a murderer, and "Bigfoot" had stalked him for a couple hundred miles.

If you ever get any ideas about raping or murdering an innocent, unprovoked, you can just chuck those ideas away. The Hand will find you, and they will destroy you. Do not play games with the Hand; they do not play games. They are the closest thing you'll find to perfect killing machines. They have given their lives to Fenris, just as Tyr sacrificed up his hand.

Words from the Hand

There is no honor in attacking the innocent. There is no glory in molesting a five-year-old or forcing yourself on a woman. These are the acts of the Wyrm, and they must be punished. Cold-blooded murders are not allowed, and the drugs that the humans sell must be stopped. From time to time, the smallest offenders can give you the names of the Wyrmling behind their crimes. The

Wyrm's roots are many and they run deep; too deep. They must be torn from Gaia! For even the smallest roots can grow again....

Mjolnir's Thunder

The Thunder do not just rumble, they kill. These guys are the ultimate killing monsters. They do not bother with humans and they couldn't care less if someone gets murdered in front of them. They stroll into places where no sane Garou would walk alone. And they come back out again. These guys are monkeywrenchers often as not, only they don't try to be subtle. They walk into Wyrm-nests and just cut loose. It is no surprise they rarely live long enough to rule a sept.

The Thunder Growls

The Wyrm is everywhere, and must be destroyed at any cost. What use is a life if Jormangundr still surrounds Midgard? Ragnarok is coming soon, and the only hope we have is to weaken the Wyrm now, before the Fimbul Winter settles upon Gaia's back. We cannot wait for the Wyrm to come to us; instead we must seek out the minions of Jormangundr, destroy them wherever they may hide. Their nests could hold the eggs of others like them.

The Fangs of Garm

The Hand of Tyr believes in avenging the innocent, but the Fangs of Garm believe in preventing the crime. They are much like the Children of Gaia, though stronger of will and shorter of fuse: they are still Get, after all, and do not take insults well. Still, of all the Get, the Fangs are the best suited to the task of negotiating with the other tribes. They have founded a few organizations to help protect others from the agents of the Wyrm; they organize neighborhood watches, and even work as counselors in halfway houses from time to time. Of all our camps, the Fangs of Garm show the most wisdom. They look out for wolves and humans alike, protecting them from the more subtle of the Wyrm's threats.

Legends tell us of Garm, the hound of hell, who will one day avenge Tyr's wrong to Fenris. Garm, too, was bound by the Wyrm's plot, but his chains are in Niffleheim, the land of the dead. According to human legend, Garm was the most horrible beast imaginable, so bad that he was bound in order to prevent the destruction of the world. Little do the humans understand that Garm teaches us a great lesson: that our Rage must be controlled or it will haunt us after death. This lesson the Fangs have learned well, but woe to those who stand in their way when their Rage is unfettered.

The Fangs Speak

Do not believe that the Wyrm's only threat comes in the form of Banes or fomori. The Wyrm can be very devious, and can hide in places that seem perfectly harmonious with Gaia. The tribes must work together if we are to defeat the Wyrm; Gaia did not intend for us to fight each other, only to stop Her illness from growing stronger.

Our most dangerous enemy is ourselves, our inner Rage. Our Rage was given to us by Fenris to aid him in his battles, but he is now bound, and can no longer help us control our anger. Garm guides us, though, by way of warning of our dire fate should we fail and lose control.

The Glorious Fist of Wotan

The Fists do not follow with a good number of the Get's philosophies. They do not leave the humans in peace, they do not involve themselves in human politics, and they do not work in jobs that could benefit the humans. The Fist does not tolerate human expansion, and will go out of their way to ensure that new development is stopped. The Fist has battled with the rest of the Get of Fenris on several occasions, particularly with those among our tribe who work in construction.

The Fist of Wotan is a radical group, and shares more beliefs with the Red Talons than is healthy. I've seen members of this camp stalk and kill humans for no greater crime than dropping a candy bar wrapper in the woods. The Fist is primarily, but not entirely, made up of lupus. Watch out for this camp of the Get of Fenris.

The Fist Howls

The humans have done too much already to harm Gaia. Most of Jormangundr's agents are humans. Have you ever seen a raven spill

oil on the sea? Do bears pour toxic waste into the air and water? The time has come to stop the monkeys from growing any stronger. We will let them have their Scabs, but we will no longer allow them to take more from Gaia and the Wyld than they have already.

Yes, Wotan is Man, but he is also Death. That is what we represent: the death of the humans and their foolish ways. Do not think that we are murderers. We are defenders of Gaia, fighting the most vile of the Wyrm's minions: the humans who have raped our mother.

The Swords of Heimdall

The Swords hold that the only humans who survive are the Kinfolk of the Garou. Some of their more radical members do not believe even that the weaker Garou have their uses, instead insisting that the weakness of the other tribes is an open invitation to the Wyrm. They have joined with human groups like the Ku Klux Klan and the neo-Nazis, praising the belief that all others must die simply because we are the strong and they are weak.

Many Get agree with the general sentiment, but not with the actions of these punks. This mentality has led to rifts in our tribe, and it cannot be permitted to grow any stronger.

The Swords are mistaken. The only way to end the problems with the other tribes is to make them understand that we are the best leaders for the coming Ragnarok, not to burn crosses in their front yards and pound them into their graves for merely existing. They have limited their sights too much, and now are as close to the Wyrm as any Get has ever been.

What's more, they have perverted our legends in taking their namesake. Heimdall was the watchman, the guardian of Bifrost, the Rainbow Bridge. His name means "world radiance," and he was called "the whitest of the gods." The foolish Swords have taken this literally. Heimdall will blow the Gallerhorn to warn of Ragnarok; the Swords claim they blow it now, to warn of the dangers of weaker races. Fools.

A Sword Decries

The other races are weak! The time for helping the other tribes grow strong is long past. Ragnarok is upon us and still the lesser tribes whimper and whine about treating the humans carefully. We have superior breeding — our flock is stronger, smarter, and better prepared to survive the final days. We cannot allow our careful breeding to be diluted by inferior races of humans or wolves.

You do not hear our Kinfolk crying out for aid from the human government, nor do our Kinfolk cry foul because of the way our ancestors were treated. No mercy! If they slink around where we live, we destroy them. The Ku Klux Klan are morally defunct and pathetically stupid, but at least they make for good tools in keeping our tribe safe from perversity and mixed breeding with the lesser races.

The so called "Pure Ones" spend their time drinking firewater and living off the land granted to them by liberal wimps; and then they cry about the horrible sins we have committed against them! If their lives are too difficult for them to function as meaningful members of society, I say we end their suffering for them. And another thing…

Allegations of Secret Camps

Ymir's Sweat

I have told you of Leif Eriksson, and how he came to the American shores to teach the Pure Ones what it meant to harm the Kinfolk of the Get. There are rumors — and mind you they are only rumors — that Leif and his pack left behind a little more than hurt feelings. There are some who claim that a group of Get stayed behind when Eriksson left, and mated with the savages that occupied these shores.

I have never met one, and I personally do not believe that they exist, but I know Get who say they have seen the pale-haired but swarthy-skinned Garou that call themselves Ymir's Sweat and run with the Wendigo and the Uktena. I have heard the legends that tell of white humans who ran with the Indians. I have even heard that they can call the winter winds, just as the Wendigo do. If they indeed exist, what a weak and useless pack of mutts they must be.

Loki's Smile

I have heard of a select few in the Get of Fenris who claim to be the secret rulers of us all. This is obviously a lie, for any such group would be destroyed at the first sign of a back-stabbing, cloak-and-dagger mentality. The Get are nothing if not warriors, and warriors handle their problems with

honor and lead their troops through example. They do not act with the same treachery as do the Shadow Lords. Should I ever meet one of this Loki's Smile camp, I will call for his head and teach him the error of his ways. Obviously, such a cowardly lot has been sleeping with Jormangundr.

Totems — Allies of Great Fenris

All Get must pay fealty to Great Fenris, for he is our creator. But we may also choose to follow his allies, others who have aided Fenris in our times of struggle. Learn of them and know that they are friends.

Fenris Wolf

Our greatest ally is the Fenris Wolf, he who called us into being. He is a harsh master, make no mistake about that, but he is fair, and he teaches us the secrets of survival. From him we gain the determination to live our lives in the proper way, like the warriors we are. He tells us that we must be strong, and we must be honorable. He personifies the goal for which we all must strive.

Alone, he is already powerful beyond measure. With us as his extended pack, he is unstoppable. Fenris did not create us to have an easy life; he created us to lead the way, to show through example what is truly required of all Garou if they would survive the Fimbul Winter and the Apocalypse. You must show respect to Fenris, even if you follow another totem, for he is the father of us all, as surely as Gaia is our mother and Luna our teacher.

Boar

Great Boar is a powerful totem, one that teaches us the ways of survival. He is set in his ways, for his ways are all that he knows. He roots through the soil and lives off the land, but he also gives to the land. Boar is thick-skinned, tougher than steel and twice as mean as a rabid bear. Boar teaches us how to tolerate the pain of our wounds and continue fighting our enemy. He teaches us wisdom as well: when to run from a fight — not out of fear, but because it is strategically useful — and where best to continue the fight. From Boar we learn to find our enemies' weak spots and to use those weaknesses against them.

Hrafn, the Raven

Hrafn teaches us to see, for he is the raven who knows the ways of the Wyrm and points to the secrets that can keep Jormangundr away from us. Hrafn reminds us to laugh, because without the Trickster's ways, we would be too grim to stomach, even to ourselves. Raven helps us pick away the dead things that would add to Gaia's discomfort, and cause Her grief. Neither the Raven nor the Crow must ever be hurt, for to do so limits the eyes of Hrafn. For all his noise and laughter, Raven is still a trusted ally.

Ratatosk, the Squirrel

There are many Get who disdain to follow Ratatosk. *What strength can a squirrel give?* they ask. But Ratatosk is no ordinary squirrel. He is the World Tree squirrel, running up and down the trunk of Yggdrassil, from the leafy boughs at the top to the earthy roots at the bottom. He sees all and hears all. He is the messenger of Fenris: he bears the Wolf-Father's words to all the totems. For this reason, he is favored by many of our Rotagar and Godi.

Ratatosk teaches us quiet wisdom. Yes, he is a coward, but he must be. He was not granted the mighty thews of the wolf, and so he must flee instead. But he flees to get aid, to deliver the cries of our lost and injured packmates to us. Know that to follow Ratatosk is to lose Honor, but to gain in Wisdom.

The Get of the Get

We are warriors, and proud of it, but we are also a family. We continue on because we must, and we find mates because without offspring, our memory would die. But do not think that we do not care for our mates. A hero's death is a fine thing, but a hero's life is important as well. We must keep the family strong. We must do our best to continue the ways of the Viking.

Fenris demands that we raise our pups in the ways of his chosen people, and that is what we shall do. We must ensure that the Kinfolk and children of the Get are strong and able to handle themselves in dangerous situations. Too often we fight against overwhelming odds, for Fenris demands that we never run from a battle. We must prove ourselves in combat in order to earn the right to fight alongside Great Fenris, when the Ragnarok is truly here and the last days are no longer on the horizon.

Discipline is the key to making the family as strong as possible, but you must try to curb your temper when dealing with your children. You have an obligation to teach them well, but you also have an obligation to leave them unscarred. I have heard the talk of fools, moaning and bitching because their children did not breed true. What they fail to see is that their children's children might be Garou. There is great honor in having a child that can join in our battles, but there is no dishonor in having children that can mate with our kind and produce fertile Get.

If we have a fault, it is that we try too hard to make warriors of our Kinfolk, even knowing that they cannot heal themselves as we can. Be stern. Make certain that your children are raised with the proper values, but do not break their arms to make a point. That way is the downfall of our tribe. Teach them well to love combat, but do not make them fear violence when they are too young to know better. To spare the rod is indeed to spoil the child, but crushing the blossom also destroys the fruit. Remember this if nothing else: A battered child is an open target for the Wyrm.

Remember also that Kinfolk do not fear the touch of silver. To put it another way: you have to sleep sometime, and better to have allies with you when you sleep, than an angry child who wants revenge. As famed Einar said to Gunnar: "Bare is the back that has no brother."

Breeds

Homid

Do not believe that the homids among us are the only ones able to fight and to lead. There are more leaders from the lupus than you believe. The homid's advantage is that they can blend in with the humans and make certain the Wyrm does not manipulate them too easily.

Do not segregate yourselves by breed; that is a trick of Jormangundr. Homids are better able to see the tricks of the Wyrm in the city, better able to read and write than lupus, but they are not better Get simply by virtue of their birth.

Metis

A metis is a sad thing, an unfortunate product of the times. Too many Garou believe that the unnatural attraction they feel for a brother or sister is acceptable. In olden times, we killed metis outright, rather than dealing with the embarrassment of them. Now we let them live — most of the time. Take a lesson from the lupus: Euthanasia is not always a bad thing. Would you want to live in this world if you were born unable to walk, or even use your hands? What good is a warrior who cannot fight? If a metis can look after itself, then we are obligated to let it live. If a metis is born without eyes, or unable to even crawl, then do the merciful thing and end its life. Better still, make the incestuous parents do the deed, for surely they must answer for their own mistakes as well.

There is a natural and understandable bias against the metis. They are impure, and can never create more children to keep our tribe strong. But, as with the Kinfolk, do not punish them for what they cannot help. Teach them the ways of the warrior, do not beat into them the ways of the coward. They, too, are Get, even for all their flaws, and they deserve the right to live and fight and die with honor and glory.

Lupus

The lupus are our greatest treasure, especially in these last days, when the Fenris Winter comes and we need to have as many Garou as possible to fight in the final battle. They are brave, and they are proud. Do not condemn them for their birth on four legs, but do not revere them for it either. All races must be equal, for without the man and without the wolf, we would not be Garou. You may condemn the weaker tribes, but do not condemn the breeds; that is not the way to Valhalla. Remember always that Fenris created us to protect the wolves, and that he himself is the greatest of wolves.

Rituals

The rites of the Get teach us tradition, and give us the sense of community that is so crucial if we are to prevail. Do not scoff at the rites, and never stop learning of our past, for there is wisdom in the experiences of our elders. More importantly, our rituals are also our testing ground. Here we learn whether those who participate are worthy of our tribe.

We are a brutal lot, and the tests we offer in our Rite of Passage are surely the truest test of our combative nature. All Get must face danger in the Rite of Passage, for only through honorable combat can any Get prove worthy of Great Fenris. Some other tribes claim that our ways are too violent. Bullshit. While the death of any Garou is a tragedy, we have our ways and they have theirs. Most of them could not survive our way of life, and most of us would be bored to tears by the tranquil existence they must endure.

The most important thing to remember about our ways is that they are violent. Do not expect mercy if you have offered or accepted a challenge; do not expect forgiveness if you screw up during a ceremony. We are warriors first: everything else must be second to that single fact of our lives.

Great Wolves

There are a number of powerful and magical wolves in our history. Many are spoken of among humans as giants or monsters. We know them as spirits, servants of Great Fenris, or as our ancestors. However, no Get may make totem alliance with these wolves, for we owe our first allegiance to Fenris. Besides, they are too busy to give of their time to mortals, whether wolf, human or Garou.

Garm

Garm is the fiercest creature ever. His Rage would know no bounds were he not chained in Niffleheim, the Land of the Dead. He is kept from Midgard, where his rampages would destroy all life. Some whisper that he is Wyrm-corrupt, and it is possible that this is so. But Fenris has not given up on him, and so we must not either. It is said that he will be free at Ragnarok, and will take revenge for Tyr's wrong against all humankind. The Fangs of Garm look to him as a model of what we will become if we do not learn the ways of peace.

Skoll and Hati

Skoll pursues the sun across the sky, and Hati chases the moon. It is said that they will catch their prey at Ragnarok. They are the sons of Fenris and an old witch who dwelt east of Midgard, in the forest called Ironwood. Hati is also known as "Managarmr" (moon hound), for he is the chosen of Luna. When he catches the moon, his power will be great, and he will wreak revenge for all the wrongs that were committed against her.

Freki and Geri

These are the fabled wolves of Wotan, and they are our ancestors. The greatest among us can trace blood lineage back to these two, and can call upon them. The humans misunderstood the truth, and thought the wolves served Wotan. It was the other way around. Humans served the wolves in those days.

Moots

Moots are more than just political, they are celebratory. During the moots, we can be ourselves. We celebrate life, victory and conquest over the enemies we have crushed beneath our bloody paws. There are two types of moots: the informal and the formal. Never make the mistake of confusing the two.

Informal moots are for fun and relaxation. They give us a chance to know each other away from the field of combat and to settle disputes that had been temporarily set aside. As with our human Kinfolk ancestors, we are a lusty lot. At these moots, you may drink yourself into a stupor, or you may join in the songs of our ancestors.

You may also join in the games of the Get — but be warned: these games are very dangerous. Do not join in an arm wrestling match over silver blades if you cannot take the pain of losing a few fingers. Bloodshed is always a part of the games. When you perform the Razor Dance, your feet will be cut to shreds. When you join in a tug-of-war using barbed wire for a rope and balancing at the edge of a fire pit, you are going to get burned and bloodied. Our games test physical prowess. If the players — winners or losers — suffer pain as a result, that is the way it should be. No loss should be without suffering, and conquest is always sweeter with the smell of fresh blood to savor after the victory.

My favorite game is Claw Tag. Trust me, you learn well how to dodge an attack after someone's claws rip hide off your back for the third time. You learn to use more than your eyes when you are blindfolded against a non-blindfolded stalker. What's that? No, you moron, the idea isn't just to avoid getting tagged, the idea is to see how many cuts you can take before you finally surrender!

These moots are sometimes open to Garou from other caerns, especially in the case of unresolved conflicts. I know a Get, Jurgi Hautala, who must be commended for his amazing patience with the lesser tribes. He once invited 17 Garou from other tribes to one informal moot, and fought each of them one after another. He won most of the battles, but that milk cow Black Fury, Hera-Moon-Bow, kicked him three times in the balls. When he had finally recovered, I asked him why he had invited so many battles upon himself. Jurgi laughed at me, spit the remains of his front tooth from his mouth, and replied: "They all offended me, but I could not fight them and fight the Wyrm at the same time. A Get has to have priorities."

There is truth to his words! You should never turn from your true enemies to make a point with other Garou. That is what an informal moot is for.

The formal moots are a different story. They take place in a great Lodge House. Understand and take my words to heart, because your life may depend it. Never, under any circumstances less than the Wyrm's invasion, fight in the Lodge Houses. In earlier times, when there were no conveniences, the houses were the only places where one could find warmth. The Vikings forbade fighting in their lodge houses, and we continue this tradition. There must be places of peace, even among the Get of Fenris.

You may bring your weapons, and you may hang them on the walls, but you must never attempt to use them within the Lodge House. These places are for discussions of tribal law, for our greatest celebrations and our deepest moments of sorrow. There is no place for violence. Three times in our

Kennings

The kenning is logically (though not always in artistic effect) a metaphor; the term is derived from the verb kenna which means 'to express or describe one thing by means of another'. The skalds were extraordinarily lavish in their use of kenningar, outdoing the most ornate of the Anglo-Saxon poets.

— E. V. Gordon, An Introduction to Old Norse

We Garou have carried our Kinfolk's traditions with us in our travels, keeping the best of them alive into modern times. While humans have forgotten what is good in their past, we remember. A poetic tradition we still use is the kenning, developed by Norwegian poets long ago.

Some examples of kennings: the sea could be referred to as "whales' pathways" or "enclosure of ships." Bjarni Herjolfsson's account of the discovery of America has the following prayer, which serves as an excellent example of the use of kennings:

I pray the sinless tester of monks may assist my journey. May the lord of high earth and the hall hold his hawk's perch over me.

The "sinless tester of monks" is God, and "hawk's perch" is his arm.

Kennings are an innovative and creative poetic technique, one that cannot be fully appreciated unless heard in its original skaldic verse. Nonetheless, I give here some of our more popular Fenrir kennings, translated into English.

Song of hearth and home = Gaia

Wearing the wolf shirt = Crinos, Hispo or Lupus form

The pathfinder = the Litany

Jewel of the sward = caern

Fleshless friend = a spirit

Singers of the song of hearth and home = ancestors

Bane of straw = fire

One who is his own kith and kin = ronin

Wearing the ice shirt = Harano

Trackless path = the way of the Wyrm

Jarl of oathbreakers = the Wyrm

Breaker of swords; piercer of armor; killer of crops; stealer of deer = the Wyrm (bad luck)

Shield brother of adders = Black Spiral Dancer

When we sing of our heroes, we often give them well-known kennings. Just as the Norsemen knew that "goat driver" often referred to Thor, we know that "lighter of pyres" refers to Gunnar Draugrbane, for the many foes he killed. Perhaps one day, if you become great, you shall have a kenning to note your deeds.

Get Lexicon

Auspices

Our names for Luna's chosen are different than the other tribes'. We refuse to honor the names used by the Fianna, for ours are older and just as good.

Ragabash = Rotagar

Theurge = Godi

Philodox = Forseti

Galliard = Skald

Ahroun = Modi

Words

When speaking human tongues, even English, we still use many Old Norse words, inherited from our great homid heroes of old.

Ancestors (Past Lives) = for-eldra

Bane = skripi

Battle = dólg

Battle Scar = bana-sar

Blood = bloth

Bone Gnawer (worthless wretch) = auvirthi

Caern = varthi

Challenge = ein-vigi

Death = bani

Death-blow = bana-hogg

Death day = duatha-dagr

Dwarf = dvergr (dwarves = dvergar)

Earth = fold

Fetishes = taufr

Fire = bál

Frenzy = jotun-mothr (to rage [verb] = geisa)

Giant = jotunn

Gift = for-mali

Gnosis (soul) = sál

Human = menskr

Lore = froth-leikr

Luck = gæfa, or hamingja

Mage = Gandwere

Monster (Wyrm creature) = forath

Nobility, courage = dreng-skapr

Poetry = brag-thattr

Poison = eitr

Rage (beast's heart) = dyrs-hjarta

Renown = vegr

Riddle = gáta

Sacrifice = blót

Shame = hneykja

Spirit = andi (spirits = andar)

Spirit summoning = varth-lokur

Vampire = draugr (vampires = draugar)

Wicked (Wyrm corrupt) = vándr

Wolf = ulfr

Wraith = haug-bui

---

history, someone has broken this law. Three times in our history, someone has died for being so foolish.

There is an arena, outside the Lodge House, where all formal combat is handled and all challenges to Jarldom are met. These battles are never to first blood, or until someone screams for surrender. There is only one survivor in these battles, for they are always to the death. Do not make challenges at the formal moots if you are not prepared to pay the price.

The Litany

F*ck the law! I want meat!

— Peloquin, from Clive Barker's *Nightbreed*

The Litany was developed to establish stability among the tribes. This is a good thing. However, there are many ways in which the words of the Litany can be misunderstood. Some other tribes have different ways of handling the Litany, as is their right. The Get of Fenris try to make certain that the rules are followed carefully, and that there is a means by which a Garou may attempt to prove his innocence, should he be wrongly accused.

Garou Shall Not Mate with Garou

Do not litter your own den, especially in such a vulgar way. There are enough metis already, but worse still, you bring shame upon our tribe by showing that you cannot control your lust.

Despite what others believe, we do not take liberties with the weaker female Garou we conquer. There is no honor in such actions, only degradation to both parties. One Black Fury claimed that she had been raped by a Get, and when her claim was proved, she was permitted to take from the rapist the offending weapon. Do not attempt to find loopholes within the Litany.

The standard punishment for breaching this part of the Litany is to raise the child and teach him or her the ways of the Get. You must care for your children in all cases, for even metis have the right to a family. If you choose not to care for your child, or if your child should accidentally come to harm, then you must dispose of the evidence in the old ways. You must consume the flesh of your offspring, allowing the child to live within you forever. That is the formal punishment for mating with your own family and causing harm to your own flesh.

Combat the Wyrm Wherever it Dwells and Whenever It Breeds

Do not suffer a Wyrmling to live. Every creature that is touched by the Wyrm has the potential to create more like itself. Destroy them. If you find a nest of Wyrmlings, make certain the creatures and their nest are both destroyed. Cleanse the land of the Wyrm's foul taint, or find someone who can. Never flee from a Wyrmling, no matter how powerful. Better to die a hero than to live a coward, for Fenris does not forgive. Nor do his Get.

Respect the Territory of Another

If you find a place that suits your needs, and you can defeat the owner of this territory in rightful combat, then, and only then, may you claim the land as your own. These challenges must be made publicly, and should your opponent refuse you the right of challenge, you may not retaliate. We do not wantonly kill our own kind over a few feet of land. We must not waste the blood of the other Garou.

Accept an Honorable Surrender

If your opponent has called for first blood, you may let him live. If he has called for a life-duel, you are honor bound to kill him, regardless of his pleas. This is our way. Know also that honorable surrender is impossible for those without honor. Kill all Wyrmlings, even if formally challenged. In wartime, and against the Wyrm's minions, this rule does not hold.

Submission to Those of Higher Station

Never question a war leader's commands. Never insult those of higher rank, unless you are willing to suffer the consequences.

The First Share of the Kill for the Greatest in Station

Give the elders their due, or they will kill you. Do not take this lightly. I have seen pups torn limb from limb for their stupidity.

Ye Shall Not Eat the Flesh of Humans

The blood-lust is great within the Get of Fenris, and this may be overlooked from time to time. Do not, however, leave any sign of human consumption.

Respect for Those Beneath Ye — All Are of Gaia

All are beneath us. Do not play with your food, and do not kill without just reason. You may test other Garou, for that is one part of our duty, but you must not insult the other tribes without justifiable provocation. Do not falsely accuse another of a crime; this is not the honorable way to provoke confrontation. You may certainly challenge the heritage of another, but know the facts before you make the challenge.

The Veil Shall Not Be Lifted

If the humans see you change, you must stalk them and destroy them. You must leave no evidence. Be aware of your surroundings, and avoid changing shapes in public places. If the Crinos is your only resort, make certain that any witnesses never have the chance to speak of the matter.

Do Not Suffer Thy People to Tend Thy Weakness

There are three honorable ways in which to grow old. You may barter with pups for food and care in exchange for wisdom. You may challenge your Jarl, knowing that you cannot win, and pray that he is merciful. You may fight the Wyrm until you fall in battle. Suicide is not acceptable, and brings dishonor to you and your tribe.

The Leader May Be Challenged at Any Time During Peace

You may only challenge for leadership during formal moots. You may challenge for renown at any time of peace.

The Leader May Not Be Challenged During Wartime

Unless your leader is grossly incompetent, and you can prove the accusation, do not argue during war or combat. Obey this rule at all times.

Ye Shall Take No Action That Causes a Caern to Be Violated

There is no forgiveness. You will be destroyed. Your name shall be unsung, and your deeds shall be unremembered. Your Kinfolk will know only shame.

Never Refuse a Challenge

The Get of Fenris are the followers of Fenris. We do not turn away from a fight. Ever. If a Garou insults your heritage and the insult is not just, rip flesh and drink deep of your enemy's blood. That is our way. But never turn from the true

enemy to settle an insult argument — if the Wyrm is near, kill the Wyrmling first, and then destroy the bastard who insulted you.

Now listen to me: if some five-year-old human brat spits on your shoe, you don't rip him limb from limb. There's no honor in damaging whelps. Instead, find his parent and calmly explain that Junior was a bad boy, then teach his parent a lesson that Junior will never forget. Children cannot be held responsible for their own stupidity, but their parents can.

Leadership

There are no councils, save the Council of War. The Council of War meets once a year, and at this time the battles for supremacy between the Jarls are held. From the victors, we choose the five greatest warriors to lead the Council. There can be no questions about their right to lead. They are the strongest and the greatest in combat. Do not question their motives; that is not for you to know. If you are called to war, be prepared to die, for we shall all meet again come the Ragnarok.

Chapter Three: Eine Welt für Nehman (A World for the Taking)

People talking in movie shows,
People smoking in bed,
People voting Republican,
Give them all a boot to the head!
— The Frantics, "Ti-Kwan-Leap/Boot to the Head"

Let me explain a little something to you about the world at large. There are forces at work you have yet to run across, forces that are vile examples of what we are fighting against. I have spoken of the Wyrm, but I have not told you about how the Wyrm works its foul tricks. Jormangundr has many powerful allies in its schemes, and you will run across some of them sooner or later. We have allies, too, but, for the most part, they are weaker than we are.

We are not well-loved by the other tribes. Oh, they care for us when the time for war approaches and they realize once again that they need us to pull their hides from the fire. This is just as well, because we do not need the love of other Garou to see us through our troubles. We have each other, and we have Gaia. We have Luna and we have Fenris. We are complete.

Our history of forced expansion is brief, but the impact from those times has been substantial. The Get of Fenris are no longer isolated in the forests of the northlands. Now there are Get on every continent of Gaia, though in some places we are still limited in number.

Humans are everywhere, trying to decide what to build next when they haven't any need for what they've already built. The humans need to be remembered, but because so few of them are warriors any longer, they choose to build memorials to themselves. Rockefeller Plaza, Trump Towers — buildings named for those with money enough to have their names inscribed onto edifices; or, worse still, the endless roads named after endless lists of paper pushers who somehow feel they have contributed to the well-being of others.

Do not fall into this kind of trap. This is false glory at best, a shallow honor that means nothing. The humans long for any acknowledgment that they are the superior race. In order to prove this to themselves, they rebuild Gaia in their own image. No other animal on Gaia is so amazingly self-righteous, so vain. The closest rival in pride is the Garou, and we know better than to mar Gaia's flesh. Instead, we record our deeds in songs and ask that our descendants remember us as well. The Get have common sense — something that is lacking in our two-legged cousins.

The World

The Get of Fenris are everywhere. Our tribe has expanded far from our homelands, just as Fenris commanded. We have made countless enemies along the way and few friends of any notice. We are warriors first. In whatever land we came to, we took up sword and shield to fight the taint of the Wyrm before we settled down, many times angering the natives in the process, as in the case of the Wendigo. Never ignore the resentment of others, for not all believe in honorable combat as a means to settle disputes. There are too many who would poison a meal before they would offer you a chance to explain your actions.

Asia

There are very few Get of Fenris in the Far East. We have little need for lands so overpopulated by humans that the Wyld cannot even hope to grow. Most in the East follow philosophies that are simply too bizarre; they would rather live in peace and study the way water falls from a tree's leaves than know the satisfaction of a well-fought battle. These places we leave to the Shadow Lords and the Stargazers.

There are many half-breeds in Asia, children of Get heritage, but tainted, mating with the Kinfolk of the lesser tribes. We will claim them if we must, but they are not true Get. These are the children of the Apocalypse. Pity them, for they will never know our glory.

The Middle East

There has never been a better place for us to hone our combat skills. The people of the Middle East claim to hold with the Asian philosophies, but they do not follow these beliefs in the same way. They believe in settling disputes with weapons and bloodshed. Unfortunately, their weapons are often bombs, and they would shed the blood of innocents on the street rather than meet their true enemy face-to-face. They are much like the Fianna in this way: they aim to create an example of their enemies, and often make claim to actions that were not their own.

If you must go to the Middle East, do not take your Kinfolk with you. Your enemies would use your family as a shield while they attempt to stab you in the back. Better that you train your Kinfolk well and trust them to defend themselves in your homeland.

Australia

A few of our tribe live in Australia, but the land is hostile, and the Bunyip Garou — those weaklings who once held the continent — are said to haunt the Umbra, troubling our brethren in the Land Down Under with their vile mind games. Do not bother trying to help this wasteland. It is not worth the trouble, for the land is far beyond our aid.

Europe

This is our Homeland, and there are many Get who live in the Old World still. All throughout Europe we have made homes for ourselves and taught the weak to fear us. The Black Forest, the hills, the valleys — all is ours. We could rule the continent if we felt it necessary. But we must allow other Garou here as well, for they would have no other place if we did not tolerate their inept ways. Even so, we continue to teach them lessons.

The northern parts of Italy still come into our territories, despite the humans and their foolish border skirmishes. The Black Furies loathe our existence on territory they claim should belong to them, but the silly cows haven't the strength to take the land away from us. We have let them keep some part of their homeland, for we are not completely without heart.

Great Britain

The British Isles have known us for a long time; to many, the Isles are as much our Homeland as are the northern parts of the continent. We share these lands with the Fianna, and we often war with them. They call us usurpers. They are not quite the warriors we are, nor are they worthy as comrades. From time to time, it is a true pleasure to provoke them in their constant cries for freedom from England. Still, their Kinfolk take human politics too seriously. And they often rebel against the rulers of their nation, the Kin of the Silver Fangs. The Fianna would do well to listen to their superiors for a change.

South America

This land reeks of the Wyrm's taint. The countries clash constantly, and the lush forests of Gaia suffer as a result. The humans have gotten out of control; Pentex rules the land, stealing what should belong only to Gaia and converting wonders of nature into more farmlands where they can raise cattle. The Amazon Basin suffers while we continue to lead the way in the war against Pentex, and we continue to lose ground in this war. Surely this, as no other sign, indicates that the final days are upon us.

You will likely be called upon to fight in the Amazon, and you should feel honored if asked. You may expect glorious battles indeed should you accept the offer.

Africa

The only good to come from the Second World War is that our numbers in Africa were strengthened once again. We are now a force in South Africa. But there are places here where the lesser races starve to death, and the bounty of Gaia is only a remembered dream. The land dies; the deserts grow stronger and devour the savannas and forests. This land is both proud and sad, for the death of so many different species is never a joyful event.

In the past, we often joined the hunters, downing an elephant or facing off against a rhino. That time is long gone, and now we must defend these weakened species. Poachers, should you find them, must be hunted down and destroyed.

America

The Great American Melting Pot is over-full and reeks with the scent of unwashed masses. Too many come from other lands, far to the east, far to the south, trying to find a better life. If they would concentrate on bettering their stations in their own lands, perhaps ours would not be so filthy.

The liberal-minded have allowed the criminals back onto the streets. Never has any land so desperately needed the Get of Fenris. The Pure Ones have failed to keep their lands pure, and so we have come to cut away the diseased flesh of Gaia, and thus permit Her to regain Her strength.

There are many Garou from around the world here. They will need us to teach them properly. Watch carefully for the Garou who cannot hold their caerns, for they are many. Already we have been forced to take control of several caerns to ensure that they do not fall to the Wyrm. This has

made us enemies in several tribes — but that is a part of life over which we have no control.

The Other Tribes
The Black Furies

The Furies are a proud tribe, and they have accomplished many feats of which they should be proud. They fight almost as well as men, and they base their lives upon the pursuit of Gaia's happiness. But they are confused. They fight against us when they should submit to us. There is no honor in denying the rights of men to rule over women. Women need the leadership of men to keep them strong in these last days. We have battled the Furies many times in the past, and I suspect we shall continue to struggle against them.

The Bone Gnawers

There is a rumor that the Gnawers once had Garou stock. These days, they mate with dogs. That does not say much for their heritage, and it says even less for their character. If there were no humans available, would they mate with gorillas? Then again, if they mated with gorillas, perhaps they would have backbones. I understand they lay claim to several members who once were among the Get of Fenris; I do not believe that nameless outcasts qualify for any other tribe. They may have them. I have never seen a more cowardly lot in my life, and I would sooner see them slaughtered than sit by and watch them mate with the Wyrm. They have no pride, no honor, and no common sense.

The Children of Gaia

They still insist on peace, when the final days are here. I understand what the Children of Gaia are after, but I do not believe all of the tribes can be united until they finally realize that we are right, and that, with the Apocalypse so close at hand, few others could even hope to lead the 13 tribes as well as we can. But they cry for peace and insist that we allow the humans to take what they need and do as they please, though it is obviously the humans who need to be culled back the most. If the time for peace is ever going to come, the war must be taken care of first.

The Fianna

Why can't the Fianna understand that songs are only a small part of our great heritage? They sing, they drink, they fight and they mate. All the while, the Black Spiral Dancers breathe down their necks and we must constantly protect them from the threat of the Wyrm-Garou. Surely we could just let them die, but the Isles are a part of our heritage, too, and must be defended. The time for harps is long past. Let them taste the savagery and pleasure of war. Then they shall be worthy to fight alongside us.

The Glass Walkers

As best I can figure, the Glass Walkers believe in fighting fire with fire. They believe that by conquering the cities, they can somehow make the cities a part of nature again. This is stupidity. They stare into the Wyrm's mouth and call for bargains and business proposals. The Glass Walkers are only steps away from a merger with Pentex. If that should ever happen, they will be destroyed. We have our sacred duties to perform, and if those duties require us to kill the Glass Walkers before they can join with the Black Spiral Dancers, then that is what we shall do. There is no excuse for worshipping the Scabs. The only difference between the Walkers and the Gnawers is that the Gnawers are more honest about their self-serving ways.

Red Talons

The Talons are powerful warriors, and worthy of our respect. It saddens me to think that we must eventually sing their funeral dirge, for they are surely the least in number of all the tribes, and the most set in their ways. Still, I believe they could make a difference, if only the Concord were not in their way. Acknowledge that the Talons are our allies, and help them when you can, but know that they are secondary to us. They are too stubborn and foolish to realize that if they would simply join forces with us, we could rule the 13 tribes with ease.

Shadow Lords

Do not trust the Lords, for they are back-stabbers and moneylenders. There are many among the Get who claim that the Shadow Lords will offer aid only if there will be a greater profit for themselves in the long run. Be wary of the Lords; always remember that they would sooner see you dead and buried than allow you the right to speak your mind. They would battle the Wyrm with words, while they manipulate others to do their fighting for them. Beneath their pompous airs and manipulative schemes, the Shadow Lords are cowards. The Get of Fenris have no need for cowardly allies.

The Silent Striders

The Striders came from the deserts and bear many features in common with the jackal. They are wanderers and vagabonds, and almost as solitary as the ronin. What is it they seek? What is it they run from? I do not feel that they can be trusted. Fight with them, but do not live with them. They come from all races of humans, and they are indiscriminate in their mating habits. How can they be trusted when they have no true heritage?

The Silver Fangs

The Silver Fangs were once almost as great as we are, but they no longer recognize the urgency of the war. Do as the Fangs request, for only by watching them carefully can we

Evaluate each of the Stargazers individually — much as with the Silent Striders — for they are very independent, and each one follows his own beliefs. They can fight, and I wish they would, because we cannot do everything.

The Uktena

I do not trust the Pure Ones, and I especially do not trust these shamans. They are both secretive and paranoid; they look for the Wyrm in places where the rocks are set just so, or where the wind blows too cold. They try to placate the Wyrm rather than doing battle against it. Also, they whine too much, crying that their lands would still be pure if not for our coming here. They would rather smoke their sacred pot and eat their sacred peyote than fight in our sacred war against Gaia's enemies. Medicine men have their place, but a whole tribe of them? No, they are weak and try to hide their weakness behind ceremonies that are ineffectual at best.

The Wendigo

There are too many of these slovenly near-warriors. They dress themselves in feathers and claim that they kept the Pure Lands free of corruption, but I notice they fell quickly enough when real Garou showed up. They sit on their reservations, drinking whiskey and whining about how poorly they've been treated, all the while swearing vengeance against us all. We have nothing to fear from these fools; they have already lost the war. Like the rednecks in the Southern states, they insist in their pride that they have only lost a battle. But it is not the Get of Fenris who now live in the deserts, feeding off lizards.

These Wendigo crawl with their tails between their legs and whine at the government, claiming that we have taken away what is theirs by right. I say let them take it back if they can; I have long grown tired of their sniveling. The only difference between the Bone Gnawers and the Wendigo is that the Bone Gnawers will openly confess to their cowardice. The Wendigo claim to mourn the loss of the Croatan tribe, and I believe they do. But at least the Croatan died with honor. The Wendigo no longer have any dignity.

Enemies

The wails of a lifetime were gathered in that train whistle from other nights in other slumbering years; the howls of moon-dreamed dogs, the sleep of river-cold winds through January porch screens which stopped the blood, a thousand fire-sirens weeping, or worse! the out-gone shreds of breath, the protests of a billion people dead or dying, not wanting to be dead, their groans, their sighing, burst over the earth!

— Ray Bradbury, Something Wicked This Way Comes

There are other creatures just as proud as the humans, and almost as deadly in their ways. They, like us, do their best to hide their existence, and like us, they do this to maintain security. They do not fear the humans, just as we do not fear them. Instead, they respect the weapons the humans have

determine when they are no longer fit to rule the tribes. They have attempted to lead the humans over the centuries, and we can see how poorly they have handled that situation. Watch them carefully, for the Silver Fangs are going mad, and must not be allowed to bring us to our knees. The Garou deserve better.

Many of the Get in Europe do not see that the Silver Fangs are insane. They want only to believe that the Fangs are their natural leaders. Do not fall into this pit of folly. The Get must be the ones who lead the Garou. Let the Fangs play their tricks with the humans and leave the Get to handle the war that must be fought.

We shall follow the Silver Fangs, we shall listen to their commands and obey their orders for now. But we will make certain that they do not lead us to the Wyrm.

The Stargazers

What do they seek in the night? The Stargazers look into the depths of the stars for answers that do not exist. They spend too much time staring into space and trying to solve meaningless puzzles, thus managing little in the war against the Wyrm. While I have seen a few who could fight, most look as if they are three-quarters asleep, and all too ready to ask questions of the Jormangundr Itself if they believe the Wyrm can answer their petty riddles.

created, and acknowledge that mankind must have his false pride, or he will surely burn off the very flesh of Gaia. They are a sad lot, but they are also deadly. You should know something of these creatures, for you will surely meet them. Their goals often come into conflict with our own. Above all else, know your enemy.

The Draugar — Undead

Vampires are real. They come out at night to feed upon the blood of the innocent. They have the power to confuse their victims, to make their victims believe they enjoy being fed upon. Should you meet one of the undead, do not be misled by its weak appearance, for many vampires are often older than the United States Government, and in some cases older than the Church. Do not trust them.

You may run across one whom you feel is trustworthy, for she will not smell of the Wyrm and she will tell you of the horrible life she leads, forever banished from the sunlight. She may even look like someone you once knew, and she may share with you her memories of easier times. It is all a lie.

If you must deal with these creatures in times of war, then do so, but be prepared to rip the hearts from their lifeless bodies when the time comes.

Vampires have family units. When they come across a human who suits their needs, they force him to join with them in their mockery of life. There are dozens of these family units, each answering ultimately to the greatest of vampires. You would think that with such a system, they could have taken over the world by now. In truth, they are divided by petty conflicts, stabbing each other in the back and stealing blood from one another.

There are a few, called the Gangrel, whom you may trust briefly. Never give them the location of a caern, or let them know where you live among the humans, but you may rely on them in times of war. They are much like the Shadow Lords: truly trustworthy only when they are asleep. Still, they have their uses. If given a choice, however, kill them on sight.

Gandwere — Mages

Mages are humans who have learned the secrets of magic. Though, most work with the Weaver, some will ally themselves with the Wyld, and others with the Wyrm. A few of the mages could potentially become our allies, but most are a threat to Gaia and to our way of life. There are many who try to make themselves into machines and then hide this fact with false skins; they are much like the Glass Walkers. Gears and wires do not make a better Garou, nor do they make a better human. It was the Weaver's capture of the Wyrm that started this whole mess in the first place.

Stay away from the mages. Work with them if you must, but do not trust them. They must each earn your trust individually, for they have no true heritage or lineage on which to rely. Do not trust those who work for the Weaver, and kill the ones who in league with the Wyrm.

Haug-Bui — Wraiths

Everyone dies. Sometimes, they come back from death. Do not be afraid of the wraiths, for they are only wretched souls who have lost their way, or were not worthy of a place in the afterlife. Many Vikings fell in fields of battle. Those who were strong and worthy went to Valhalla. Those who were weak became ghosts who still haunt the world.

We believe that it is those humans who are weak in will and determination who become wraiths. We cannot hope to kill the wraiths, for they are already dead. Instead, leave them to their own. They suffer as few have suffered, for they cannot find Valhalla.

The Faerie

We have a long history with the faerie. To some, we have sworn oaths of alliance. The Dvergar — the Dwarves — are our friends. The Jotunns — the Giants — and the Trolls are our sworn enemies. Do not take any action against a faerie until you know for certain that he intends to do you harm. Most of them share our love of Gaia, and for that reason alone, they should be treated with respect. While you may work with the changelings, do not expect straight answers to any questions you may ask. They are like the spirits; their motives are too alien for us to understand.

Appendix One: Seidar (Powers)

Tribal Weaknesses (Optional)

An optional rule was introduced in the first of the **Werewolf** Tribebooks: tribal weaknesses. These are quirks each member of a particular tribe possesses, usually due to the social or even genetic nature of a tribe. Weaknesses should not always be enforced. There are some situations where a Bone Gnawer may not suffer a higher difficulty on Social rolls. These situations may be rare, but they can occur. For instance, Black Furies suffer from an inborn anger against men, but a Black Fury may not feel anger towards a man with whom she has a trusting relationship.

It is up to the Storyteller to enforce these rules when an appropriate situation occurs in the game. A player may be unwilling to remind a Storyteller that her Uktena's curiosity will get her into trouble.

Get of Fenris Weakness

Intolerance

Each Get of Fenris has one thing that she will not tolerate. If a situation arises in which this object of contempt is near, she will be unable to endure its presence and will do everything in her power to rid herself of the annoyance. If this object of intolerance is a fellow Garou, then woe unto him....

The player may either define a specific Intolerance for her character (with the Storyteller's approval) or choose from the list below. Wyrm creatures may not be chosen — all Get are expected to hate such monstrosities as a matter of course.

• Cowardice — You hate cowardice in all its forms, whether it is fear of the battlefield or fear to stand up to others in social situations. You openly scorn those you deem cowardly. If you ever go into a fox frenzy, you will turn your hate inward, and must do everything possible to make up for your act of cowardice, becoming quite reckless in the process.

• Compromise — You hate to compromise; you view this as a tactic for those who are not strong enough to get their way. You scorn those who use compromise as a means to settle disputes (such as the Glass Walkers and the Children of Gaia), and you yourself will never compromise in a situation. Your way must be enforced. If a leader forces you to compromise, that is acceptable, but you will begin to doubt that leader's ability to rule.

• Lower Animals — You have only contempt for creatures lower than you on the food chain. Such creatures are meant to be kicked around by your kind. This includes humans and even wolves. While you believe it is your duty to defend them to a degree (such is Gaia's will), you will not accept condescension or insubordination from them. A grave insult from a human is enough to drive you to frenzy.

• Peaceniks — You despise those who speak of peace when war is the proper response. War tempers the warrior and prepares him to fight against the Wyrm as the Apocalypse approaches. Yes, there are times for peace, but when attacked, you must strike back. Never turn the other cheek.

• Weakness — You hate weakness in others, whether it is a lack of physical strength or a lack of backbone. You will openly scorn those you deem weak and will never tolerate such qualities in yourself. You can only be merciful when there is a risk involved, a chance that it could lead to danger; otherwise, mercy is the hallmark of those too weak to punish criminals (whether they are servants of the Wyrm or Garou).

• Weaver Stuff — You hate all things of the Weaver, especially technology. You may even feel that Klaives bear too much of her taint; only claws and fangs would then be pure enough. You especially despise the Glass Walkers and all Urrah. You must never willingly use technology when more traditional means will do.

Merits and Flaws

Alcohol Tolerance (1 pt. Physical Merit)

With a successful Stamina roll (difficulty 5), a Garou with this Merit can shake off the effects of intoxication, suffering no coordination penalties that might normally affect a drunken fighter. This Merit also works against all natural intoxicants, though not against poisons. It will also take a Garou with this Tolerance longer to get drunk.

Mixed Heritage (1 to 2 pt. Social Flaw)

Get of obviously mixed heritage are scorned by others. They are less likely to be accepted, must work harder to gain Renown (at the Storyteller's discretion) and are often treated as poorly as metis by the more militant members of their tribe. The Get suffers penalties on all Social rolls with Get of Fenris (+1 difficulty with 1 pt. Flaw; -1 die with 2 pt. Flaw). Note: This Flaw does not affect the Pure Breed Background.

Physically Impressive (2 pt. Physical Merit)

A Garou with this Merit can add one die to all Social rolls that involve intimidation. The Get appears dangerous both in outward demeanor and in physical bearing, and exudes a confidence that assists in impressing opponents.

Gifts

• **Troll Skin (Level Two)** — With this Gift, a Garou can make her skin grow tough and thick, covered with warty knots of hard, armored flesh. This Gift is taught by an Earth Elemental.

System: The Garou spends one Gnosis point and rolls Stamina + Primal-Urge (difficulty 7). For each success, the Garou receives one extra die on her soak roll. This Gift does not protect against fire or silver, and lasts for one scene. However, when embued with Troll Skin, the Garou is +1 difficulty on Social rolls due to the ugly skin and its accompanying smell.

• **Wearing the Bear Shirt (Level Two)** — When a Garou with this Gift frenzies, he will always enter a berserk frenzy, never a fox frenzy. This Gift is taught by a Bear-spirit.

System: No roll is required; once this Gift is learned, the effects are automatic. In addition, the Garou can make a

Willpower roll to resist any Gifts, Disciplines, Arcanos or other powers that incite fear, even if a resistance roll is normally not allowed.

• **Endurance of Heimdall (Level Five)** — This powerful Gift grants the Garou great endurance and hardiness for a time. This Gift is taught by a Boar-spirit.

System: The Garou spends one Gnosis point and rolls Willpower (difficulty 6). If successful, the Garou's Stamina rating is doubled for the duration of the scene. This will aid Stamina and Soak rolls.

• **Strength of the Einherjar (Level Five)** — This Gift allows a Get to call upon his greatest ancestors, the heroes of Valhalla, the Einherjar, for assistance. It is only used in dire situations, when the lives of more than one Garou are endangered. Calling on the strength of the Einherjar allows a Get to increase his Attributes substantially for a limited time. The Einherjar come to the aid of a Get only in times of great peril, and punish any Get who attempts to call on them without need. This Gift is taught by an Ancestor-spirit.

System: Only Get with at least one dot in the Past Life Background may learn this Gift. The Get spends one Rage point and rolls Charisma + Rituals (difficulty 10); she may subtract one from the difficulty for every dot she has in Past Life. During the casting of this Gift, she must carve the specific runes of her ancestors into her flesh. For each success, she may add one dot to any Attribute, or distribute the dots to different Attributes.

If the Storyteller believes this Gift has been used inappropriately, the Einherjar will still give assistance, but then turn on their descendant, permanently removing a number of Attribute dots equal to those they granted. They will show no mercy.

• **Call Great Fenris (Level Six)** — The Get may summon a spirit avatar of Fenris Wolf. The avatar will assist in combat, slaying all who are not Get of Fenris or under their protection. There is always a sacrifice demanded in return, traditionally the right hand of the summoner. Once Fenris has claimed the hand, it does not regenerate. If there is not a good reason for calling the avatar, or the summoner will be devoured whole. This Gift is taught by a wolf spirit.

System: The Garou spends one Gnosis point and rolls Stamina + Occult (difficulty 6). The summoner permanently loses one Health Level as his right hand is bitten off by Fenris in return for daring to summon him. See the sidebar for the Fenris avatar's Traits.

The Spirit Avatar of Fenris Wolf

The avatar of Great Fenris appears as an enormous wolf, 10 feet tall at the shoulder. His eyes burn with rage and his jaws drip with the blood of countless enemies. His fur is brown with red and black markings. The avatar of Fenris can run at up to 100 miles per hour, and never seems to tire.

Willpower 10, Rage 10, Gnosis 8, Power 75

Charms: Airt Sense, Materialize (Power cost 40; Strength 10, Dexterity 7, Stamina 10, Brawl 5, Dodge 3, Claws: Str + 3, Fangs: Str + 4, Health 15), Reform, Tracking

---

Get of Fenris Ragabash (Rotagar)

• **Loki's Touch (Level Three)** — This Gift is rare among the Get of Fenris, but the Rotagar often find it necessary to cool the rages of their comrades. With just a touch, the Garou may cause a target to go into uncontrollable fits of laughter or simply to have a better sense of humor. This Gift is taught by any Trickster spirit (most often Ratatosk, the Squirrel).

System: The Garou must touch an opponent and roll Manipulation + Empathy (difficulty equal to the Rage plus the Rank of the target; maximum difficulty of 10). The fits of laughter will last for one round per success, during which time the target may not take any offensive action, although he may defend himself if attacked.

Ymir's Sweat Gift

• **Call of the Early Frost (Level Three)** — Per the Level Three Wendigo Gift. Only members of the Ymir's Sweat bloodline (if they truly exist) may learn this Gift.

Rites

The rites of the Get of Fenris are bloody, savage affairs; few are ever performed without retribution or punishment in mind.

Rite of Heritage (Level One Renown)

This rite reveals the lineage of a Get, often allowing rival's numerous claims of poor breeding to be disproved without resulting in a bloodbath.

Rite of Rune Carving (Level One Mystical)

The Theurges (Godi) of the Get of Fenris are taught early on to respect and appreciate the power of runes. This rite allows them to carve the runes that they can later cast. The runes must be carved into the bones of enemies slain in battle and, once dedicated, may never be lost by the Get. (See the **Rite of Rune Casting**, below.)

Rite of War (Level Two Renown)

An Ahroun must successfully complete a vigorous series of trials before she is allowed to become Rank Two, regardless of what she may already have accomplished. During this rite, she may use no weapons except her natural body, and she must battle with two more Ahroun, both of whom are armed with silver. The scars achieved during the rite are then painted with dyes made from various plants, and become permanent reminders of the Ahroun's success. This rite is ceremonial in nature, and simply marks the successes of the Get as a warrior.

Rite of Challenge (Level Three Renown)

This long rite is a formal challenge for leadership of the sept and may only be performed at formal moots. The challenger must step forward and recite his full lineage, announcing the proud heredity that permits him to call for battle. He must also call out the reasons for his challenge, and make a formal accusation against the present Jarl. The Jarl may not refuse this challenge. No weapons may be used in the ensuing combat.

Rite of the Lodge House (Level Three Mystical)

This powerful rite is performed at all formal moots, and works to soothe the Rage within all Get of Fenris. Once this rite has been performed, any Get within the lodge are supernaturally calm, and all Rage rolls have a difficulty of 9. They are thus capable of rational thought and reasonable discourse.

Rite of Rune Casting (Level Three Mystical)

The Theurges use this rite to cast and understand the meaning runes. The Storyteller is encouraged to come up with exactly how much or how little of the future can be interpreted by the casting of the runes. The answers should always be vague, but accurate enough to give hints.

Rite of Conquest (Level Five Mystical)

This rite is performed whenever one Jarl has defeated another. The rite acknowledges the history of both the fallen Jarl and the new Jarl, and is actually more ceremonial than mystical. The heart of the slain Jarl must be consumed by the new Jarl, who symbolically gains the wisdom to rule his sept properly. In the case of the World-Jarl, the leader of all the Get of Fenris, the symbolic act is accompanied by the actual knowledge of the predecessor's Gifts. This rite ensures that Get of Fenris leaders will always be strong. The possessions of Jarls defeated in combat are turned over to the new Jarl, but any relatives who have a claim on the fetishes and weapons may challenge the new Jarl for the right to keep them.

Fetishes

Dagger of Retribution

Level 2, Gnosis 5

This fetish allows a Garou to know who has stolen a prized possession. While concentrating on the stolen item, the Garou must hold the ornate dagger forward and follow the gentle tugs it gives until it reaches its mark. The fetish inflicts Strength damage, but the difficulty to hit is only 5.

Hammer of Thor

Level 5, Gnosis 5

These hammers are forged from silver-laced iron and cooled in the blood of freshly-slain enemies. Each hammer inflicts Strength +3 damage and causes aggravated wounds. As with Thor's hammer, Mjolnir, a hammer always returns to its rightful owner. There are seven of these hammers, and most are in the hands of the Jarls of various powerful septs. Killing blows from

The runes (Futhark):

ᚠ	ᚢ	ᚦ	ᚨ	ᚱ	ᚲ	ᚹ	ᚺ
f	u	th	a	r	k	w	h	n

ᛁ	ᛃ	ᛈ	ᚷ	ᛉ	ᛏ	ᛒ	ᛖ	ᛗ
i	j	p	r	s	t	b	e	m

ᛚ	ᛜ	ᛟ	ᛞ
l	ng	o	d

these weapons send out a powerful thunderclap; this does no damage, but announces to everyone in the vicinity that a foe has fallen.

Shield of Heimdall

Level 5, Gnosis 8

This small wooden token, shaped like a shield, is worn around the neck. When activated, the shield adds +5 dice to the wearer's soak roll, but only against cowardly attacks. Only one opponent per round will have a direct shot at the wearer; for all other attacks, from behind or from cover, the wearer receives the +5 soak dice.

Wotan's Spear (Gungnir)

Level 5, Gnosis 7

This powerful spear causes aggravated damage, and will only harm minions of the Wyrm. The bearer of this spear may use the Gift: Sense Wyrm. If a foe can be seen, it can be hit, for the spear suffers no range penalties. The spear does Strength + 5 damage. There are two known in existence.

Totems

(See also Chapter Two)

Totems of War

Boar

Background Cost: 5

The savage and powerful boar is feared by many hunters. With its ferocity and anger, it will fight long after weaker warriors fall in battle. Many combative young packs choose Boar as their totem.

Traits: Boar gives his Children an extra point of Stamina and Brawl 2.

Ban: Children of Boar must never hunt or eat boars.

Fenris Wolf

See **Werewolf: The Apocalypse** Second Edition rulebook, p. 262.

Totems of Wisdom

Hrafn, the Raven

Background Cost: 5

Hrafn is a Trickster-spirit favored by many lupus. He plays with their cubs and teases the yearlings and adults. He is always hungry; in fact, he is the hungriest of all the totem creatures. Hrafn often leads wolves to prey, but lacks the strength to kill

the animal himself. He feeds upon what is left after the wolves are finished with the carcass. He is also a totem of wealth. He makes sure the wolves want for nothing and always have the resources they need.

Traits: Hrafn teaches his Children Survival 3, Subterfuge 1 and Enigmas 1. Each pack member gains a bonus of one temporary Wisdom point. Children of the Raven are favored by the Corax wereravens.

Ban: Hrafn asks that its Children carry no wealth, instead trusting in Hrafn to provide.

Ratatosk

Background Cost: 4

Ratatosk sees and hears all from his secret pathways up and down the trunk of the World Tree. While he is small and puny, he knows much and teaches his Children craftiness.

Traits: Children of Ratatosk learn Subterfuge 2 and three dots in any Knowledges of their choice (Lupus characters can even choose Knowledges normally restricted to them). Children of Ratatosk will always gain one fewer Honor Renown point than usual (they must gain at least two points on any occasion to get one), but they get an extra point of Wisdom Renown every time they earn Wisdom (Storyteller's discretion.)

Ban: Children of Ratatosk become skittish and jumpy. They will always enter a fox frenzy rather than a berserk, and they may not learn the Gift: Wearing the Bear Shirt.

Appendix Two: Jung Fenrir (Young Fenrir)

> *...The Old Norse word for wolf,* vargr, *being also the legal term for outlaw.*
> —Adam Douglas, *The Beast Within: A History of the Werewolf*

To the last human or wolf among them, the Get are tough and mean as hell. But while they may seem culturally and behaviorally homogenous to outsiders, they actually hold many individual beliefs. Get can be warriors, wise thanes, stern shamans or crafty (and cruel) tricksters.

Judge, Jury and Executioner

Quote: *Excuse me, I think you left this noose behind when you murdered that little girl. (Snarl) I thought you might like it back, you twisted sonova...*

Prelude: You grew up in the city, more often than not left to your own devices, as both of your parents were forced to work. By the time you were 10, you had been in trouble with the law several times for boosting cars and even for shoplifting. You tried dealing drugs once, for the easy money, but the desperate look on the junkies' faces led you to change your mind. It just wasn't worth the fast cash to do that to someone. Instead, you drifted into the neighborhood protection group as you grew older. Your First Change happened when you were 15. By that time, you had developed a reputation for reporting crimes to the cops. They no longer thought of you as a threat, but as an ally.

After your Rite of Passage, you took the action to a new level. Now, you locate the criminals who prey upon your neighbors and teach them a harsh lesson about civic responsibility. Your prey rarely lives long enough to forget the experience.

Concept: You are now a beat cop, working the worst parts of the city to hunt down the sleaziest individuals and the most corrupt gangs. You try to avoid being seen too often in action; if you are seen, this might come back to haunt your Kinfolk.

Roleplaying Hints: You know the language and the rituals of the streets. You also know where you can get information with little more than a veiled threat. You always play by the book when on duty, and you lead by example as a responsible member of the community. But when night falls, the game begins. You love the smell of fear on your victims and you love the taste of blood on your fangs. You are a friendly, cheerful man, and a savage, merciless Garou.

Equipment: Ratty street clothes, various confiscated weapons, used to hide the true cause of death, handcuffs, nondescript car, donuts and coffee

GET OF FENRIS

Name: _____
Player: _____
Chronicle: _____

Breed: Homid
Auspice: Ragabash
Camp: Hand of Tyr

Pack Name: _____
Pack Totem: _____
Concept: Judge, Jury & Executioner

Attributes

Physical
Strength _____ ●●●○○
Dexterity _____ ●●●●○
Stamina _____ ●●●○○

Social
Charisma _____ ●●●○○
Manipulation _____ ●○○○○
Appearance _____ ●●○○○

Mental
Perception _____ ●●●○○
Intelligence _____ ●●●○○
Wits _____ ●●○○○

Abilities

Talents
Alertness _____ ●●○○○
Athletics _____ ●●○○○
Brawl _____ ●●○○○
Dodge _____ ●●○○○
Empathy _____ ○○○○○
Expression _____ ○○○○○
Intimidation _____ ●●○○○
Primal-Urge _____ ○○○○○
Streetwise _____ ●●●○○
Subterfuge _____ ○○○○○

Skills
Animal Ken _____ ○○○○○
Drive _____ ●○○○○
Etiquette _____ ●○○○○
Firearms _____ ●●○○○
Leadership _____ ●○○○○
Melee _____ ●○○○○
Performance _____ ○○○○○
Repair _____ ●○○○○
Stealth _____ ●○○○○
Survival _____ ●●○○○

Knowledges
Computer _____ ●○○○○
Enigmas _____ ○○○○○
Investigation _____ ●●○○○
Law _____ ●○○○○
Linguistics _____ ○○○○○
Medicine _____ ●○○○○
Occult _____ ○○○○○
Politics _____ ○○○○○
Rituals _____ ○○○○○
Science _____ ○○○○○

Advantages

Backgrounds
Allies _____ ●●●○○
Kinfolk _____ ●●○○○
Resources _____ ●○○○○
_____ ○○○○○
_____ ○○○○○

Gifts
Blur of the Milky Eye
Resist Pain
Persuasion
_____
_____

Gifts
_____
_____
_____
_____
_____

Renown

Glory
●●○○○○○○○○
□□□□□□□□□□

Honor
●○○○○○○○○○
□□□□□□□□□□

Wisdom
○○○○○○○○○○
□□□□□□□□□□

Rank
[ ]

Rage
●●●●○○○○○○
□□□□□□□□□□

Gnosis
●●●○○○○○○○
□□□□□□□□□□

Willpower
●●●●●●○○○○
□□□□□□□□□□

Health
Bruised _____ □
Hurt -1 □
Injured -1 □
Wounded -2 □
Mauled -2 □
Crippled -5 □
Incapacitated □

Weakness
INTOLERANCE:
Criminals

Attributes: 7/5/3 **Abilities:** 13/9/5 **Gifts:** 1 Level One from breed, auspice and tribe; **Backgrounds:** 5; **Freebie Points:** 15 (7/5/2/1)

Caern Guardian

Quote: *Little far from home, aren't you? Looks like the park's pretty full up today. Why don't you get back in your car and leave before things get ugly?*

Prelude: You were born different from others, less than perfect in the eyes of your people. Despite your deformity, your people still gave you affection as a child and helped you to overcome your physical limitations. While it's true they often made life hard for you, never letting you favor your club foot, they instilled in you a sense of pride in your worth, and gave you the chance to prove yourself. You have always lived in the country, surrounded by the sounds of the natural world. As time went on, you moved closer to the periphery of the human world. Now you work as a park ranger and make certain that no one defiles the haven of Gaia. You take your duties seriously, as you are also the first defense of the caern in times of danger.

Concept: Your love of the Wyld is strong, and when it is mistreated your anger is ferocious. You still live near the woods, working as a park ranger and as a guardian of the caern. You do not ask questions more than once, and you enforce the rules about campsite safety with an iron fist.

Roleplaying Hints: You seldom lose your temper, but you never back down from an argument with some city fool who wants to give you grief. You try to be friendly, but are also very firm in the rules you set down. If a potential troublemaker comes to the park, you ask him to leave, and if he declines, you teach him the error of his ways.

Metis Deformity: Club foot. You can only run at half the normal speed.

Equipment: Jeep, ranger's uniform, two-way radio, portable fire extinguisher

54

Get of Fenris

Name: **Breed:** Metis   **Pack Name:**
Player: **Auspice:** Theurge   **Pack Totem:**
Chronicle: **Camp:**   **Concept:** Caern Guardian

Attributes

Physical
Strength ●●●●○
Dexterity ●●●○○
Stamina ●●●○○

Social
Charisma ●●○○○
Manipulation ●●○○○
Appearance ●●○○○

Mental
Perception ●●●○○
Intelligence ●●○○○
Wits ●●●○○

Abilities

Talents
Alertness ●●○○○
Athletics ●●○○○
Brawl ●●●○○
Dodge ●●○○○
Empathy ○○○○○
Expression ○○○○○
Intimidation ●●●○○
Primal-Urge ●○○○○
Streetwise ○○○○○
Subterfuge ○○○○○

Skills
Animal Ken ●●○○○
Drive ●○○○○
Etiquette ○○○○○
Firearms ○○○○○
Leadership ○○○○○
Melee ○○○○○
Performance ○○○○○
Repair ●○○○○
Stealth ●○○○○
Survival ●●○○○

Knowledges
Computer ○○○○○
Enigmas ●●●○○
Investigation ●○○○○
Law ●○○○○
Linguistics ○○○○○
Medicine ●○○○○
Occult ○○○○○
Politics ○○○○○
Rituals ●●●○○
Science ○○○○○

Advantages

Backgrounds
Totem ●●●○○
Past Life ●●○○○
  ○○○○○
  ○○○○○
  ○○○○○

Gifts
Sense Wyrm
Spirit Speech
Razor Claws

Gifts

Renown

Glory
○ ○ ○ ○ ○ ○ ○ ○ ○ ○
□ □ □ □ □ □ □ □ □ □

Honor
○ ○ ○ ○ ○ ○ ○ ○ ○ ○
□ □ □ □ □ □ □ □ □ □

Wisdom
● ● ● ○ ○ ○ ○ ○ ○ ○
□ □ □ □ □ □ □ □ □ □

Rank
□

Rage
● ● ● ● ● ○ ○ ○ ○ ○
□ □ □ □ □ □ □ □ □ □

Gnosis
● ● ● ● ● ○ ○ ○ ○ ○
□ □ □ □ □ □ □ □ □ □

Willpower
● ● ● ● ● ● ● ○ ○ ○
□ □ □ □ □ □ □ □ □ □

Health
Bruised		□
Hurt	-1	□
Injured	-1	□
Wounded	-2	□
Mauled	-2	□
Crippled	-5	□
Incapacitated		□

Weakness
INTOLERANCE:
Tourists

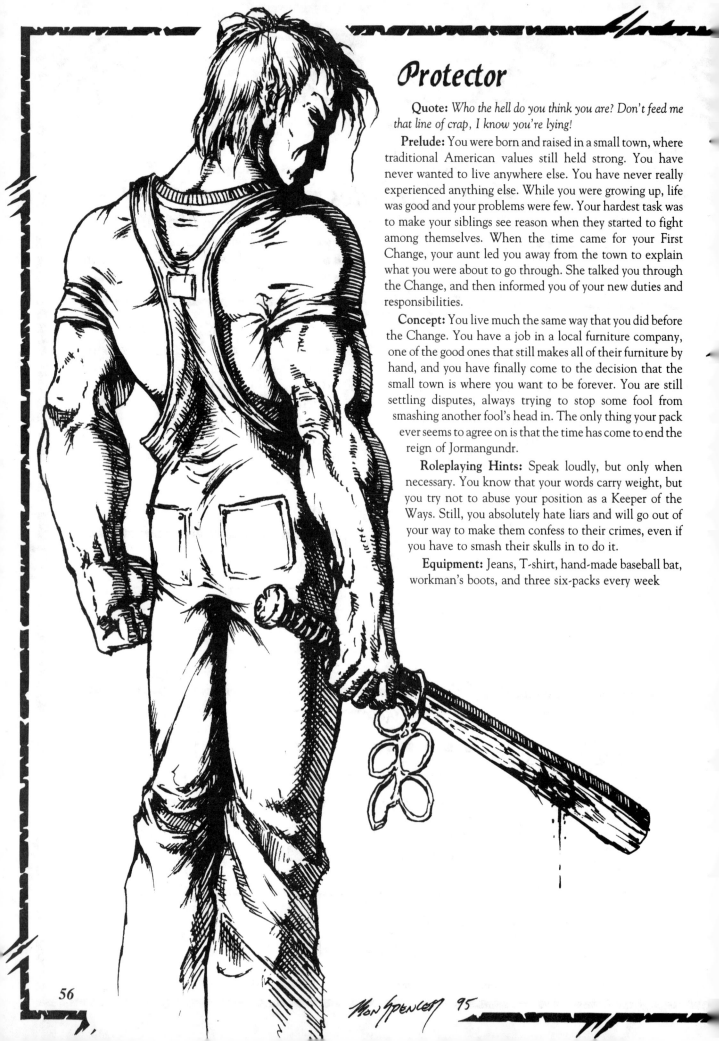

Protector

Quote: *Who the hell do you think you are? Don't feed me that line of crap, I know you're lying!*

Prelude: You were born and raised in a small town, where traditional American values still held strong. You have never wanted to live anywhere else. You have never really experienced anything else. While you were growing up, life was good and your problems were few. Your hardest task was to make your siblings see reason when they started to fight among themselves. When the time came for your First Change, your aunt led you away from the town to explain what you were about to go through. She talked you through the Change, and then informed you of your new duties and responsibilities.

Concept: You live much the same way that you did before the Change. You have a job in a local furniture company, one of the good ones that still makes all of their furniture by hand, and you have finally come to the decision that the small town is where you want to be forever. You are still settling disputes, always trying to stop some fool from smashing another fool's head in. The only thing your pack ever seems to agree on is that the time has come to end the reign of Jormangundr.

Roleplaying Hints: Speak loudly, but only when necessary. You know that your words carry weight, but you try not to abuse your position as a Keeper of the Ways. Still, you absolutely hate liars and will go out of your way to make them confess to their crimes, even if you have to smash their skulls in to do it.

Equipment: Jeans, T-shirt, hand-made baseball bat, workman's boots, and three six-packs every week

Get of Fenris

Name: _____ **Breed:** Homid **Pack Name:** _____
Player: _____ **Auspice:** Philodox **Pack Totem:** _____
Chronicle: _____ **Camp:** _____ **Concept:** Protector

Attributes

Physical
Strength _____ ●●●○○
Dexterity _____ ●●●○○
Stamina _____ ●●●●○

Social
Charisma _____ ●●○○○
Manipulation _____ ●●●○○
Appearance _____ ●○○○○

Mental
Perception _____ ●●●○○
Intelligence _____ ●●○○○
Wits _____ ●●●○○

Abilities

Talents
Alertness _____ ○○○○○
Athletics _____ ●●●○○
Brawl _____ ●●○○○
Dodge _____ ●●○○○
Empathy _____ ●●●○○
Expression _____ ○○○○○
Intimidation _____ ○○○○○
Primal-Urge _____ ●●●○○
Streetwise _____ ○○○○○
Subterfuge _____ ○○○○○

Skills
Animal Ken _____ ○○○○○
Drive _____ ●○○○○
Etiquette _____ ○○○○○
Firearms _____ ●○○○○
Leadership _____ ●●●○○
Melee _____ ●●○○○
Performance _____ ○○○○○
Repair _____ ●●●○○
Stealth _____ ○○○○○
Survival _____ ○○○○○

Knowledges
Computer _____ ○○○○○
Enigmas _____ ●●○○○
Investigation _____ ○○○○○
Law _____ ●●○○○
Linguistics _____ ○○○○○
Medicine _____ ○○○○○
Occult _____ ○○○○○
Politics _____ ●○○○○
Rituals _____ ○○○○○
Science _____ ○○○○○

Advantages

Backgrounds
Kinfolk _____ ●●○○○
Past Life _____ ●●○○○
Resources _____ ●○○○○
_____ ○○○○○
_____ ○○○○○

Gifts
Persuasion
Truth of Gaia
Resist pain
_____
_____

Gifts
_____
_____
_____
_____
_____

Renown

Glory
○○○○○○○○○○
□□□□□□□□□□

Honor
●●●○○○○○○○
□□□□□□□□□□

Wisdom
○○○○○○○○○○
□□□□□□□□□□

Rank
[ ]

Rage
●●●●●●○○○○
□□□□□□□□□□

Gnosis
●●●●○○○○○○
□□□□□□□□□□

Willpower
●●●●●●●○○○
□□□□□□□□□□

Health
Bruised		□
Hurt	-1	□
Injured	-1	□
Wounded	-2	□
Mauled	-2	□
Crippled	-5	□
Incapacitated		□

Weakness
INTOLERANCE:
Weaklings

Attributes: 7/5/3 **Abilities:** 13/9/5 **Gifts:** 1 Level One from breed, auspice and tribe; **Backgrounds:** 5; **Freebie Points:** 15 (7/5/2/1)

Wyrm Hunter

Quote: *Grrr... You stink like a corpse. Now you'll look like one, too...*

Prelude: Your life among the wolves was easy until the humans started cutting down the forest where your family had made their den. Three times you were forced to move because of the foul scent that brought the felling of the trees — the odor of diesel fuel and machine oil. When you saw the great metal-

lic beast that tore the land apart, your First Change assaulted you and you fell into a fit of lunatic Rage. The humans with their machines fell before your fury as easily as the trees had fallen to their chain saws.

You were content for a time. But then the foul things came, the Wyrmlings in their false human skins. They tore up the woods and killed your family, and they would have killed you, too, had not others like yourself shown up — others who could change their shapes. Severely wounded, you watched as the first other Garou you had ever seen attacked and destroyed the Banes. Afterward, the Garou patiently taught you their heritage, although you had no desire to learn. When you became too aggressive toward your teachers, they tore your fur to make their point. Eventually, you learned your place in the pack, and were taught more about the humans. You soon learned how to imitate humans, and to like the taste of their flesh...

Concept: You spend your time in the woods near the big Scab, and you hunt and kill those who would destroy your home. You know the humans have foul weapons that can hurt Gaia, and you are determined to stop them before they put them to use.

Roleplaying Hints: If it's human, kill it. If it is of Gaia, respect it. You do not like the city, and you avoid it when ever possible.

Equipment: Claws, fangs and a serious attitude problem. You keep human clothes hidden away for the times when you must go to the city to hunt Wyrm creatures.

Get of Fenris

Name: **Breed:** Lupus   **Pack Name:**
Player: **Auspice:** Galliard   **Pack Totem:**
Chronicle: **Camp:** Glorious Fist of Wotan   **Concept:** Wyrm Hunter

Attributes

Physical
Strength ●●●●○
Dexterity ●●●○○
Stamina ●●●○○

Social
Charisma ●●○○○
Manipulation ●○○○○
Appearance ●●●○○

Mental
Perception ●●●●○
Intelligence ●●○○○
Wits ●●○○○

Abilities

Talents
Alertness ●●●●○
Athletics ●●●●○
Brawl ●●●○○
Dodge ●●○○○
Empathy ●○○○○
Expression ●●○○○
Intimidation ●○○○○
Primal-Urge ●●○○○
Streetwise ○○○○○
Subterfuge ○○○○○

Skills
Animal Ken ●●○○○
Drive ○○○○○
Etiquette ○○○○○
Firearms ○○○○○
Leadership ○○○○○
Melee ●●○○○
Performance ○○○○○
Repair ○○○○○
Stealth ●●○○○
Survival ●●●○○

Knowledges
Computer ○○○○○
Enigmas ●●○○○
Investigation ○○○○○
Law ○○○○○
Linguistics ○○○○○
Medicine ○○○○○
Occult ○○○○○
Politics ○○○○○
Rituals ●●●○○
Science ○○○○○

Advantages

Backgrounds
Kinfolk ●●●○○
Pure Breed ●●○○○
_____ ○○○○○
_____ ○○○○○
_____ ○○○○○

Gifts
Heightened Senses
Beast Speech
Razor Claws
_____
_____
_____

Gifts
_____
_____
_____
_____
_____
_____

Renown

Glory
●●○○○○○○○○
□□□□□□□□□□

Honor
○○○○○○○○○○
□□□□□□□□□□

Wisdom
●○○○○○○○○○
□□□□□□□□□□

Rank
[ ]

Rage
●●●●●●●○○○○
□□□□□□□□□□

Gnosis
●●●●●○○○○○
□□□□□□□□□□

Willpower
●●●●●●○○○○
□□□□□□□□□□

Health
Bruised		□
Hurt	-1	□
Injured	-1	□
Wounded	-2	□
Mauled	-2	□
Crippled	-5	□
Incapacitated		□

Weakness
INTOLERANCE:
Non-Kinfolk/Non-Garou

Attributes: 7/5/3   **Abilities:** 13/9/5   **Gifts:** 1 Level One from breed, auspice and tribe; **Backgrounds:** 5;   **Freebie Points:** 15 (7/5/2/1)

War Monger

Quote: *Are you talkin' to me? Come here, you little shit! I've got something to tell you. Hey, come back here! I'm not done killing you yet!*

Prelude: You were never happy with second best. All through Little League, you had to outdo the others around you. If someone could run faster, you practiced until you could beat them. If someone could take pain better, you toughened yourself and learned to thrive on pain. If someone was a better fighter, you learned how to break bones to make your point. Then the First Change came, and everything just got better. You could outrun them all. You made star quarterback in high school. You even made it to Golden Gloves Regional Championship. All while you were learning the ways of the Get.

Concept: You still strive to be the best, and you're pretty sure there aren't many who can beat you in a fair fight. Of course, not everyone fights fairly, so you've started learning a few new tricks along those lines, too....

Roleplaying Hints: You are aggressive and unstoppable — at least in your own eyes. You always meet the enemies who face you on their terms, whether you like those terms or not. You prefer to use your hands in combat; use of weapons almost seems like cheating. You live for the challenge and the thrill of defeating your enemies. Nothing pleases you more than to hear your foes, crying for mercy which you will not deliver.

Equipment: Shit-kicker boots, Harley Davidson motorcycle, leather jacket, chain, .357 Magnum with spare clips, brass knuckles, big pig-sticker knife, attitude

Mon Spencer 95

GET OF FENRIS

Name: _____ **Breed:** Homid **Pack Name:** _____
Player: _____ **Auspice:** Ahroun **Pack Totem:** _____
Chronicle: _____ **Camp:** _____ **Concept:** War Monger

Attributes

Physical
Strength_____ ●●●●○
Dexterity_____ ●●●○○
Stamina_____ ●●●○○

Social
Charisma_____ ●●●○○
Manipulation_____ ●○○○○
Appearance_____ ●●○○○

Mental
Perception_____ ●●●○○
Intelligence_____ ●●○○○
Wits_____ ●●●○○

Abilities

Talents
Alertness_____ ●●○○○
Athletics_____ ●●●○○
Brawl_____ ●●●●○
Dodge_____ ●●○○○
Empathy_____ ○○○○○
Expression_____ ○○○○○
Intimidation_____ ●●○○○
Primal-Urge_____ ○○○○○
Streetwise_____ ○○○○○
Subterfuge_____ ○○○○○

Skills
Animal Ken_____ ○○○○○
Drive_____ ○○○○○
Etiquette_____ ○○○○○
Firearms_____ ●●○○○
Leadership_____ ●○○○○
Melee_____ ●●●○○
Performance_____ ○○○○○
Repair_____ ●○○○○
Stealth_____ ○○○○○
Survival_____ ●●○○○

Knowledges
Computer_____ ○○○○○
Enigmas_____ ○○○○○
Investigation_____ ●○○○○
Law_____ ○○○○○
Linguistics_____ ○○○○○
Medicine_____ ●○○○○
Occult_____ ●○○○○
Politics_____ ●●○○○
Rituals_____ ●○○○○
Science_____ ○○○○○

Advantages

Backgrounds
Kinfolk _____ ●●○○○
Pure Breed _____ ●●●○○
_____ ○○○○○
_____ ○○○○○
_____ ○○○○○

Gifts
Smell of Man _____
Inspiration _____
Razor Claws _____

Gifts
_____
_____
_____

Renown

Glory
●●○○○○○○○○
□□□□□□□□□□

Honor
●○○○○○○○○○
□□□□□□□□□□

Wisdom
○○○○○○○○○○
□□□□□□□□□□

Rank
[ ]

Rage
●●●●●●●●●○○
□□□□□□□□□□

Gnosis
●●●○○○○○○○
□□□□□□□□□□

Willpower
●●●●●●●○○○
□□□□□□□□□□

Health
Bruised		□
Hurt	-1	□
Injured	-1	□
Wounded	-2	□
Mauled	-2	□
Crippled	-5	□
Incapacitated		□

Weakness
INTOLERANCE:
Peaceniks

Attributes: 7/5/3 **Abilities:** 13/9/5 **Gifts:** 1 Level One from breed, auspice and tribe; **Backgrounds:** 5; **Freebie Points:** 15 (7/5/2/1)

Appendix Three: Hamarar Fenrar (The Hammers of Fenris)

Those Who Will Fight at Ragnarok

Many Get of Fenris have had songs sung about them. In the future, many more will be so remembered. The Get do not long tolerate cowards, nor do they permit the weak or honorless to walk among them. The following figures are examples for all Get to follow, examples of the goals toward which all Get of Fenris must strive.

Brynhild-Blood-Avenger

Brynhild lived in Scandinavia in the early 800s AD. Brynhild-Blood-Avenger changed late in life. For a time, no one even knew that she had bred true. Brynhild was married to Jon, son of Halthar, and she gave him three strong sons and two healthy daughters. Their marriage was blessed.

When Brynhild's mother grew ill, she left her husband's village and made her way to the town where her mother lived: because her father had been killed in battle, there was no one else to care for her. While she was away, the Trolls came to her husband's village; when Brynhild returned home after her mother's death, she found her husband and sons dead, and her daughters missing. She underwent her First Change as she stared at the rotting flesh that was all that remained of Halthar.

With no training beyond that given to any Kinfolk, Brynhild stalked the Trolls, running many leagues as a wolf, and feeding off the land. Eventually, she came upon her daughters, poorly used and discarded by the monsters. She was proud to see their bloodied hands, which spoke of a valiant fight. Nevertheless, Brynhild was deeply saddened. For three fortnights, she chased after the Trolls, speaking with the spirits and learning what she could from Gaia.

Along the way, Brynhild fought other enemies: a servant of Jormangundr who sought to seduce her to the ways of the Wyrm, and three giants who sought to make her their wife. All of them fell to her anger. On the night before she found her prey, Great Fenris approached. He asked her what she wanted more than life itself. Brynhild did not pause, nor did she cower before the lord of wolves; she replied with only a single word: "Revenge."

Satisfied with her answer, Fenris taught Brynhild Gifts she could use in her battle against the murderers. He granted her the Rage of a hundred warriors, and then sent her on her way. By daybreak, she found the slayers of her kin, 40 Trolls, all totaled. Armed with only her claws, her fangs, and the Gifts of Fenris Wolf, Brynhild attacked the forces that had killed her family. The Trolls fought with silver and with vile poisons. They came at her in great numbers. But still, Brynhild's Rage was too much for them.

Gravely wounded from the fierce battle, Brynhild removed the heads of her enemies and carried them back to her husband's village. There, she called for all to see that her family had been avenged. When the Get came forth from other villages, they took note of her deed and named her Brynhild-Blood-Avenger. After she had been named, Brynhild fell dead from her wounds. We sing her song at the formal moots, for she has been a lesson to us all. Nothing must stop us in our quest for vengeance.

Gere-Hunts-The-Hunters

Stone-Fist-Thunderhowl

Stone-Fist led the Get of Fenris in their battle against the Black Spiral Dancers in Britain. Although most of the lands the Vikings invaded were pure, Great Britain had been tainted by the Wyrm. The Fianna fought well, but they were no match for the Dancers. And so what had started as a simple conquest of new lands soon became a full-scale war. Stone-Fist-Thunderhowl discovered strategic locations from which the tribe could defend the lands against the Wyrm-Wolves.

In Ireland, he founded the town of Dublin to protect a caern that was threatened with certain destruction, and in England, he forced the Dancers back in a wave that freed a great part of the country from the Wyrm's domination. Stone-Fist then carried the battle back to Scotland, where he led a combined force of the more sensible Fianna and the Get of Fenris, and destroyed the foul Kinfolk of the Dancers wherever they tried to hide. He would have driven the Black Spiral Dancers all the way to the sea, had the Fianna not betrayed him and brought about his brutal murder.

Krieger-Silver-Mane-Tears-At-The-Heart-Of-The-Wyrm

Krieger is old, a lupus who has battled against Jormangundr for 80 years. Over the course of his life, he has slain hundreds of Wyrmlings; his body is now riddled with battle-scars. He has sired many broods, and from most of these at least one pup has bred true. Krieger moves across the lands, teaching the ways of the Get to all he meets, and reminding us that the Get must respect Gaia and all of her creatures.

During the Great Depression, Krieger and his pack, the Bane Breakers, fought and defeated a powerful Bane left over from the times when only the so-called "Pure Ones" ruled the Americas. Wind Spear tore through the lands, bringing with it a Wyrm-Storm known now as the Dust Bowl. Had not Krieger-Silver-Mane-Tears-At-The-Heart-Of-The-Wyrm led his pack against the great Bane, the farmlands would not be here today. The great Wyrmling slaughtered many Garou before the Bane Breakers arrived. Krieger used his powerful rituals to force the creature into a slumber, and then he and his pack banished the Bane from the land. Some say it has returned to work its evil in Africa, but there is no proof that this is the same servant of Jormangundr.

During the Great Moot of 1942, it was Krieger who forced the issue of the great folly of the German Get who joined with Hitler. Though, many opposed him, he won over the majority with wise words. He challenged the few who would not listen to his arguments for combat. All were defeated. He spared them because they were of his own tribe, although Krieger is not known for his mercy.

Krieger is the greatest Get alive today. Respect and obey him, for surely he will be among the leaders of our tribe come the final days of Ragnarok. There are rumors that he is in Alaska, and it is also rumored that he is in the Amazon. In truth, he is in the Homeland preparing for a great concolation. In Krieger, we see the ultimate example of Get ideals: He is wise, fair, deadly and honorable. He knows when strength is the only answer. But he also knows when tolerance for others is most effective.

Gere hunts in Alaska. He has declared open season on the wolf hunters. Gere believes in teaching his prey lessons: He has recently taken to stripping the hunters he catches of all of their weapons and leaving them to survive alone in the frozen tundra. If the hunters have actually killed any wolves, he slices their hamstrings and dresses them in the fur of the animal they slaughtered — after removing their tongues. Those who do not bleed to death either starve, or manage to get shot by other hunters.

If they have not actually killed any wolves, he takes their shoes and clothing, and leaves them to fend for them- selves as they walk back across the tundra. One has survived to tell of his experiences, and he has sworn never again to hunt wolves.

Tor-Brundvandt-Scab-Slasher

The Scab-Slasher has already made a name for himself as a warrior and protector of Gaia. In the two years since he earned his name, he has worked diligently to destroy all attempts by big business to build in the areas outside of his home city of Atlanta, Georgia. His terrorist activities have many times delayed road construction work and the development of new housing projects. More importantly, he has increased the humans' fear by hunting down and mutilating the worst Wyrm-corrupt beings in his territory.

Along with his multitribe pack, the Hammer of Justice, Tor has slain numerous humans guilty of dealing drugs or committing rape, murder or prostitution. He has made a habit of tracking his enemies to their homes and ending their miserable lives in ways that protect the Veil. Many of the "domestic violence" cases that have come before the media and the law in Atlanta have actually been the work of Scab-Slasher and his pack, but their subtle approach and careful manipulations have ensured that the Garou do not gain unwanted attention.

One of Tor's favorite maneuvers is the deliberate derailing of trains carrying important supplies for Pentex. There are rumors that he has Kin working as low-level file clerks and passing information to him at irregular intervals. The number of accidental industrial spills on railroad lines is second only to the number of tractor trailers that crash and burn in his hometown.

Many believe that tornadoes in the areas surrounding Atlanta aim for trailer parks, but the Get know better: Scab-Slasher aims for trailer parks, specifically the ones known for frequent drug transactions. His ability to make almost any action seem as if it is simply the work of fate should be commended. The time will come when the humans once again know of our existence, but that time is not yet here, and we could all learn a few lessons in strategy from Tor-Brundvandt-Scab-Slasher. Violence is the way of the Get, but that violence need not leave behind the shredded remains of humans to fuel the Inquisition.

Lars-Vandergot-Wyrm-Crusher

Only three years after his Rite of Passage, and already the Wyrm-Crusher has made a reputation for himself. On the West Coast he has battled against the Leeches, leading them away from his family in Oxnard and taking them far into the desert where none could see the carnage to come.

He has been seen running with his pack, the Savage Seven, in Arizona where they did battle against Black Spiral Dancers, and in New Mexico where they fought valiantly and killed three Thunderwyrms. He has been seen with the remainder of his pack in Alabama, where he battled against Pentex and destroyed a factory releasing Wyrm-ridden toys to unsuspecting humans. Most recently, he has been spotted walking alone — for his pack mates have all gone on to Valhalla — heading to the Southwest, where he claims that the time has come to put an end to the woes of Mexico City.

Along the way he has found new members for his pack, promising them great glory and a proper death. Learn well from his example, for it is said that he suffers from Harano. Even in Harano he fights the Wyrm mercilessly.

Get of Fenris

Name: _____ Breed: _____ Pack Name: _____
Player: _____ Auspice: _____ Pack Totem: _____
Chronicle: _____ Camp: _____ Concept: _____

Attributes

Physical
Strength_____ ●○○○○
Dexterity_____ ●○○○○
Stamina_____ ●○○○○

Social
Charisma_____ ●○○○○
Manipulation_____ ●○○○○
Appearance_____ ●○○○○

Mental
Perception_____ ●○○○○
Intelligence_____ ●○○○○
Wits_____ ●○○○○

Abilities

Talents
Alertness_____ ○○○○○
Athletics_____ ○○○○○
Brawl_____ ○○○○○
Dodge_____ ○○○○○
Empathy_____ ○○○○○
Expression_____ ○○○○○
Intimidation_____ ○○○○○
Primal-Urge_____ ○○○○○
Streetwise_____ ○○○○○
Subterfuge_____ ○○○○○

Skills
Animal Ken_____ ○○○○○
Drive_____ ○○○○○
Etiquette_____ ○○○○○
Firearms_____ ○○○○○
Leadership_____ ○○○○○
Melee_____ ○○○○○
Performance_____ ○○○○○
Repair_____ ○○○○○
Stealth_____ ○○○○○
Survival_____ ○○○○○

Knowledges
Computer_____ ○○○○○
Enigmas_____ ○○○○○
Investigation_____ ○○○○○
Law_____ ○○○○○
Linguistics_____ ○○○○○
Medicine_____ ○○○○○
Occult_____ ○○○○○
Politics_____ ○○○○○
Rituals_____ ○○○○○
Science_____ ○○○○○

Advantages

Backgrounds
_____ ○○○○○
_____ ○○○○○
_____ ○○○○○
_____ ○○○○○
_____ ○○○○○

Gifts
_____
_____
_____
_____
_____

Gifts
_____
_____
_____
_____
_____

Renown

Glory
○○○○○○○○○○
□□□□□□□□□□

Honor
○○○○○○○○○○
□□□□□□□□□□

Wisdom
○○○○○○○○○○
□□□□□□□□□□

Rank

Rage
○○○○○○○○○○
□□□□□□□□□□

Gnosis
○○○○○○○○○○
□□□□□□□□□□

Willpower
○○○○○○○○○○
□□□□□□□□□□

Health
Bruised		□
Hurt	-1	□
Injured	-1	□
Wounded	-2	□
Mauled	-2	□
Crippled	-5	□
Incapacitated		□

Weakness
INTOLERANCE:

Attributes: 7/5/3 **Abilities:** 13/9/5 **Gifts:** 1 Level One from breed, auspice and tribe; **Backgrounds:** 5; **Freebie Points:** 15 (7/5/2/1)

Get of Fenris

Homid	Glabro	Crinos	Hispo	Lupus
No Change	Strength (+2)___	Strength (+4)___	Strength (+3)___	Strength (+1)___
	Stamina (+2)___	Dexterity (+1)___	Dexterity (+2)___	Dexterity (+2)___
	Appearance (-1)___	Stamina (+3)___	Stamina (+3)___	Stamina (+2)___
	Manipulation (-1)___	Appearance 0___	Manipulation (-3)___	Manipulation (-3)__
		Manipulation (-3)__		
Difficulty: 6	Difficulty: 7	Difficulty: 6	Difficulty: 7	Difficulty: 6

INCITE DELIRIUM IN HUMANS

Other Traits

_____ OOOOO
_____ OOOOO
_____ OOOOO
_____ OOOOO
_____ OOOOO
_____ OOOOO
_____ OOOOO
_____ OOOOO
_____ OOOOO
_____ OOOOO
_____ OOOOO
_____ OOOOO
_____ OOOOO
_____ OOOOO
_____ OOOOO
_____ OOOOO
_____ OOOOO
_____ OOOOO
_____ OOOOO

Fetishes

Item: _____ ☐ Dedicated Level ____ Gnosis ____
Power_____

Item: _____ ☐ Dedicated Level ____ Gnosis ____
Power_____

Item: _____ ☐ Dedicated Level ____ Gnosis ____
Power_____

Item: _____ ☐ Dedicated Level ____ Gnosis ____
Power_____

Rites

_____
_____
_____
_____
_____
_____
_____
_____
_____
_____
_____

Combat

Maneuver/Weapon	Roll	Difficulty	Damage	Range	Rate	Clip

Brawling Chart

Maneuver	Roll	Difficulty	Damage
Bite	Dex + Brawl	5	Strength +1†
Body Slam	Dex + Brawl	7	Special
Claw	Dex + Brawl	6	Strength +2†
Grapple	Dex + Brawl	6	Strength
Kick	Dex + Brawl	7	Strength +1
Punch	Dex + Brawl	6	Strength

† These maneuvers do aggravated damage.

Armor: _____

GET OF FENRIS

Nature: _____   Demeanor: _____

Merits & Flaws

Merit	Type	Cost	Flaw	Type	Bonus
___	___	___	___	___	___
___	___	___	___	___	___
___	___	___	___	___	___
___	___	___	___	___	___
___	___	___	___	___	___

Expanded Background

Allies
_____
_____
_____
_____
_____

Kinfolk
_____
_____
_____
_____
_____

Resources
_____
_____
_____
_____
_____

Pure Breed
_____
_____
_____
_____
_____

Past Life
_____
_____
_____
_____
_____

Pack Totem
_____
_____
_____
_____
_____

Possessions

Gear (Carried) _____

Equipment (Owned) _____

Sept

Name _____
Caern Location _____
Level _____ Type _____
Totem _____
Leader _____

Experience

TOTAL:
┌─────────────────┐
│   │
│   │
└─────────────────┘

Gained From: _____
_____

TOTAL SPENT: _____
Spent On: _____
_____
_____
_____

Get of Fenris

History

Prelude

_____
_____
_____
_____
_____
_____
_____
_____
_____
_____
_____
_____
_____

Description

Age_____

Hair_____

Eyes_____

Race_____

Nationality_____

Sex_____

	Height	Weight
Homid		
Glabro		
Crinos		
Hispo		
Lupus		

_____
_____
_____
_____
_____
_____
_____

Battle Scars————————————————————————
_____
_____

Metis Deformity——————————————————————

Visuals

Pack Chart   Character Sketch

HAZARDS IN THE WORKPLACE

Story by: Emery Barnes   **Art by: Brent Trammel**

3

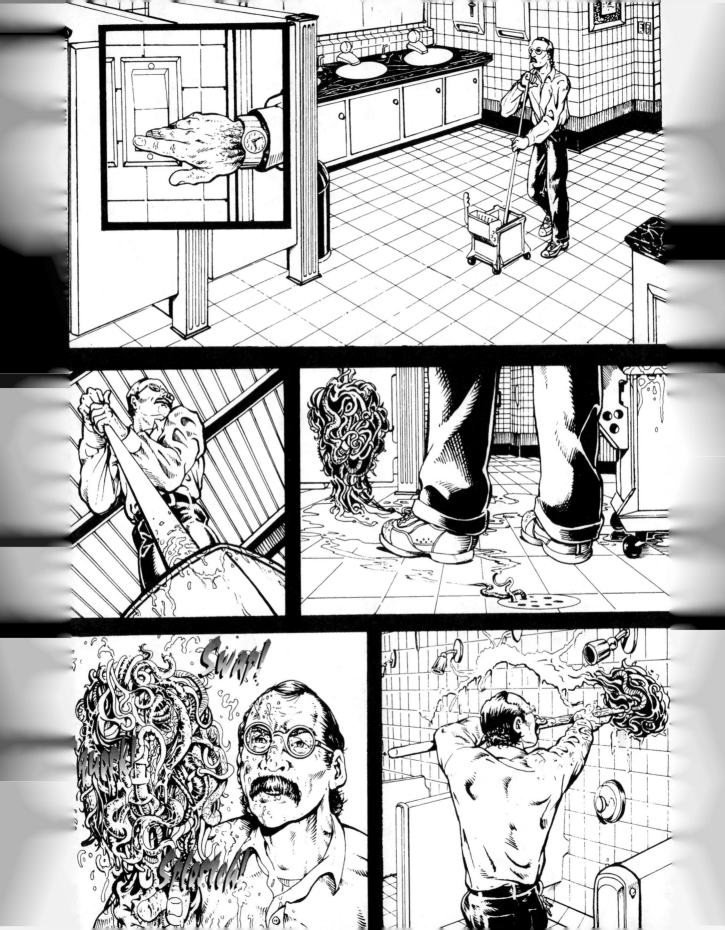

6

GLASS WALKERS

Wolves at the Gate

By Emrey Barnes

Credits

Written by: Emrey Barnes
Developed by: Bill Bridges
Editing: Annie Schultz
Art Director: Richard Thomas
Comic Book Art: Brent Trammel
Interior Art: Brian LeBlanc and Mike Chaney
Back Cover Art: Joshua Gabriel Timbrook
Front and Back Cover Design: Lawrence Snelly
Typesetting & Layout: Kathleen Ryan

**735 Park North Blvd.
Suite 128
Clarkston, GA 30021
USA**

Special Thanks

Andrew "Antedeluvian" **Greenberg** for the hordes of neonates slavering for his position.

Phil "Hassan chop!" **Brucato** for his gift to future generations.

Mike "Thumbilina" **Tinney** for being a girly man who can't lift a desk.

Ian "The Fisher King" **Lemke** for suffering Rob's Dolorous Stroke.

Jennifer "Goth girl" **Hartshorn** for her nocturnal singing.

Ken "Ralidium poisoning" **Cliffe** for his big buy at the miniatures convention.

Cynthia "Invisible Girl" **Summers** for hiding away in her office.

Laura "Zipped" **Perkinson** for her cool outfit at the World Horror Con.

Ethan "Home on the range" **Skemp** for placing his desk where the tumbleweeds blow.

Author's Dedication

To the machines that realize that a couple of humans have respect for them. To the co-workers and relatives who died during the writing of this book: Henry, Todd Smith, Grandma Pease and Phyllis Kutner. Thanks to the guys at the Sunday night game: Chris, Rick, Brad, Steve, John and Russ. Thanks to my parents for never telling me that trying to be a writer is a foolish maneuver. Don't let the media pull the wool over your eyes. Live life the way that you think it should be lived. Long live liberty. Fight for freedom.

GLASS WALKERS

Introduction: Metal Organism   12

Chapter One: The March of History   14

The history of the Glass Walkers.

Chapter Two: High Society   28

The culture of the Glass Walkers.

Chapter Three: Worldly Contacts   42

The Glass Walkers around the world.

Appendix One: Powers of the City   50

New Gifts, rites, fetishes and totems.

Appendix Two: Residents of the Naked City   55

Five ready-to-play characters.

Appendix Three: If We Built Statues....   66

Famous Glass Walkers of the past and present.

Contents

BRIAN LeBLANC '95

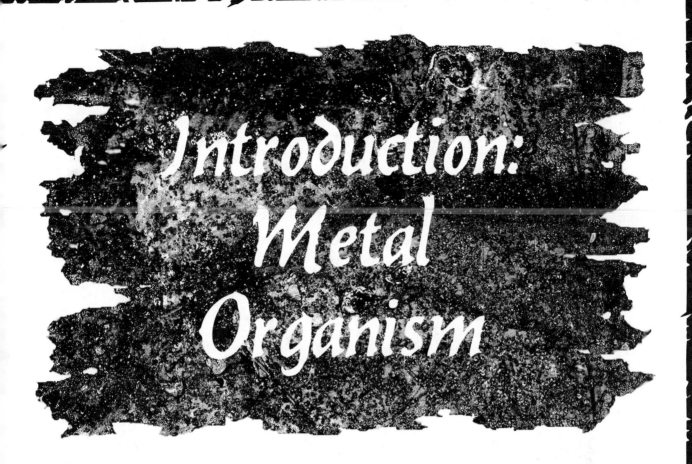

Introduction: Metal Organism

In the city, the quiet city, the lion sleeps tonight.
— Weiss/Peretti/Creatori, "The Lion Sleeps Tonight"

Watch the new life grow. Look at it. The long wires are seeking outward. The pulse is throbbing at 60 hertz. Its mouth is broadcasting information and its eyes and ears are absorbing it. A metal organism. Humans befriend it and steward its children — new models with stylish improvements and add-on gadgets. A symbiotic relationship of give and take. So goes the cycle of mechanical evolution. The ecosystem of the City. The City grows and changes, just like the wilderness. If only the other Garou would take the time to look, they might understand — this world needs both cities and forests! They are both of Gaia!

We are the Glass Walkers, the lions of the City. We have always dealt with the young spirits of mechanism. These young spirits bring the greatest returns on our spiritual investment. Don't listen to the other Garou who say we are of the Wyrm. We guard the City from the corruption of the Wyrm.

Don't listen to the lies proclaiming that the Wyrm thrives within technology. The user perverts technology. Sure, Wyrm-tainted technology exists; however, the use of a tool makes all the difference in the world. Metal doesn't lust or yearn. The flesh is weak. We are closer to our human side than any of the other tribes. Sure, the wolf is weak within us, but this only makes our connection to the new life stronger! Yes, we know that the Wyrm hides in the hearts of humans. Through them, it seeks to dominate and subvert the world. We won't let it. We're going to win this war. Not through claw and fang, but with cunning and strategy.

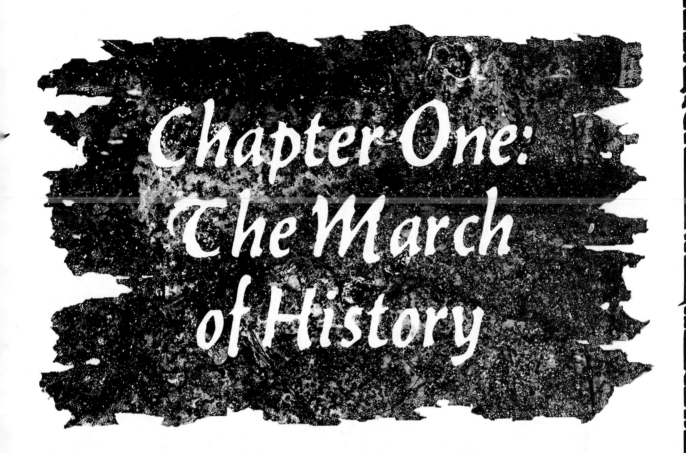

Chapter One: The March of History

Even a crude tool is powerful because it can be used to make other tools. Later, the bow and arrow gave an advantage, as did metal and the wheel. In each case, the tribe interested in mechanical manipulation survived, while those less interested declined. This leaves us in today's paradoxical state. We are bio-technophiliacs; we are lovers of the Wild Earth and of technology. Today, we have both elements in our genetic heritage; we love the natural world and we love machines, so we flit back and forth between the two realms, never quite sure where our allegiance lies.

— Frank Waters, "Strange Mindfellows: Can Biophilia and Technophilia Co-exist?", *Wild Earth*

My bones ache and my muscles atrophy. Even the cyber-fetishes implanted within me long ago have begun to rust. The spirits inside of them taunt me. "You're lazy!", they say. "You are old!" It is true. I am only a shambling corpse of what I once was. But I can still howl and rush into battle.

Procrastination — Lethargg, the Urge of Apathy — drags me down and warps my being. Yet I must continue. There are things I must tell you before I die. But what of procrastination? What can be done to kill this beast? It haunts us all. You lie when you say you have never fallen under its evil spell. It is a curse of those who live within the City!

I am Samuel Carlos Scapini. My Garou name is "Vacuum Tube" (shows you how old I am!). Sammy "Vacuum Tube" Scapini. I've never run with the crowd. I've always been somewhat of a monkeywrench among monkeywrenchers, and I've got something to tell you about the Glass Walkers. I've been inside and outside of the tribe, so I've gotten a pretty good view.

Listen and take heed to this information. I can only hope that you're smart enough to learn from the mistakes of others. Our tribe has the most complete, written documentation of historical events of any of the Garou. But I haven't read all of it. I'm no expert on history. But listen well. Listen, and I will tell you what I know of being a Glass Walker.

Before the City

…It seems possible that the traditional relationship [between stone flakes and cores in the tool-making process] might be reversed: the flakes may have been the primary tools and the cores often — although not always — simply the byproduct of manufacture… and therefore indicative of neither the maker's purpose nor the artifact's function.

— Nick Toth, "Ape at the Brink", *Discover*

Sometime during the unrecorded days of history, the Silver Fangs ordered a group of Garou to form a pack to watch over humanity, ensuring that the little troublemakers wouldn't get too dangerous. They were called the Warders of Apes.

In these days, humans were hardly a threat to us, but we watched them anyway. Their antics had always seemed strange. There was another pack set to watch over wolves as well, but the wolves didn't do much.

Now, the Warders, after watching the humans for a while, realized the humans were on to something — something big. They used wood and stone tools to make up for their lack of natural weaponry. The Warders thought this was clever. They also realized, after watching the human medicine men, that humans didn't figure all of this out on their own. They received help from the tools themselves. The Warders went into the Spirit World to meet with the spirits of rock and stone, to learn the Gifts they were teaching to the humans.

The story goes something like this:

The pack leader spoke to the gathered rocks. "Listen to me, spirits of stone and rock. We have watched you and the apes. You have taught them powerful Gifts. Will you teach these Gifts to us?"

A large, speckled rock moved forward from the others and spoke with a voice sounding like shifting gravel. "Yes, but you must make a promise to us. The apes began to lose respect for us because of our abundance. Humans use our children and then toss them aside. You must swear to always respect us." A rumbling like an avalanche followed as the others mumbled amongst themselves.

The pack leader replied, "Are we not Garou? Do we not always keep our promises? I vow to respect you and to call upon your strength to aid me. I will not discard you as do the apes. My kind and I will carry you with us and make your kind grow even stronger!"

"If what you say is true, we will always aid you. Call upon us, and we will break your opponents' bones and draw forth blood in raging torrents!" Several rocks and stones began bumping into the speaking spirit. "But there is one more thing. To prove your truthfulness to us, you must grant us one favor."

The pack leader's chest swelled with pride. "Name the favor you wish, and it shall be yours!"

"Help us to fly like the birds," the spirit said. The pack leader's gaze fell to the earth. "We have always dreamed of soaring through the air as they do. The most we ever get to do is fall from a cliff. This works fine as a means of reproduction, but it is not the same as flying through the air."

"I think this favor is going to take a little while," the disgruntled pack leader said, and he traveled back to the world.

Glass Walkers

And so an oath was sworn to the rock spirits. The Warders struggled for a long time to figure out how to make the rocks fly like birds. The spirits of the air would not deign to help them lift the rocks so they always fell quickly, even when tossed by the strongest Garou among them.

One day, they saw a human chip a small piece of stone and tie it to a stick. He placed bird feathers on the other end of the stick. Then he picked up the stick and fit it to another stick that had animal gut tied tightly to the ends, making the stick curve. The human pulled back the gut and let go. Zoom! The stick and stone flew through the air, farther than any Garou had been able to throw!

The Warders then discovered the answer. They all began using bows and arrows soon after that. Their vow to the rock spirits was accomplished; in return, the spirits ensured that their arrows always struck with great might.

Word of the Warders new magic soon spread, and other Garou began to use bows and arrows. The Warders became very popular and they continued to watch the humans for new tricks. Many Ragabash found it great fun to follow the humans and steal their secrets. The Warders watched the humans summon forth sharp, cutting edges out of stone. But the humans would use them and then haphazardly discard them. The abandoned rock spirits would call to the Warders; thus, their supply of tools grew.

Then the humans figured out that fire spirits hid within rocks and wood. The Warders watched them carry out their spirit-calling, in awe of their cunning. They began to fear the human Theurges who we now call mages. Garou feared fire, for they had no control over its power to consume things. Fire is of the Wyld.

Around that time, the rock spirits said that the humans were calling upon them to assemble into new shapes, in much the same manner that the spirits of mountains called lesser spirits to them. These new shapes were odd, but fascinating; like caves, but without a mountain to host them. The mountain spirits threatened to rise in anger at the imitation of their power. The surface of Gaia shook with their anger, but the Warders went into the Umbra and coaxed them into complacency.

Lurking in the shadows, the Warders watched the apes create their artificial caverns and hillsides, living in fear of everything else. The building did not stop with these few simple houses. The next thing the Warders knew, there was a City.

The First City

In case you haven't guessed, the Warders were the first Glass Walkers. As the years passed, more and more Garou began following them, until they were no longer a pack, but something like a multi-tribal faction. It wasn't until after the Impergium that they became an actual tribe of their own. But that story's still a way off.

The Warders of Apes never dared to go within a stone's throw of the First City. They sensed something wrong

within those walls. Later legends say that it was full of the vampires. We — the Warders, that is — were content to sit back and to marvel at these structures the humans had created. Though odd, this city of theirs held the shining beauty of newness within it. The First City burned to the ground. We saw its destruction, and — Gaia help us — we secretly mourned its loss.

The Impergium

We willingly shared our human-based knowledge with other Garou. Many Garou feared the human ideas, listening more to the wolf in their hearts than to the human. You see, most other Garou even to this day forget that they — most of them, at least — were born human. Only later did they become Garou. But we have never forgotten. Why give up our birth heritage for drums in the woods when we can have screaming amps on stage?

The Silver Fangs saw the human's new ideas and ways as a threat. They declared that the humans were too close to the Weaver and that we had coddled them when we were supposed to be warding them from such evil ways. The tribes called a Grand Moot and the decision was made. Impergium. You all know what that was.

In the beginning, the Impergium worked to eradicate the creative urges of the humans (mainly by killing their mages) and to trim their herds (by killing the old, the weak and sick and the unprotected young.). Slowly, the methods of enforcing the Impergium mutated. Garou corralled humans and killed selectively killed them.

We knew something had to be done, but our small numbers held no sway among the tribes. Our neo-tribe puzzled over the problem for many turnings of Luna. Eventually, a plan came to us. In order to stop the rampant killings, we bred freely with as many humans as we could, then claimed them for Kinfolk. Kinfolk were spared the cullings, so we were able to save whole tribes of humans from the jealous claws of our fellows.

We also took time to explain the Impergium to our Kinfolk. We taught the humans to "sacrifice" troublemakers to the other Garou. These sacrifices went over so well that several nomad tribes managed to survive the Impergium just by giving sacrifices to the Garou! Who knows, maybe this is where the old saying "throw him to the dogs" came from.

We also went to our respective tribes for help. The Children of Gaia and Stargazer elders agreed with our pack. So did the Black Furies, who I guess still had enough motherly instinct to realize that the culling was wrong. But it would take a long time before they could act.

Coming to Grips with the City

We understood that the City was a new type of spirit struggling through its birth. We could hear it crying like an infant in the Umbra. It drew humans away from the

dangerous animals and offered them a place to live in peace. We told stories to the humans about the First City and helped to nurture the idea of new cities within their minds. Eventually, we talked them into building a second city.

Of course, the other Garou rose up in rage. The Silver Fangs called in the tribes once again. They wished us to be punished. The Get of Fenris asked for the right to slay us. The Shadow Lords requested that we disband, for we had grown too large. The Children of Gaia, Black Furies and Stargazers voiced their opposition to the Impergium. The Bone Gnawers agreed, but would not come forward. As the days of the Grand Moot grew to a close, the Silver Fangs ordered the destruction of the second city.

The Shadow Lords responded first, followed by the Get of Fenris. The other tribes followed to witness the destruction. An army of Get of Fenris and Shadow Lords swept down nearby hillsides and rushed into the city. Neither its walls nor gates could hold back the raging Garou. Humans fled in terror as the two tribes destroyed everything in their path. The fury drew to a close as the city burst into flames.

Spent in both body and rage, the two tribes regrouped with the watching Garou. We sat and watched as the city burned and crumbled to the ground. We heard the last of the human's screams end as they suffered an agonizing death. The city smoldered for days. The Garou maintained a vigil until the fire spirits could be completely banished. Now they began to feel the sorrow of its destruction.

Before the Garou assembly disbanded, the Children of Gaia stepped forward to challenge for an end to the Impergium. Their Stargazer allies won the challenge with gamecraft, outsmarting the Silver Fang king who was forced to end the centuries-long practice. In many ways, we were also finally free. It was sometime after this that we became our own tribe.

We Built This City

We struggled for what seemed an eternity to get the humans to build a third city, but once it was built, it stood for a long time. It eventually burned and crumpled to the ground. At least they built another city on top of it! When they needed strong bodies to build new cities, we happily helped them and learned the Gift of City Building. (This Gift is now forgotten. It may have never existed in the first place.)

Once the cities where built and began to grow — like saplings in the forest — we moved within their walls and claimed them as our territory and dared any Garou to take them from us. None did. They didn't care — but they would later, when it was too late and we were too strong to be pulled from our homes. We felt the strength of the cities, in the same way that we feel the power of mountains and roaring rivers. Our tribe expanded along with the cities. We broke into multiple septs, which we began to call families, just to be different from the others. Each family retained their original sept leader's name. Without other Garou to contend with, we continued to dramatically increase our numbers.

The Bone Gnawers realized that city predators left more excess than those of the Wyld. They, too, came into the city and began to follow the humans. Before long, the Bone Gnawers learned to live happily in the cities with us. Well, okay, so it wasn't that simple. It was our territory and we tried to kick them out at first. But have you ever tried to rid a city of rats? It's almost impossible. They just keep coming back. So, we just let them stay. They were far more useful as friends than enemies.

The Shadow Lords complained to the Silver Fangs about our sudden surge to tribal status and accused us of being Wyrm tainted. The Silver Fangs sent mixed packs into the cities to check us out. This marked the beginning of our treatment as scapegoats by the Silver Fangs and their cohorts, the Shadow Lords and the Get of Fenris.

The Coming of Commerce

We took time to observe skilled humans and kept their secrets to ourselves. We shared this knowledge only within our families, for we had grown untrusting of the other Garou. We loved using human knowledge and did so constantly. Certain members of humanity (mages) began to realize this fact and persuaded us into doing their work for them. It started as barter, but beautiful, shining metal spirits were soon used as reward. Mages thought of this as a method to control us, but we were no old dogs! We had plenty of time to learn a few good tricks. Several families turned to the spirits of metal for guidance. Soon, humanity did our work for us.

It wasn't long until a faction of metal spirits broke away from their brethren to become the coin spirits, worth far more to humans than their simple metal. This was a revolution of sorts; the idea that something was worth more than it seemed simply because a king or official said so. The Weaver's Pattern was spreading. I mean, these objects were just hunks of bronze or copper at first, but people killed for them anyway. Those damn coin spirits loved it when people fought over them. Damn it, we loved them, too.

As cities grew, so did the Weaver's influence. Humanity strayed from the path of animals, who followed the Wyld, and labored to mold the world into a pattern of their choosing. They had learned to create tools to mimic the abilities of the animals and, most importantly of all, they learned how to leave markings that conveyed a certain meaning. We were quick to jump on this idea and we crafted all sorts of symbols. Soon we were making lists of the spirits. We began to chart our travels and, more importantly, our adventures within the Spirit World.

Burning Down the House

The City is our territory, and as such, we are its caretakers. We have to ensure there is always room for new growth by clearing out the old, so we sometimes burn cities down. This enables new buildings to go up, like fresh saplings in the wake of a forest fire. It's an old concept, really. Native peoples all over the world have long used controlled burning to ensure the healthy growth of their lands. The difference is that they burn trees; we burn buildings.

Some of the great city fires were set by us, all for the greater good of the city. San Francisco was ours. So were the recent Los Angeles brush fires (alas, not enough was done). Chicago wasn't us; vampires did that. Same with Atlanta, although were not sure who was behind that one.

When next you see a city burn, don't cry. It's only the old giving birth to the new. Of course, if we didn't set the fire, then we're damn sure going to find out who did and teach him how to really play with matches!

The Machine

One of our great Theurges, Sheba Arrow-of-Gaia, traveled into the Realm of Dreams. She found a giant, mechanical human who's body was formed of all manner of tools. The being grew larger as more tools appeared to attach themselves to the sleeping giant. She traveled within the giant's mind to find its dream within a dream. This conglomeration spoke to her. She sensed that this was the dreaming image of a sleeping Incarna, not yet born. Sheba learned many secrets before leaving it to peacefully rest. She could feel the Gnosis slowly seeping from the spirit, bleeding into the physical world in strange ways.

Sheba returned to us and told us of her vision of the sleeping giant who would one day awaken. She told us to prepare for it, to steward its way into the world. It would take years and many generations, but her vision was so powerful that many of us followed her.

While watching the early human inventors from the Umbra, we began to learn how they influenced spirits. These were secrets of the Weaver Way. Animals couldn't follow this way because they couldn't think. But the humans could, and so could we. We also learned that these human inventors were tapping into the dreams of the sleeping giant, later to be called the Machine. This slumbering Incarna-to-be and its Jaggling and Gaffling minions

were unlike other spirits. They were Weaver spirits, built of the dreams of humans interacting with the Pattern Web. The humans were actually changing the Web through their dreams and visions! We realized our great secret. The Weaver was not mad, simply unguided. She needed beings like us to guide her in the right direction.

Some humans caught onto this idea later, like the Sons of Ether mages and the Technocracy, but they don't understand it on the primal level that we do. And we don't care for the kind of guidance the Technocracy prefers. No matter how enamored of the Weaver you are, you can't forget Gaia.

What the Machine taught us is that technology is alive. It's an organism. It exists on a different level than most, a level of pattern and abstraction, part in the spirit world and part in the physical world. Quite possibly, the most important aspect of the Machine manifested itself in the early days. The true power of the Machine grew from its ability to store information within itself. Information recording became an important part of human existence. It helped humanity remember its mistakes and how problems had been solved in the past. But the Machine… well, it's the ultimate recorder. We believe that records dealing with just about every subject ever in existence are hidden within it. It just takes a lot of wits to get to this information. But until recently, the Machine slept without knowledge of its own existence.

The Golden Age of Growth

The tribe soon decided that keeping abreast of the technological advancements of humanity should take precedence on a tribal level. We sent our tribe out across the world to discover the secrets of the burgeoning technology.

The Silent Striders held the Egyptian delta and told us that we weren't welcome. They didn't trust us, even though their Kinfolk excelled in science. They held fast to the land and blocked all Moon Bridges. We were unable to make contact with the technological spirits who lived there. So much of that early race's technology has been lost. By 1500 B.C., we moved into the Greek city-states, then into Black Fury territory. The Black Furies did not live inside the cities and rarely attempted to learn the skills of humanity. We gained a shaky alliance with them, swearing to ensure that women were treated well within the cities. One of our families fled from Troy to Italy with a large contingent of humans. Two Kinfolk brothers, Romulus and Remus, later contested for rulership of the new land. Romulus won and named the new city Rome. As our tribe came into Italy, our family leaders took control of organizing the new cities. Our Kinfolk held places of great honor. Rome was built from the sweat of our brow.

Our tribe had also awakened to the arts of war. Clashing Boom-Boom's voice broke out of the sleeping Machine's dreams and cried out to us through all manner of armament and weaponry. We quickly organized ourselves, our Kinfolk and the humans into an armored force. We sent our youngest off on travels for conquest and wealth. In return, those who survived gained great wisdom and glory.

Our tribe expanded once again as we continued our policy of frequent mating with humans. Even then, we started to feel the lack of the wolf within our blood. Our young felt the pull of humanity and often feared darkness like a human child. The power we maintained over human society began to dwindle as the human population increased. We fought hard for positions in political circles, but there were too many against us. We organized our own underground governments and manipulated trade from behind the scenes.

We felt the wanderlust — the Wyld yearning — and traveled with our Kinfolk on great quests and adventures, seeking new lands and lore. We voyaged together on great journeys, calling upon the spirits of the stars and planets for the secrets of navigation. We calmed the spirits of the seas and rivers. We communed with the odd spirits of commerce from foreign lands. With the land travels of the Greeks and Romans, we managed to travel far and spread wide. We forged trade routes in order to maintain a smooth flow of goods on a regular basis. Moon Bridges became our secret trade routes. We became rich and the tribe rose in status once again. Some families, like the Glass Walkers of China, disappeared into far lands and we didn't see them again until modern times.

The Glass Walkers of Ancient China

The Glass Walker household in China often consisted of multiple wives, many children, nannies for the children, grounds keepers, cooks, manservants, concubines, night watchmen and often their extended family as well. Only merchant status or government position could insure the wealth necessary to keep such a household going. With the help of spirits, our tribe had gained merchant status in every civilization it entered. Merchant status allowed our tribe not only the time needed to battle the Wyrm but also the money to buy supplies and pay retainers. Those who were capable of passing written examinations based on classic writings and philosophical ideals were given positions as Public Officials. Galliards often read the minds of examiners as a means of improving their exam results and insuring a government position. Among our tribe, the position of Magistrate was most coveted. The Magistrate decided criminal punishment and oversaw the execution of his judgments before an assembly of city folk. All knew the crime and all witnessed the punishment. This taught the people the value of living righteous lives.

There's Always a Hitch

It was a glorious time, but it was not without its problems. The cities hid many Wyrm beasts and Banes loved to feed on the hearts of humans. The most dangerous threat to us was the vampires. The vampires lorded over the humans. They attempted to run us out of many cities. But this was our territory, damn it! We fought hard for it. We could walk around in the sun and our spirit eyes could find many havens…. Soon enough, we came to a rough truce with most of the vampires in our cities. A sort of mutual ignorance pact. We would pretend they didn't exist, so as not to get blamed for an alliance with the Wyrm; they would leave our Kinfolk alone and let them prosper. Needless to say, this unwritten pact is broken all the time.

The Roman Republic and Empire

Veni, Vidi, Vici
(I came, I saw, I conquered.)
— Julius Caesar

Greek culture surpassed the fledgling country, but the Romans soon invaded Greece and seized control of it. Those of us among the Roman army took advantage of anything useful: technology, religion and culture. We often commandeered any technological items we could find.

The Greek people ruled themselves by forming democratic councils composed of adult males. This seemed to be a reasonable method of weakening the behind the scenes power of the Silver Fangs, whose Kinfolk often ruled through the nobility. We spread the democratic idea among the merchant class. Eventually the Roman government reformed into a Republic that was controlled mainly by rich land-owners. Candidates for election often bribed the populous with sporting events and huge feasts. The Wyrm slowly snaked its way into Roman government. The plan we originally had thought would wrest the vampires and Silver Fangs from politics had backfired. There was little we could do to fight the corruption. The other tribes were unwilling to help us; they hated us for helping to strengthen the humans. We tried to pay them for their services, but they had no respect for coinage.

Knowing that nothing could be done to save Rome, we convinced Constantine to move the seat of the Empire to Byzantium (later renamed Constantinople and much later Istanbul). Much like the original cities, Rome was left to crumble. Barbarians began to sweep down from the North. First the Visagoths came on horseback to trample Rome. Next came Attila the Hun with his elephants. This was the end of the Roman Empire and most of European culture.

The Dark Ages

In hoc signo vincas
(In this sign, we will conquer)
— Constantine, A.D. 313

The northern barbarians, among them the Get of Fenris and their Kinfolk, systematically destroyed the centers of science that helped to evolve human culture over the centuries of Greco-Roman rule. The burning of the Library of Alexandria marked the end of humanity's technological progress and the beginning of scientific decline.

The mages declared war among themselves and those who followed the One God rose in power. The vampires took advantage of the chaos caused by the mages to gain control in many political circles. Our elders began squabbling with the Bone Gnawers over beggars guilds and public sanitation. The combination of these problems led to society's fall on the ladder of civilization and cultural advancement.

The Umbral Fire

Sometime during the Dark Ages, our tribe witnessed a huge Wyld fire streaking through the Umbra. Reports conflict on just when this happened; some say 550 A.D., others say 700 A.D..

By that time, the Machine was no longer just a conglomeration of physical and mechanical contraptions; it had evolved into political, legal and economic "thought machines" as well. The Umbral fire swept through the Machine and destroyed large sections of its enormous form. Reality trembled with the repercussions. Many tools ceased to function. Human culture staggered backwards. Scientists hid within monasteries and subjected themselves to the censure of the Christian church rather than expose themselves to the raging mobs of the common people. The church would often destroy their works, but at least the scientists were still alive. Eventually, with our help, the Machine slowly began to grow anew and filled the void that the Umbral fire had created.

The Plague

Humans released dogs into the sewers beneath their cities in order to kill rats. The Bone Gnawers went into a frenzy and infested the cities with fleas. During this time, the Wyrm spewed its toxins into the cities. As a result, the hygienic practices of the humans suffered and disease ran rampant. We were also partly to blame for this. We pushed hard for trade development with foreign lands. It seems that some diseased rats which made their way from China wound up in Italy. You see, some big river over there had overflowed and killed a lot of people. Lots of disease popped up, due to the rotting bodies floating in the water.

When these rats came over, they brought the disease. Just goes to show you that everything is connected. A disaster in China leads to a disaster in Europe.

Cities closed their gates to keep out plague-ridden people. Beggars were driven from cities. Rich people were locking their doors and hoarding their food. The Bone Gnawers were beside themselves with anger and hatred for the suffering that surrounded them. Scientists and Glass Walkers alike found themselves falsely accused of being witches and were burned, drowned or tortured to death. We narrowly survived by begging the Bone Gnawers for help. The vampires, immune to the sicknesses of the living, took the opportunity to regain their power over much of the European populous. Utilizing our trade routes, they struck quickly from city to city.

The Plague died down by the 1400's. We managed to reclaim the trade routes throughout Europe. Through all this, the central base of our power continued to reside in the coastal lands to the north of the Mediterranean Sea. The Garou said that the cities made the plague worse than it would have been otherwise. They're right. But that's no reason to give up on cities. The trick was to learn from misfortune, then figure out a way to keep it from happening again.

Other bad things also happened here. During the rise of Christianity, the vampires managed to convince the Europeans that evil personified as the Devil, Satan and/or Lucifer created the spirit religions and that worship of nature would lead to eternal damnation. Vampires puppeteered rulers and prayed upon humanity's superstitious fears.

Of course, they were taught a big lesson when it backfired on them during the Inquisition. But the Burning Times, as the Black Furies called those days, hurt us too. The rich often were accused by the poor of being devil-worshippers. Therefore, we lost a few to the screaming mobs.

Duty Beyond Death

We performed as many favors as we could for the other tribes during these dark days and struck deals with them for future returns. We figured out that if we made honor-bound obligations with some Garou, and these Garou wound up getting killed before they could pay it off, they'd have to pay it off after death. In other words, the past lives of other Garou owed us, and we planned on collecting the favor later on. Of course, not every dead Garou still felt bound to the deal, but that's why we built up the importance of honor in our pacts. A Garou who broke the pact was lower than dirt. We even learned a Gift to ensure it. On the other hand, our departed spirits never stick around. They go somewhere else. We can't find them after death, so we are free of the post-mortem obligations created by our same pacts.

B. LeBlanc

Renaissance

It's alive! It's alive!

— Dr. Frankenstein, *Bride of Frankenstein*

We worked hard to foster the idea of an organized, logical science. It was a stabilizing force. The City once again gained strength. The Machine finally broke through the dream barriers and began to mold reality. Meanwhile, we made deals with a multitude of new technological spirits born around ingenious human inventors. Like I said before, humans seemed able to actually change the Pattern Web, whether they knew it or not. One of the effects of this was the birth of a host of science spirits. Few humans are aware that their science is alive.

Status quo scientists chose to ignore many scientific advancements, labeling them as idiotic and blights against God. But we didn't allow these resources to go untapped and we took these ideas into the Umbra where we could do some tinkering of our own. We built Umbral flying machines based on human designs. While the humans had problems with their versions staying aloft, we called on spirits to aid us in our flights. We easily took to the Umbral sky and sailed into many realms.

In the Middle Ages, craftsman guilds formed with an idea in mind: Knowledge yields money; money is power.

We agreed. We spread trade information only among our Kinfolk and kept it a secret from others. We had a meeting with the vampires of Italy and organized contracts regarding property ownership and acceptable business practices. Private papers were signed to insure compliance and agreements were enforced by well-armed families who orchestrated the illegal business activities within a given city. Of course, this was kept hush-hush from the other Garou who wouldn't understand.

Houses

The other tribes finally grew accustomed to the cities and many new cities were built without the high, stone walls once necessary for protection. We set up houses to aid Garou during their travels through cities. This allowed us to take advantage of their lack of city knowledge and money smarts. Soon, these houses rose in power and lorded this strength over nearby houses, eventually leading to the world-wide network we have today.

The Black Furies continued to stay in hiding in the forests and avoided the cities. Our businesses transactions with them had to be done through the females of our tribe, but we did our best to stay on their good side as both our tribes considered the northern Mediterranean area as our homelands.

The Advancement of the Machine

The Renaissance marked the reawakening of humanity's connection to the Machine. Instead of making a tool to do a job the way it had been done for hundreds of years, human mages began to look closely at the forms and processes of nature and worked to construct tools based on their findings. Now humanity created machines to reach their dreams rather than simply assembling tools to ensure their food supply. Italian scientists formed colleges in the manner of ancient Greece and Rome, but only scientists who bought into the status quo of the early colleges had their works recorded for future generations. A lucky few had rich patrons (us) who coveted their cunning achievements. It wasn't until the next growth spurt of the Machine that we began to realize what was really happening. Without past-life experiences to lead us, we weren't fully aware of the Machine's phases of advancement. The next surge caught us by surprise.

Industrial Revolution

Suddenly, humans began creating devices that worked independently. Using horses and windmills to grind grains into flour began the process, but the invention of the cotton gin marked the real start of humanity's ability to mutate the environment with ever-faster methods. It made sense that the quicker and easier something could be done, the greater the profit margin.

As our power grew, the Wyrm reared its ugly head to break down efficiency and belch forth the smog of burning coal. Children were forced to work in factories full of hazards and death. The Countess of Desire and the Chamberlain of Lies mated to secrete Collum, Lord of Sludge and Lady Yul, Mistress of Toxins. We feared that the Apocalypse had come to claim our tribe as it had the White Howlers.

Death ran rampant and eventually humanity understood that coal pollution was choking everyone to death. The Garou, of course, blame us for the corruption of the cities, but we had a long list of favors due us from their ancestors; therefore, we escaped punishment. Okay, we had been lax. We were so enamored with the wonder of the New Life, we had forgotten that the Wyrm can corrupt anything, no matter how pure. The Wyrm rose in the Penumbra like a perverted storybook dragon breathing its toxic sludge and smog. Banes frolicked. We knew what had to be done… what sacrifices had to be made. And we were the only ones who could do it.

We took the battle to the front. We, the predators of the City, set upon the economic supports that stabilized industry. With quick blows of reason, we halted the downward spiral of the Machine. We revealed the foul Wyrm taint

for what it was and set the stage for workplace and work practice reforms. We always defend profit, but not at the cost of Gaia. The Industrial Revolution had taught us that much.

Progress

August 16, 1807 marked the start of gaslight use in London. England lead the rush forward into a new age and learned to work into the night. The world followed closely on England's technological tail. While we were strong in parts of France and England, the majority of us stayed firmly entrenched in the banking system and colleges of Italy. We flexed our muscles in the streets and took control of the local gangs. Businesses were built upon the idea of capital and dividing up capital assets among multiple individuals. These agreements on paper were known as stocks, and new Pattern Spirits were born of these relationships. We made deals with these stock spirits as we had done with the coin spirits. No one believed — and most still don't — that money is alive. It's an organism, a sort of parasite, but one that can work for you as easily as against you.

Communication technology once again surged forward with the invention of the electronic telegraph, the telephone and the phonograph. In 1851, transatlantic cables connected telegraph lines from America to Europe. After the 1870's, electricity began to replace gas as a source of lighting. With safer and brighter lighting, factories extend their hours of operation to generate higher profit. In 1881, the First International Electric Congress in Paris set down the formula of $I = V/R$ (one amp = one volt/one ohm), calcifying the laws of electricity.

We took technology into the Umbra once again and crafted devices to explore the depths of the oceans and inner reaches of the planet. To this day, our houses have huge Penumbral storage rooms with some of this old equipment. But today's youth would rather explore the world inside a computer than go on adventures to the center of the earth.

The Ones Who Walk Among the Glass

The Garou who helped us turn back the Wyrm tide of the Industrial Revolution came from the forests. Some of them had never been to the larger cities before this. For most of them, the truly astounding feature of the cities was the abundance of a transparent material known as glass. When these Garou returned to their tribes in the wilderness, they took with them the legend of our tribe, "the ones who walk among the glass." They started calling us by this title at every moot we went to, but it sounded stuffy to us. So, we took the name and made it our own. From then on, we were the Glass Walkers.

World War I

Most wars sprout for economic reasons. They stimulate the economy. Nobody can argue that fact. They decrease the population and steal the riches from those who fight. Some tribes split on which side to follow in the war, but it usually came to Kinfolk. If the krauts were bashing your flock, then you bashed them back. If it was the Yanks bashing, you bashed them instead.

Clashing Boom Boom was born anew amid the clatter of modern weapons of destruction: machine guns, trench shotguns, grenades and mortars. We could see her in the tanks, but she mostly filled the aircraft.

Most of the war took place in mud-bottomed trenches. Chemical warfare (mustard gas), used for the first time in 1915, appalled many nations and was made illegal at the Geneva Convention. By 1918, the fighting drew to a close. Formed in 1919, the League of Nations attempted to ally the nations of the world, but, given no power to insure balance, it was doomed to failure from the start.

The shock of World War I brought America out of prepubescence and into adolescence. Many of our houses migrated to the big American cities where the Machine surged with power and commerce was king. We began making deals with O' Mighty Dolla', the totem of American currency.

World War Two

The Germans once again made their move to improve their cash flow the old fashioned way. Many Get of Fenris joined their ranks. We hated the Nazi treatment of humans (it reminded us of the Impergium) and saw the Beast of War behind the Nazi's actions. Many of us, and a good many Bone Gnawers, joined the allied forces to wage war against the Axis. We didn't like the war. It disrupted our kind of commerce, although it did help some others. But we didn't want it to end the way it did. There's a rumor that some of us helped build the A-bomb. I hope that's not true. But if the Machine could be fooled, so could we.

The Self-Aware Machine

The internet is nothing like a super-highway. It's an organism.

— John Perry Barlow, *US News & World Report* (Jan. 23, 1995)

The Machine had its greatest growth spurts when the Wyrm took direct action in the physical world, forcing the Weaver to urge the Machine to stop the Wyrm's progress. As the Beast of War slithered through the trenches and foxholes of the World War II battlefields, the Machine kicked into full gear. The Machine went into a frenzy of blind flailing at the hideous creature and tensed its newly realized muscles. Cities fell. Nations toppled. Metal rose

from the earth to move about as if alive! Then, in an instant — 9:15 A.M.; August 6, 1945 — half of Hiroshima ceased to exist. Another blitz three days later and Nagasaki crumbled into blackened ruins. Humanity was in shock. The Machine stopped. It tried to comprehend itself. It struggled to find understanding. The Beast of War laughed and prepared for the return of the Eater of Souls and the turning point of the Apocalypse.

The Machine sent questions outside of and within itself. The responses it received puzzled it. Each answer held differences, though many had mutual points of agreement. The Machine, sorely used by the Wyrm for its own ends, rationalized the need for a focused vision in its existence and sought to eliminate confusion. It fought to achieve consciousness. Soon after, the computer age was born. Thinking machines came into existence from the new consciousness of the Machine. Its consciousness helped Gafflings become Jagglings, and the power of these technological Jagglings in turn allowed humans to create thinking machines.

New Tactics

[Virtual Reality] is making training simulations more realistic than ever, turning financial managers into masters of the universe, endowing surgeons with x-ray vision, reducing the national debt by letting soldiers blow up virtual tanks instead of real ones... .

— Michael Antonoff, "Living in a Virtual World", *Popular Science*

We no longer feared the other tribes. We used humanity as a buffer and called upon the aid of the Machine if that buffer was breached. However, we needed the other tribes; we could not protect the whole of the City, the Machine and the Weaver from the Wyrm. We maneuvered to convinced the Silver Fangs that we needed their help — not as leaders, which we let them believe, but as soldiers in our war against the Wyrm. We pointed out targets to the Silver Fangs so that the other tribes would do the fighting for us. We asked the Bone Gnawers to add their on-the-street information network to our already extensive one. In return, we gave them our outdated technology; you know, the old cars, toasters and TVs. They seem to appreciate used things more than new things. Ridding ourselves of it helped keep us on the cutting edge.

During the World Wars, the Machine seemed to constrict the planet. In 1946, the United Nations brought together the nations of the earth in peace, but Clashing Boom-Boom gained more power daily and yearned to be released. We tried to redirect humanity's war-like tendencies toward space travel, but this seems to have failed miserably. Lesser wars continued to spring up, but we finally began to understand them. Like forest fires, they serve to destroy stagnation so that new technology and ideals can have a chance to grow.

Today

Outlaw freedom, and only the outlaws will be free.
— Unsigned wall scrawl, 1985

The Machine makes it increasingly easier to communicate. Computers and telephones link together to span the surface of the planet. Humanity turns inward and away from the exploration of space. The Information Revolution is here. Our tribe plunges daily into the raging thrall of a new virtual world… the Digital Web.

But don't think that we're not in big trouble. Yeah, this is the Apocalypse. Pollution is increasing everyday; useless junk filling our mail boxes and ever-increasing numbers of toxic chemicals are being created. Gaia's tortured soul screams in pain! You can't let it get to you like it has the other tribes. We have a purpose. We've got progress on our side. The upper hand of evolution is ours! The trick is to guide the Weaver, not fight her. Never forget that everything is alive. The trees, the rocks and the toasters. It's all of Gaia. It's one giant ecosystem. And it's our responsibility to run it. For Her sake.

Nature's voice can also be heard in the city, on the highway, in airports and in slums, in hospitals and schools, in Disneyland and shopping malls. The weave of nature excludes nothing from its fabric, not even the crazy and destructive, creative and inspiring ideas of human beings.
— Joan Halifax, *The Fruitful Darkness*

Chapter Two: High Society

Obsessed with technology, especially technology that is just beyond their reach... the cyberpunks are future-oriented to a fault. They already have one foot in the 21st century and time is on their side. In the long run, we will all be cyberpunks.
— Philip Elmer-Dewitt, "Cyberpunk!" *Time*

If you've seen one city werewolf, you've seen 'em all. Yeah, and I own some Mokolé-guarded swampland in Florida, too. Ya wanna buy some? Sure, many of us follow the standards of our tribe, but a lot of us have different agendas. Glass Walkers are known by their pack, family, house and by the camp they claim to follow (if they follow any at all). We also have our totems. I, myself, follow the Monkey King — Totem of Freedom — and I don't fit into any of these categories. I am Glass Walker and Garou; these titles alone do I need to be forever linked to Gaia. We build our own cages, but we gotta make sure that our cages are big and that we've got the key. There are enough cages built around us by others; let's not lock ourselves in those of our own making.

The Prime Directive: Co-existence

Even in the days of the Impergium, we strove to live with humans in order to protect Gaia as best we could. Now humans are in control of Gaia's delicate balance and we must direct them into battle against the Wyrm. The humans' strength rises from their numbers and their ability to cooperate. Their cunning, like ours, gives them power over many of Gaia's creatures. But, unlike ourselves, they must link with the Machine to gain any physical advantage, using tools because they don't have fangs, or clothes because they don't have fur.

Except the outright ravages of the Wyrm, humankind's abuse of the Machine threatens Gaia more than anything else today. Humans unknowingly allow the Wyrm to enter their machines and then use them for corrupt causes. They must learn to love the Machine; too many of them hate and fear it. We don't have the strength to destroy the Wyrm completely. We must learn to co-exist with many evils, great and small. Everything has its place. Once the Garou battled the Wyrm in nature, but now the Wyrm gathers strength and festers within the City. Most Garou hate the City and hatred gives the Wyrm great power.

The City has become too big for only two tribes to protect. The Bone Gnawers guard the streets and wastes and we watch over the buildings and technology. But in addition to this, we've got to battle the other Garou just to get anything done outside the City. If we can't co-exist with our own, how can we save Gaia?

The Camps

MOBILE, Ala. —A howling, snarling werewolf escaped from a foreign freighter, savagely bit seven cops and turned a police cruiser over before he was captured in a darkened alley near the docks.

— Weekly World News

Long before the Industrial Revolution, we knew that we could accomplish more through specializing than by trying to learn all of Gaia's Gifts. Luna taught us this with the five Auspices. Why shouldn't we take advantage of this principle? Camps help us find our area of expertise and link us to others with similar interests. To us, they're sort of like guilds.

Wise Guys

These guys are Sicilian throwbacks with an attitude and, unfortunately, they pull the strings of our tribe. If you want guns and people who can use them, who you gonna call? They're gun totin' maniacs who want to rule as much as the Silver Fangs, but at least the Silver Fangs haven't figured out that money is king. That's right. Money is power and the Wise Guys take the cake *and* eat it when it comes to controlling the flow of money. That's why they're still in command of the Glass Walkers. Money talks; bullshit walks.

When the whole banking system got started way back yesteryear, people were already manipulating its flow. Of course, members of our tribe were onto the idea like debutantes on caviar. The various organized crime families of the world grew from that seed. The Wise Guys still lock into that power base today, but they can see the corruption that runs rampant within those organizations. They know that the control and manipulation of society in order to increase money-making potential can easily become a Wyrm-tainted activity. Wise Guys strive hard not to fall prey to the Urge Wyrms who pursue them, but they've been skating on thin ice for a long time. This is a lesson that all city Garou should pay heed to.

A Wise Guy Spills the Beans

I have to admit, I like the set-up Lefty had rollin' with the gambling casino. Lure the Banes in to taunt the humans and then nix 'em out — the Banes, I mean. What I love most is getting paid by one Wyrm-fetid jerk to assassinate another Wyrm flunky. Now that makes my day! And ya just can't beat the money. Oh yeah, sure, some of the money is Wyrm-tainted. What did you think the Rite of Cleansing was for anyway?

City Farmers

The City Farmers can make plants grow in the city as if it were wilderness. Nobody else can do that; most people can't get anything to grow. The Farmers think plant life should take over the city from within and live in peaceful co-existence. Or maybe they're just trying to protect the green parts of Gaia within the hard, protective shell of the City.

It doesn't make sense. If you don't want to live outside, then why drag nature inside? It's retro and pointless. I mean, plants don't exist in the Cyber Realm, do they?

City Farmer Spiel

Let us bring the Wyld into the City. Face it: We will always be dependent upon nature as long as we are animals — even the humans are animals. The best defense of Gaia is for us to go on the attack. What once was nature is now the Machine. I do not wish to destroy the Machine; I merely believe that we should bring nature into our lives and our homes. Here in the city, we can protect nature from humanity by buying into their system and using it for our own means. The rest of our tribe is too concerned with the Machine. Nature is the important thing. This is the lesson we were meant to teach.

Urban Primitives

These guys believe that Gaia has allowed the forest to grow into a new form of life — the City. The Urban Primitives struggle to unlock the feral side of the City and to gain power from the technological spirits. A lot of them pierce their bodies, tattoo themselves and sport weird hairstyles in order to remind themselves of their dedication to Gaia.

Urban Primitive Rant

We must strive to connect deeper into the beat of the City. We are here to defend Gaia, not solely to destroy the Wyrm. It is also our part to nurture and study the world about us. Our connection to the spirits of technology will give us the power we need to thwart the Wyrm.

Late at night, when I'm in my artificial cave, I hear the voice of the Machine through its whining hum. I feel the pulse of the electrical and water spirits rushing through the walls. Everything about me is alive, and I'm at peace. What surrounds me is not my enemy, but my ally. I revel in the power that surges and wishes to be free. I want to run wild with them in the Umbra, and I do — every chance I get!

Random Interrupts

Some would call them Luddites for their wanton destruction of machinery, but they're really working to free the Machine of Wyrm-taint and for the freedom of information. If you want to get in tight with the Cyberwolves, these guys are the way to go. They know the ins and outs of the Net here, in the Penumbra and beyond. Computer access codes and security cameras mean nothing to them. They're beyond all that. I, however, think these guys spend too much time with the Machine and not enough time interfacing with flesh and blood beings.

Random Interrupt E-mail

Information wants to be free; the Wyrm is stagnation. We must learn better methods to disseminate information among our race. We take too much pride in hoarding it. We as a people must learn to share with one another.

Enough of that.

Tomorrow night we hit the toy factory on 8th and Parson. Last Wednesday's excursion into the Penumbra was fruitful. We've got some info on the Wyrm-generator they're using to inject Banes into an action figure toy line. This info is courtesy of Wonder Hacker, Hexachrome and their House O' Wyld cards! Same deal as usual. The Clean-Cuts go in as janitors, security guards and temporary workers. The Wyld Boys hit the systems through the Penumbra. Coordinate and send me back info — pronto.

Corporate Wolves

This is some kind of cabal of big business types, the Glass Walkers who really go for the suits and stocks line of work. A bunch of them are owners and CEOs of environmentally aware corporations. They tend to get involved in caern politics as well, serving in caern positions.

A Corporate Wolves Meeting

I have found it necessary to call a central operations meeting with the board of trustees. I need your help preparing for this. It seems that a financing group trying to buy stock in one of our corporate arms is tainted with the Wyrm. As of yet, we are unsure if they realize that Garou own enough stock to manipulate the company. We will need several charts and graphs on how a buy-in might affect us if we allow them to go through with it. I do not see this as being a major problem, and we do not need an intensive stock analysis at the present time. Of course, any buy-in on their part would simply bring them into our trap.

I've already begun the process of juggling the internal paperwork and employees. Nothing has been done on the corporate level that can be traced through the computer networks or banking transactions. By the time they sign the contract, we will have already begun restructuring for bankruptcy. Please take time to duplicate copies of all keys used in that branch's facilities. Make sure that our techs wire in security bypass systems that we can control through spirits. I don't want any traces of our tampering left. All this information should be stored at the local caern until we need it or we are ready to begin Phase A of our counter-seizure.

Umbral Pilots

These freaks are hyped on exploration of the farthest fringes. They're always off on jaunts to the Umbral Hollow Earth or the dangerous void of the Deep Umbra. I think they've got some allies among the Sons of Ether, some like-minded mages. It's hard to say much about them because a lot of them never come back from their journeys.

An Umbral Pilot Orates

While exploring one of the back rooms in the warehouse, I discovered the drilling device our ancestors had modified from the designs of an early Renaissance inventor. It seemed in good condition but for the lack of several Gafflings and Jagglings necessary to operate it properly. I must say that our ancestors did quite a good job crafting these devices and making sure they were stored properly for our future use.

At any rate, I am interested in bringing this device back-up to full potential and using it to explore the earth's crust, thereby locating Black Spiral hives. I have already pulled several of the guidance and sensing fetishes out of the atom rocket we used to travel into the Deep Umbra two years ago — I can only hope that the disasters associated with that journey will not dissuade you from joining me on this expedition. We'll need help moving the craft about once we're inside the warehouse. It seems that part of it has begun to meld with the fins of a diving craft. I am unsure of how common this state is, but the books I found in the debris of an abandoned storage building mentioned the effects generated by exposure to Wyld winds. More and more curious, I dare say.

The Mechanical Awakening

I'm not sure what these guys want. They're a bunch of ranters. I think they're fighting for the independence of the Machine from humankind. But I'm not sure that's the Weaver Way. It seems like this would break the pattern to me, but these guys claim otherwise.

The Mechanical Awakening Shouts

How can we bear to sit back and watch humanity force our spirit brethren into servitude? Must the Machine awaken only to find it is chained? What will happen when it breaks free? The Machine will fall back, for it is locked into humanity and humanity into it. They cling to one another for survival and we stumble into the same trap. We must break the cycle of dependence!

Once we hunted and killed animals for food. Now we pay others to make machines to do our hunting for us. The media tells us how to act and what is expected of us, but the media sleepwalks in its responsibility. Humans can't burp or fart without shame; they don't want to be regarded as animals. They think they have transcended nature to become one with the

sterility of the machine. Is this what the machine wants? What is enjoyable to a machine? Surely not to be broken to pieces by abuse or driven into the ground by lack of maintenance!

Totems of the City

Humans rely on the power of the City and the Machine, but they neglect both. Humans run from one feeding ground to the next like sheep lead by a ram. Look at the sorry state of the city! Urban decay and collapse of the infrastructure are the result. We are Garou. We can feel the pull of the spirits, and we know their power. We know why it takes money to make money — it takes the respect of one spirit to gain the support of another. Do not forget the totem you follow, or it will forget you. And as you are forgotten, so will your Gifts dissolve away, your spirit will become insubstantial and your life will become dull and dreary until your final days are done.

Cockroach

The cockroach knows a good thing when it sees it. When humans began to store food, the cockroach was there to take part in the abundance. Let it not be said that its earthly children don't know how to evolve. Cockroaches can feel the hum of the Machine and know that where the Machine exists, so do humans and their food supply. This is how the cockroach became linked to the Machine. Humans have left offerings for the cockroach for countless centuries without everr realizing it. This has given the Cockroach great power. As Glass Walkers, it was only natural for us to link our efforts toward co-existence with such a hearty and resilient force of nature as cockroach.

Clashing Boom-Boom

I like anchor sandwich
Served on aluminum side
I like rusty fences
Locomotive pie
— Pete Townshend, "I Eat Heavy Metal"

Clashing Boom-Boom is a weird totem of the Weaver and the Wyld. She rules over weapons of all types, from simple axes to mortar shells. No one knows where she came from, but some Theurges say she's a dream sprung forth from the interaction of human anger and the Machine's productivity. She was once raw and ugly in her primal form of animalistic tendancies. Look at her now, embodying the strong graceful beauty of a stealth bomber — wow. She's not my totem, but I saw her once while I was in WWII. She came screaming out of the sky, her long metal wings swept back. The earth rumbled as she raced over it. Her lips cried out with metal resonance, "Fall before me!" Human bodies flew like flies. The field glowed with the fiery glory of her after-presence. I'll never forget that day. I'll never forget how I trembled in awe of her power.

I could understand why some of the other Garou in the squad prayed to her every night. She prevented their rifles from jamming and kept their aim true. She even fouled up the enemy's tools of destruction from time to time. If you're a warrior or a Wise Guy, she's a good one to have on your side. If she's against you, your goose is as good as basting in the pan.

Monkey King

Who is that splendid young ape that ridicules both Heaven and Earth?
— Milo Manara and Silverio Pisu, *The Ape*

Born a mortal child of Gaia, the Monkey King struggled and studied until he refined his being and rose above this plane of existence to become a Totem Spirit. He respects the hairy primates most of all. He doesn't hold much compassion for humans. He's a totem of freedom and knowledge as well as being a trickster.

The legend holds that he went around beating up older, lazy Incarna to steal their powers for himself. He has some items of power: the staff used to level out the Milky Way, which can become any length and any weight; a pair of boots for cloud treading; a hat of invisibility and a jacket of invulnerability. He is a master of the 108 Taoist magicks — the 72 transformations and 36 form changes. What can I say? Whenever I've been in a tight spot, he's always gotten me out in one piece… well, more or less.

O' Mighty Dolla'

When you were broke you would come to me
And I would always pull you 'round
Now I call your office on the telephone
And your secretary tells me that she's sorry,
But you've gone out of town.
— The Kinks, "Catch Me Now, I'm Falling."

The Glass Walkers began their dealings with this totem after World War I. O' Mighty Dolla' existed before then but possessed only limited power. He was once a coin spirit, but grew from a little Gaffling (a nickel's worth) into a Jaggling (a whole quarter) and finally into the big, bruisin' totem spirit he is today — the all-mighty dollar.

When we first met him, he took the form of a hefty man with a 10 gallon hat, expensive suit and a big, smoke-belching cigar full of Banes. I'm told that he constantly complains of aches and pains and that his bum knee is infested with Wyrm cancer. He called upon our aid to cut the Wyrm-taint from him and his children have been struggling to do so ever since. O' Mighty Dolla' used to hang out with the Bone Gnawer totem, the American Dream, but O' Mighty Dolla's left him behind to pursue other goals.

There are other totems like him overseas, but they don't get along with each other too well. They're always trying to one up the other. I guess when they learn to get along, we'll finally have a one-world economy. Yikes! Who wants that? Keep fighting, O' Mighty Dolla'!

Sex and Cubs in the Modern World

… Lycanthropes are actually genetic variants of basic human stock. The genes that make you a werewolf are scattered throughout the human species. Not everyone has them, of course — fewer than one in thirty thousand these days, according to computer analyses.

— Brad Strickland, "And the Moon Shines Full and Bright"

It's not like the old days. Child support puts a damper on the old "love 'em and leave 'em." Media hype stops a lot of Kinfolk women from mating and losing their girlish figures. Daycare centers, run by humans, insist that we medicate our children because they're hyperactive.

If we continue with our current rate of reproduction, the Garou will die out as a race within the next few decades. One fact becomes increasingly clear: Although few of our children turn out to be Garou, the rest possess our blood and understand our plight. This resource must not be forgotten. I've heard it said that we have too much human in our bloodline and not enough wolf. We smell so much like humans that wolves don't want to be around us. But we don't like mating with wolves anyway. The wolves in the City are mostly dog. The bottom line is this: Humans make better sexual partners.

The Breeds

Do your best to bring about the birth of as many Garou as you possibly can. That means breeding with Kinfolk. I'm not saying don't mate with non-Kinfolk, but they're less likely to understand why you need to fight for Gaia.

Homid

We're 98% human stock. Being homid Garou allows us to travel the City without revealing ourselves to lesser Wyrm minions. It also makes it easier to gain the support of human allies. Without their help, we fight a futile battle against the Wyrm.

As homid Garou, we sometimes find ourselves bound by the values of human society. We strictly adhere to schedules controlled by calendars and mechanical time pieces. We undeniably rely upon money for our existence. Even though we fight against it, the media quietly seduces and sedates us until we follow the hype. We like to dress well and we like to have the newest, coolest things. Deal with it.

Metis

Nature curses us. We should be able to breed with one another. It's not right that the Litany holds us back from breeding with our own and forces us to take mates from races that do not and cannot understand what we are. Maybe this part of the Litany has been Wyrm tainted all along. The Wyrm must laugh at this cruel joke. Maybe the Wyrm tainted us long ago — corrupted our line so that we must breed with humans and wolves.

Listen to me! Metis are Garou, maybe more so than any of us. Isn't their natural form Crinos? Keep them in your care. Hold them close and show them love and truth. Let them live in the Garou community, since they must be kept separate from humans and wolves until they can control the change. They must not be lost to the Wyrm. We must help them to be strong.

Lupus

We love our lupus Kin with all our being. They don't know the pressures of city life. What a joy it is to introduce them to technology; to show them that the box with flashing pictures is actually a television and that it does makes sense!

To wolves, we often stink of the City and humanity. They disdain that. They're right, of course. Wherever we go, the spirits of the City follow us, even in the wilderness. Our lupus Kinfolk tend to be overly docile and they have a hard time gripping the Rage that should be instinctual to them. More often then not, they grow-up in captivity in a zoo or live as pets in someone's home. We need them, for they are very strong in the spirit. Soon, humans will kill the remaining wolves, just as they have eradicated so many other races. When they vanish, we might quickly follow.

Organization: The Four Houses

Our tribe has a structure composed of four main "houses." Houses only take up part of our position in the tribe. We usually join together in houses independent of these groups as well, but we are all duty bound to join or lend aid to the appropriate house as requested by the local Don. In each locality, there is a Don who runs the local houses and a bunch of leaders in each house. But each house also has a Head House; the one house to which all of the local houses are answerable. The leader of the Head House (there is one for each of the four houses) is called the Lord or sometimes Godfather.

The Central House

The elders of our tribe all hold a seat within the Central House, as do all house leaders. The Central House forms the primary leadership of our tribe on a city level. The Central House votes upon the position of Don. He usually controls the biggest hunk of turf, runs the most action and takes the local City Father as a totem. Anyone who wishes to challenge the Don's authority must do so at a moot held at the Central House. The Don heads the Central House and sets the status quo of all the houses within his city. Those who break the Don's mandates will find punishment swift and harsh, while those who follow him find their needs fulfilled.

The Central House's major purpose is to keep track of Wyrm-taint within the city by use of Gifts and investigations through both the physical world and the Umbra. Since this house has traditionally been run by Wise Guys, the Head House is in Italy. It tends to shift with different elections to either Venice or Rome.

House of Technological Advancement

As we depend upon new spirits for our source of future allies, the House of Technological Advancement is important in every city. It tends to be populated by Corporate Wolves, Random Interrupts and the tribe's Theurges. Its functions include: handling initial contact with newly birthed technological spirits, maintaining the awakened state of technological spirits within a city and monitoring scientists who are responsible for the potential birth of technological spirits. The Head House tends to shift location with each successive Lord, but it is currently in San Jose (Silicon Valley), California.

House of Urban Defense

The Theurges and Galliards of our tribe meet weekly at the House of Urban Defense to teach and perform the rituals and rites of our forebears. This work house is open to anyone who wants to learn the secret ways of our tribe. The applicant must swear loyalty to a Garou mentor of this house, who will then lead the applicant down the path of spiritual development. In addition, this house works in a preventative manner to cleanse and maintain the city and keep the Wyrm at bay. The Head House is in Rome, where it has been for many years.

House of Rightful Justice

The Central House appoints and removes individuals from the ranks of the House of Rightful Justice as it sees fit. Once the Central House has chosen a Wyrm-tainted target to be removed, they devise a plan of attack and then issue orders to the House of Rightful Justice. The house takes responsibility for the eradication of the targeted Wyrm infestation. Members of this work house rely upon their combat abilities and street smarts in order to survive. The local caern warder is also the chairperson of the House of Rightful Justice. Ahrouns see placement in this house as either a chance for immense glory or a death sentence. The Head House is in New York, where many worldwide Glass Walker assassinations are contracted.

Moots: Big Throwdowns

By electronic culture, I suppose we mean a certain cybernetic swipe at metaphysics. To a large extent, cybernetics have been superseded by the more sophisticated discipline of artificial intelligence.

— Gary Wolf, "Avital Ronell on Hallucinogenres," Mondo 2000

We follow the Weaver Way, yet the wolf still resides within us. Our allegiance to the Weaver must not overshadow our duty to protect Gaia. This dichotomy of our existence is clear to those who know us. Our moots and rituals tell the tale. They define our existence and focus our everyday lives. They align our spirits so that we become aware and stay true to our cause.

Most moots occur on the 23rd of each month. The location can change, depending upon the state of the sept, but conventions start exactly at 12:37 A.M. by the sept leader's watch. However, rigidly upholding this stance, has lead to stagnation within our tribe. Even the staunchest of elders agrees that half of our moots should be held as raves in order to maintain our link to the wolf.

Conventions: The Weaver's Rules of Order

We must be calm and resolute. We can't lose our heads when we battle the Wyrm. We can't give in to the raging beast and fly down its gaping maw. We find peace in structure, as do humans. Organization allows us to manipulate humans into battling the Wyrm for us. As we age, we tend to want everything to fall neatly into place. It makes things easier. I want to say it's wisdom, but I think laziness makes us think this way. I know that I don't have the strength in these old bones that I had as a pup — maybe that's part of it as well. Our meetings, presided over by the Philodox, might seem overly rigid, but the elders must use order to formulate plans insuring the safety of the City for today and tomorrow. We must have forethought in our planning. Once a course of action has been formalized, Theurges call upon the aid of the necessary spirits and the local Don assigns each house with its individual goals for the following two month period.

Follow the rules of order. Each house must select a single spokesperson. In moot, each spokesperson has a chance to express his or her viewpoint. House members are sometimes allowed to speak at open forums after requesting time via paperwork. If the elders don't want someone to speak, they make him travel a route of red tape to get permission, such as filling forms out in triplicate and getting certain signatures, etc. It's better to present your ideas to a sympathetic elder who can then use her influence to lend credibility to the idea.

Appeasing and gaining the aid of Weaver spirits takes precedent at our moots… expect rigid formality.

Raves: Reaffirming the Wyld

The wolf rages within us. The City cages us. The Wyrm tries to enshroud us.

Calling upon the power of the Wyld, the roaring music fills us with electronically augmented pulses of surging sound. Multicolored flashes of lighting shoot within our minds. Howling and screaming, bodies contort and change form as they slam into me, and I into them. The Galliards fill our minds with ancient tales and we fall into our roles. Forgotten beasts rise from the boiling steam of the past. The armies of corruption fall before our cleansing path as we tear through the City. Our souls scream pure with renewal. In the end, we collapse in piles about the dance floor. We are at peace, for the wolf has been sated and we have reaffirmed our bond to the Wyld. The night is done.

Elder's often find themselves standing back and trying to make sense out of these raging parties. Music and adrenaline take control. Between songs, the younger Garou, and often all Ahrouns present, are expected to make meaningful statements over the PA system.

Organization is secondary to the thrill of the moment. One slip of the tongue in drunken banter can often mean a jump in logic that would never come out otherwise. Everyone knows to ignore insult and to promote well being.

Seasonal Rites
All Machines Day

Many spirits are often rejected and ignored, but the servant spirits of machinery find themselves performing redundant labor on a daily basis forced upon them by humans. The humans drive them until they break or dissipate for lack of Gnosis. But we respect the spirits who thrive within technology.

All Machines Day celebrates our dependence on the Machine and our reverence toward technological spirits. The festival begins with Vulcans Day on the preceding Friday and ends with Sister Science Day on the following Saturday, although the moot itself takes place on the Ides

of March, the 15th, each year. On this day, we clean and repair our machinery from the early morning until the evening. This includes the cleansing of both home and office with rites and rituals. As the sun sets, we power up our machinery and invite the spirits to frolic with us through a festival of light and sound. The festivities go into the Penumbra where we commune with the technological spirits who aid us in our daily lives. When the celebration finally dies down, a peaceful calm settles within both the structure that houses the main festivities and the Penumbra that surrounds it.

All hail the Machine!

Promethean Daze

Filled with eating and communing, this week-long celebration, occurring between Christmas and New Year's Day, falls into two distinct parts.

The first phase clears the mind of delusional, self-imposed boundaries that were constructed during the course of the previous year. The individual seeks to break down her own boundaries, while the houses work to break down repressive structures they have erected. When this event occurs on a tribal level, the whole tribe works to remove the previous order and leave a clean slate for reorganization. The second stage works to predict the events of the new year. Drumming is used to call upon the harmony of the past and to welcome new spirits into existence. We hope to find the new spirits birthed from Gaia's womb and promise our allegiance to them. In turn for protection, we ask the spirits to aid us in future times. We try to expand our minds and find new direction and insight.

The Litany

I once helped catch a Shadow Lord who was trying to infiltrate our tribe and report breaches of the Litany to the Silver Fang hierarchy. We held him down and tattooed "Fink" on his chest. We made it clear that his treachery was not appreciated. We stare right at the Wyrm while the other tribes run around the woods having a good ol' time. Who are they to judge our battle against the Wyrm?

Enough of that. You need to know the Litany the way we see it. Straying from it could mean death. Pay attention.

Garou Shall Not Mate with Garou

Sometimes I wonder if this part of the Litany wasn't originally "It is the duty of all Garou to breed with another Garou at least twice during their lifetime in order to insure the existence of Garou in this generation, lest the Wyrm take advantage of our dwindled numbers (due to the fate of recessive genes) in any one generation or another." Makes too much sense, doesn't it? But don't tell the Silver Fangs this. They'll come after us with their flunky tribes.

Lingo of the Techno Wolf

Bionics — Mechanical devices designed to replicate the functions of biological organisms. Sometimes called "six million dollar ware."

Cipherware — Computer software that appears to be something other than what it actually does.

Conferencing — The linking of several different users to one another through any two-way communications device.

Cracking code — 1) Writing or breaking into another person's computer programs, 2) Writing programs in machine language.

Crowbar — Prying into something by use of something else. "I crowbarred my way into Pentex by dummying up to a couple of Black Dog Games execs."

Cyberfetish — A technological fetish, usually implanted into a Garou's body.

Cyberpunk — Someone who carts technology around with them and integrates it into as many aspects of her life as possible.

Cyberware — Hardware that links directly to a living organism.

Family — A Glass Walker sept.

Flushing — 1) Removing everything from a computer system or IC chip, 2) Turning on all the fire sprinklers in a building, 3) Filling a given location with noise, smoke, water, etc. in order to force something out.

Hacker — One who hacks.

Hacking — 1) Breaking into computer systems, 2) Working through things by trial and error, 3) Programming [archaic].

Interface — 1) Setting up an equal connection between two parties, 2) Trading information, 3) Joining two things together.

House — The organizational structure of the tribe. There are four main houses and many sub houses.

Jack-in — 1) Plugging into a system, 2) Gaining control of a piece of machinery.

Lamer — 1) A computer user who does not program, 2) Someone who doesn't help out.

Linking-up — Sending and receiving information from another computer system or person.

Lurking — 1) Linking into other people's communications and not letting them know you're there, 2) Sneaking around in the Penumbra to observe people in the physical world.

Managing — 1) Getting other people to do your work, 2) Being the brains behind a plan.

Monkeywrench — To sabotage.

On-line — Being in a situation where one can send and receive information from an outside source.

Power out — 1) Getting out of a situation as fast as possible, 2) Temporarily banishing electrical spirits from a certain area.

Set date — 1) Planning an activity that is to occur at a certain time, 2) Synchronization of watches.

Spook — Coined off the nickname for CIA agents. 1) Someone who watches people from the Penumbra, 2) Someone who listens or looks into other places through mechanical means, 3) Someone who pulls information out of communications networks or computers from the Penumbra.

Spoon-bending — 1) Using electromagnetic spirits to destroy magnetic media, 2) Making a solid object take another shape.

Trojan horse — Making something appear to be something else, especially if it is where the other thing should be and it is used to trick people into a false sense of security.

Uplink — 1) Sending information from a communication's satellite, 2) Sending information to a larger computer system, 3) Sending and receiving information from an outside source with more information.

User — Someone who utilizes a piece of machinery.

Virtual reality — An artificially constructed environment.

Workaholic — A person who falls into work so deeply that she does not know when to stop working and feels she cannot rest until everything is done.

Other words for that piece of machinery over there: doo-hicky, gadget, gizmo, thing-a-ma-doodle, thing-a-ma-jig, what-cha-ma-call-it and widget

Combat the Wyrm Wherever It Dwells and Whenever It Breeds

The Wyrm fills the City with its stench. If we raged out at every Wyrm scent we smelled, we'd be in constant frenzy. Don't worry about the little Wyrm things unless they get in your way. If you do, the little ones'll wear you down until you're easy pickings for a big one. Select your targets carefully. Take time to plan all attacks. Take no prisoners. Destroy all Wyrm-tainted machinery.

Respect the Territory of Another

Follow this rule for land and property. Be careful; some Garou still mark what's theirs the old fashion way. Take time to make sure that you're not going to step on any toes when you make business dealings. Inside the Machine, nothing can truly be owned. Information wants to be free. No one owns the Cyber Realm. Data held prisoner should be freed if possible.

Accept an Honorable Surrender

There's too much killing among our race. Accept any surrender — except, of course, from the Black Spiral Dancers, who should be killed and the Shadow Lords, who should be made to grovel if at all possible. In any case, make sure you get something cool out of it.

Submission to Those of Higher Station

Look… you're going to go through your phases, but it's best to respect and to listen to those above you in any situation. Sometimes, if you have a good idea, you're going to have to speak up even if it is against the views of the elders. Just remember, if you are told to hold your tongue and don't, you're liable to get shot a time or two for speaking out of turn.

The First Share of the Kill for the Greatest in Station

Don't let the Wyrm get a hold of you if you're the "top dog." Remember, what you might want, someone else might need or know how to use better than you do.

Ye Shall Not Eat the Flesh of Humans

Chomping on someone is one thing, ripping a hunk out and swallowing it is another! If we catch you doing it, we're gonna skin you alive with our klaives — and you can post that on the BBS!

Respect for Those Beneath Ye — All Are of Gaia

Don't shove people around. Ask them to do things for you and explain to them why it's necessary if time allows. We ensure that our people, our allies and those individuals who we protect have their needs fulfilled. No one should go without food, shelter or decent entertainment (hey, it's a priority these days!).

The Veil Shall Not Be Lifted

Don't even joke about telling the tabloids about us. We'd be attacked both by Garou and humans. I know you could make a lot of money, but get a life! Take a hint from the vampires. If you have to say something about the Garou's existence, blow it out of proportion so no one will believe it.

Do Not Suffer Thy People to Tend Thy Sickness

Medical science can help people live far longer than they should. Death's a natural process. Holding onto life too long is Wyrm fetid and without honor. When your time comes, turn to the woods. Live your final days as a tribute to the Wyld. I'm on my way there soon. Don't mourn me when I'm gone; I'll be back!

The Leader May Be Challenged at Any Time During Peace

The Leader May Not Be Challenged During Wartime

Do we really need to repeat ourselves in the Litany? Come on, make some sense already. Do we ever see peace in the City? Bottom line… don't fight among yourselves while fighting the Wyrm. Don't quarrel as a house in front of other houses. Don't defy our tribe in front of other tribes. Do your fighting for leadership in private. Try to solve things logically before regressing to tooth and talon. Save your strength for battling the Wyrm.

Ye Shall Take No Action that Causes a Caern to Be Violated

Be very careful with our secrets. Mages and Wyrm followers want to steal or destroy what we hold dear. If you violate this part of the Litany, you'd best just kill yourself. Your death will be long and painful if we have to do it for you.

Punishment

As a tribe, we understand that we're animals. We like to treat our kind justly, but when they have done wrong, it's necessary to punish them in a way that will have a lasting impact. Firearms have become the first line of punishment for the Glass Walker pups. Everyone knows what they do to a human. Garou in Crinos form will feel the pain, but they'll heal rapidly without lasting scars. Greater offenses usually lead a house to abandon a Garou deep in the wilderness without any technology: no television, no radio, no matches and of course, no clothing. The harsh environment and the lack of suitable entertainment usually lead to reform. Once you've been through it, I promise you won't forget it.

A repeat offender will find his money becoming useless. Any transaction, other than bartering, becomes unattainable. In addition, information about the offender will be removed from as many sources of documentation as the house or tribe can manage. Non-Garou will often become unable to verify his identity. These punishments will continue until the Garou has learned the error of his ways.

When a Glass Walker goes to the Wyrm, the tribe must do what is necessary. Death of the Garou takes precedence over all other actions. We leave no remains and purify the site of the Garou's death.

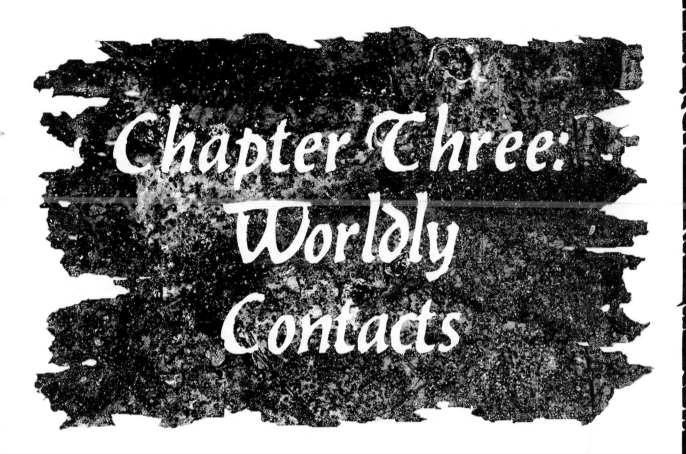

Chapter Three: Worldly Contacts

Walking on
Walking on
Broken glass
— Annie Lenox, "Walking on Broken Glass"

The City

Friends will help you better than any sidearm or weird doo-dilly-bob that you happen to find. You're hearing me right. Friends are better than money, too. Listen to what I'm saying. Make an ally of the spirit within the machines you use. Talk to the programmer who runs your database. Know who you can trust. Even better, know who you can't.

So I'm cynical. I've seen young punks come and go. I'll tell you right now, I've been throated by better than the likes of you. So you have a lot of raw power — I did too. So what's the big deal? Prove it to the Wyrm. I don't have time to fight with my own people. I'm too old to be wasting my time. Claw me up if you have to, then I can get on with my life. If you want my help, I'll give you something that you don't have: my knowledge. I have more in this chrome-plated skull then you'll ever get if you keep acting like a reckless cub.

The City has been our shelter and provider since our tribe's beginnings. In return for maintaining urban caerns, the Weaver has been nice enough to help us make allies with the City spirits. This should be more than enough proof that the City fills an important niche in the whole of Gaia. For some reason, the other tribes insist on arguing against us and labeling us as Wyrm tainted. However, if we weren't here to fight against corruption, then every city would have been a hellhole long ago.

I know the other Garou find their roots in the Wyld while we have followed the Weaver. Maybe Gaia has reasons behind what she does. We fill a niche, helping to retain what remains of the fragile balance of the Triat. It is general practice for at least one house in a city to select the City Father or Mother as its totem. City totems are of little or no power once you are outside of their limits, but while you are within their domain, their power reigns supreme. Houses must take care to tend to the local City spirit or risk having the whole City turn to the Wyrm and then against them.

It may seem hopeless, but we must fight 'til the end. Even through death, we return to protect the City. Just because we can't look into our past lives like other Garou doesn't mean that we don't reincarnate just as often.

The Machine

The human body will not evolve beyond its present state. Their mission is to give birth to the new life form that will replace them. That is why we cyberdroids have come into being. But humans are unwilling to turn the world over to us and so they have locked up our souls.

— Tony Takezaki, A.D. Police

Technology, like everything else, is a part of Gaia. How can the others be so blind? They look at nature and say "Nature is Gaia." How can their view be so narrow? There are spirits within the machines just as there are spirits within animals and plants. No matter. We are who we are and we know who we are. We know what we believe in and we will do our part to retain the Balance of Gaia.

The Weaver spawned the Machine just as she did the City. There's no question that parts of it smell like the Wyrm. But parts of nature stink of the Wyrm, too, but the Garou aren't trying to destroy nature, are they? Of course not! Almost every piece of machinery has its own spirit. I've seen comput-

ers with several spirits. A majority of technological spirits are of the Weaver, but there are a few of the Wyld as well.

The CyberRealm

The creation of technology begins in the CyberRealm. Those new spirits who need our help slowly grow to strength here, knowing that we will protect them.

Up there is the Computer Web. It networks the thinking machines together as no other machines have been able to link up before. The strata of mechanical networks lies below. All machinery is connected — each wheel and gear works together. Beneath this, things become dank with the darkness and ooze of the Wyrm. Slimy, bestial forms of sludge and goop lurk just behind the pristine surfaces of Umbral office walls. There are no roads beneath the skyscrapers anymore; just a dank emptiness that stretches ever downward.

We've got gargoyles; local spirits who defend our gleaming penthouse offices. Still, the Wyrm extends its grasping tentacles. It reaches out, unnoticed, until its tentacles are large enough to drag us from the skyscrapers into the soot and grime of that which waits below.

We are friends of the Machine. You will be permitted access through this realm. Do not panic. The Weaver is our friend. But that doesn't mean that the Weaver always knows what she is doing. She needs guidance. I think it's the Wyld creeping in and maligning her patterns, but the

BLEBLANG

others insist that it is the Wyrm and that the Weaver herself is out of control. We know better, don't we?

The Rest of Our Race

The Bone Gnawers and Children of Gaia always look out for us. Give your junk to the Bone Gnawers and they will forever love you for it. The Children of Gaia talk peace first in every situation, but don't let them talk you into becoming a martyr. The Fianna and Silent Striders will follow our lead and help us out of a jam. Both tribes know what it's like to be outcasts. The Fianna tend to be entrapped by the cultural heritage of their Kinfolk, but I hear they can communicate with fairies and other mystical creatures. The Silent Striders can travel really fast, but they keep secret what ideas they deem dangerous. I trust both tribes only as long as we're making a profit.

The three mystic tribes like to remain separate from us. This doesn't mean they hate us, they just like doing their own thing by themselves. The Black Furies hate men, so let the females among us do the talking — and stay away from their fetishes! The Uktena delve into occult lore constantly; if you have questions about spirits, they're the ones to politely ask. The Stargazers study the mysteries of the Umbra through their own minds. If you think that's cryptic, try talking to one! Don't try to manipulate any of these three tribes or they won't deal with you again in this life. Treat them with respect and they'll at least keep you from getting killed.

The ruling tribes have always hated us. The Silver Fangs fear us for the power we have in human society. Most Shadow Lords are cunning and hateful and all too often they try to muscle in on our corporate territory. The Get of Fenris are a bunch of thugs who fight anyone they can. Placate these tribes and stay away from them as best you can. Many of them hold their status in Garou society because of their breeding and connection to their previous incarnations. I think that this tends to hold them in the past and blind them to new ways of life. I'm not even going to go into the inbreeding part — and they're the ones so adamantly against metis!

The Wendigo and Red Talons would kill us as soon as they would a Black Spiral Dancer. To them, we are the enemy. Both tribes fill themselves with the Wyld and run free in the wilderness. The Red Talons form our opposite among the Garou because their tribe consists of only lupus. The Wendigo are as bloodthirsty as the Get of Fenris and have no one to help hold their rage in check. Don't run into either of these tribes in the wilderness. It's a good thing for us they hate the cities.

Everyone and Everything Else

But… but they changed the original design! They cut down on building materials. Cut corners; used a lot of cheap substitutes! The psychotecture was ruined! God knows what effects

the actual city is having on all our minds! Why did Simon allow it, knowing the consequences?

— Los Bros Hernandez, Mister X

We're not the only supernatural creatures running around. I'm sure I haven't heard of all the mystic weirdness that exists, but I'll tell you what I can.

A Monkeywrencher's Guide to Battling the Wyrm

A lot of Glass Walkers are Monkeywrenchers; It's a loose-knit gang of trouble-makers — trouble for Pentex, that is. These are their tenants for Wyrm smashing, starting with the unstated but obvious: Know your target.

1) Always plan in advance including an escape route.

2) Trick the Wyrm into attacking itself.

3) Crowbar, whenever possible.

4) Use surprise and distraction to your advantage.

5) Destroy communication and power networks around your target just before you go in for the kill.

6) Always target the greatest enemy.

7) Never strike at a target twice in the same manner.

Vampires

Yes, vampires! Undead, immortal parasites that subsist off the blood of the living. For some reason, they don't all smell of the Wyrm — but be careful; this doesn't mean they aren't evil. Some vampires are too useful to kill, unless their Wyrm scent becomes too strong or they become treacherous. Remember, we have bigger Wyrm fiends to fry. Don't provoke the old vampires; they're usually too busy fighting their own undead offspring to bother us and they're highly dangerous if riled.

Vampire Cliques

There thrives a secret society known as the Ventrue. They, like our tribe, manipulate the business world and economy. Try not to bring the wrath of the Ventrue upon yourself; these vampires are the most organized of Wyrm minions. They might seem like good allies in business deals, but don't try it. It's not worth the hassle. However, you might want to let them know if you're going to make any power plays. No need to step on any toes and cause a corporate war to snowball into a supernatural one. I hear they have rules like we do and they respect other people's property. Keep this in mind if they try to take over anything you own. Point any transgressions out to them sensibly.

Another clique is the Giovanni. While they don't number as many as the Ventrue, we've had better dealings with them, since our mutual homebase is in Italy. We fought a lot at first, but eventually came to some mutual understandings. Legends say that the Wise Guys have an ancient pact with them. The contingent known as the Nosferatu is filled with mostly gentle beings who came into their immortality malformed. This makes them look the most Wyrm-fetid of the night stalkers, but most of the time they're actually the least tainted. I find this especially odd when the other vampires treat them in the same manner as metis are treated among our tribes. Oh, and stay out of the sewers — it's their home. Let the Bone Gnawer Rat Finks take care of any transactions you might want to make with the Nosferatu.

Mages

It's legend that the mages like to find our caerns and drain them. Everything else in legend seems true, so don't disregard anything you might have heard. I've heard elders talk about making deals with some mages for weird technology or to trace the presence of new technological spirits — which some mages apparently don't believe in or ignore. I, myself, don't want to have anything to do with them. They don't seem to be trying to protect Gaia and magick doesn't have anything to do with technology.

If you see what you think is a mage, clear the hell out of the area and contact the nearest Uktena. They don't like mages and they'll do your battling for you. The Uktena'll

leave all the technology spirits behind, because they don't like them either. No reason getting our hands dirty if we don't have to; that's the first sign of a good manager.

Wraiths: Trapped Souls

Ghosts. I've heard the same stuff that you have. They're trapped to haunt the world of the living until they find a way to right a wrong or stop the evil that killed them. Your guess is as good as mine and I don't know who's side they are on, so don't ask.

I think it's best to hold places of the dead as holy. I always tell business colleagues not to build on graveyards, but sometimes they don't listen. Something weird always happens.

Exploring the World at the Speed of Sound

I tried to get another Glass Walker to tell you this, but he was too set on talking about how great a surfer he is and where all the best waves are. Most of you aren't surfers and you don't really have time for all that nonsense. I'm trying to sort out what he told me, but I don't know what he's trying to say half the time… damn surfer lingo. It's like talking to a banker about currency. He's sort of famous, though. He's the guy who the spirits first taught the Gift of Phone Travel to. Since he learned it, he's been traveling around the world surfing. It's an

BL

abuse of Gaia's power, but I'm going to make something good out of it by compiling this.

North America and Europe

Most of our tribe lives in North America and Europe and stays linked together by the ever-increasing simplicity of the telephone and computer nets. Soon it won't make a difference where we are; we'll still be able to talk to each other like we're next door.

Unfortunately, the cities are getting old. The Wyrm is starting to corrupt them with its smog and sludge and human neuroses. I've been in the wilderness once or twice. The sky is blue out there, not gray like in the cities. The air tastes fresh — not like the junk we cough out of our lungs.

Japan

Technology pulses with youth in Japan. There is neon and glass covering everything in sight. Recycling is important because the country has few natural resources, but the Wyrm's power causes industry to pollute the ocean and destroy sea life.

Quite a few new types of technological spirits have been found in the Penumbra around Japan. Rumor has it that Japan's Gauntlet is thin and has many holes in it. The local Shadow Lords have most of them mapped out, but they don't want to give up their secrets to those of our tribe who live there.

What I'm worried about is that recurrent, waking dream the Japanese keep putting into their films about giant Wyrm creatures coming out of the polluted Pacific Ocean and befriending the children of Japan. It all smacks too much of the Apocalypse to me. A Wyrm-joke created to lure children into summoning a Nexus Crawler into existence with what limited spiritual power they possess. Unfortunately, as I said before, the Gauntlet tends to be thin in many places.

Coastal Asia

If you want to get something and you can't get it any place else, the trade centers of the Orient are the places to check. Coastal Asia's full of open air markets and money exchanging. There's even some technology here and there, but most of it is shoddy. Go for trade only; not many of our kind around those parts — from any tribe.

I've heard rumors that Ratkin live in these regions. The few native Bone Gnawers would know if this is true, but their lips are sealed.

Mainland Asia

My surfer pal didn't go inland… no waves. He heard that weird stuff goes on in the jungles and said that he felt bad mojo rising out of them whenever he was near. Stories abound of different breeds of shapeshifters and armies of fomori gathering for a giant battle. It all seems like a bunch of bunk aimed at getting us nervous and stopping technology from moving into that area of the world.

The Amazon

We've backed none of the development in the Amazon, but working in political circles to stop deforestation only does so much. Some of us have found that the best way to stop the Wyrm from devouring these primal lands is to buy it and stop all industrial expansion. Though this seems somewhat backward to us, we alone among the tribes have the monetary means to execute this kind of counter-attack.

You want a war, young pup? Well, there ya go! You got a hot one. Kill them all and hopefully only the good ones'll reincarnate. Pentex-controlled money is tilting toward 75%+ of the Amazon market, or so my sources claim. Don't worry about destroying the City or the Machine down there; it's all pretty much corrupted by the Wyrm.

Whatever you do down there, keep your eyes open! The natives think that we're the enemy! I'm including the other changing breeds in with the whole lot of them, as they still have a grudge from the old days when the Garou declared the War of Rage.

The Third World

As a policy, the Glass Walkers have vowed not to aid in the development of any new city or the expansion of technology outside of already existing cities. This was part of our plea to bring about the end of the Impergium and to stop the others from trying to commit genocide on us. Breaking this policy will lead the Red Talons down our throats. I'm sure the Silver Fangs and their two side-kick tribes, Shadow Lords and Get of Fenris, would be more than happy to help those savages do us in, so don't tempt them!

Remember: Only use the technology that is available to you. Do not front the expansion of cities. It is acceptable to rebuild areas inside of a city as long as they are built to match their surroundings. Let humanity do the footwork and "buy in" later. In doing this, we can shift the blame from us to the humans for the cities increasing in size.

It's sad. The media talks about the suffering in these countries all the time. We could help the Third World so easily with so very little effort if the rest of the Garou would free us of our ancient promise.

Appendix One: Powers of the City

Tribal Weaknesses (Optional)

An optional rule was introduced in the first of the **Werewolf Tribebooks**: tribal weaknesses. These are quirks each member of a particular tribe possesses, usually due to the social or even genetic nature of a tribe. Weaknesses should not always be enforced. There are some situations where a Bone Gnawer may not suffer a higher difficulty on Social rolls. These situations may be rare, but they can occur. For instance, Black Furies suffer from an inborn anger against men, but a Black Fury may not feel anger towards a man with whom she has a trusting relationship.

It is up to the Storyteller to enforce these rules when an appropriate situation occurs in the game. A player may be unwilling to remind a Storyteller that her Uktena's curiosity will get her into trouble.

Glass Walker Weakness

Weaver Affinity: Cannot regain Gnosis in wilderness.

The Glass Walkers are tied closely with their cities, their city spirits and the spiritual life unique to the city, with its mishmash of tyrannical Weaver and tempered Wyld. Because of this, they lack an inherent connection with the Wyld and may not regain Gnosis points when in the wilderness. The exception to this is when they are at a caern; they may regain Gnosis as they normally do at these sacred sites.

Merits and Flaws

Jinx (3 - 4 pt. Supernatural Flaw)

Probably due to your actions in a previous life, technological spirits tend to avoid you. You cannot learn Gifts from technological spirits (including Net and Pattern Spiders), and you cannot use technological fetishes or talens. In addition, these spirits may cause technological devices you use to malfunction — you're just a jinx.

Fortunately for you, there is one technological spirit that does believe in you. It likes you and thinks that you have been unjustly accused of whatever annoys the other spirits. This spirit lives inside of a piece of machinery, although it is not a fetish, and you must have it present when dealing with technology spirits or you will be ignored. With its aid, you can use any technological fetishes or talen and learn tech Gifts. If this spirit is ever killed, you are out of luck in dealing with technology. A dangerous quest into the CyberRealm may yield you a new ally, at the Storyteller's discretion. If you purchase the 4 point version of this Flaw, then your spirit ally does not exist and you suffer all the drawbacks listed above.

Machine Affinity (4 pt. Supernatural Merit)

Working and repairing equipment has always come easy to you. Your connection to machinery spontaneously awakens technological spirits in your presence and allows you to add one to all dice pools when dealing with them.

Gifts

• **Pennies From Heaven (Level Two)** — The Garou can convince money spirits to improve the value of his money by changing the denominations of the coinage or currency. This Gift is taught by money spirits.

System: The Garou spends one Gnosis point and rolls Charisma + Politics. The difficulty depends on the final desired denomination. It doesn't matter what the money already is, although few Garou will change dollars into pennies at a loss. The amount of money changed depends on the number of successes. (Storytellers of non-U.S. chronicles should adjust the following chart to the closest equivalent foreign currency.)

Denomination changed to:	Difficulty
Penny	3
Nickel	4
Dime	5
Quarter	6
Dollar bill	7
Five dollar bill	8
Twenty dollar bill	9
Any other currency	10

Successes	Amount (in coins or bills)
1	5
2	10
3	20
4	50
5	100

Glass Walker financial managers frown on the blatant use of this Gift, since it tends to attract the attention of other supernaturals who are concerned with money (such as the mage Syndicate). If too much of this mutant money hits the market too quickly, there will surely be supernatural retribution from other parties.

• **Steel Fur (Level Two)** — Garou with this Gift can temporarily convert their fur into steel. This Gift is taught by metal or earth elementals.

System: The Garou must spend one Willpower point and roll Stamina + Science (difficulty 7). Each success adds one to the Garou's soak dice pool. The effect lasts for one scene or until the Garou decides to convert the metal back into fur. While this Gift is active, the Garou suffers a +1 difficulty to all Social rolls (except among Glass Walkers) and Dexterity rolls.

• **Tech Speak (Level Four)** — By mentally interfacing with the Machine, the Garou can send communications through any technological device. By concentrating her will upon the individual(s) whom she wishes to communicate with, communication devices will project the information at the intended individuals: telephones shout, stereos blare and printers print out the message. If no communication device is present, other devices can be activated: alarms will go off, lights flash or plumbing turns on. This Gift is taught by Pattern Spiders.

System: The Garou spends a Gnosis point and rolls Manipulation + Science. The difficulty depends on the distance to the target: the next room is 4, the same building is 5, one block away is 6, one mile away is 7, one time-zone away (from Eastern to Central Standard Time) is 8, anywhere in the world (as long as there is a technological device present at the location) is 9. The clarity of the message depends on the number of successes. One success may only communicate one word, such as "run," while five successes may allow a reading of the Gettysburg Address.

• **Tractor Beam (Level Four)** — The Garou can transport non-dedicated objects with her to the Umbra when she steps sideways. She may not take living creatures, only objects. This Gift is taught by Weaver spirits.

System: The Garou spends one Willpower point for each object brought over to the Umbra. It must be something she can carry and it must weigh no more than her own body weight. However, two or more Garou with this Gift can team up and carry larger items into the Spirit World. Despite it's name, the user of this Gift does not emit a beam.

City Farmer Gift

• **Agro Culture (Level One)** — The Garou can cause plants to take root and grow in places where it is usually impossible for plants to grow. This Gift does not make plants grow supernaturally fast; it simply gives them a chance for life where none existed before. The plants must still be tended to and watered. However, the plants can use artificial substances such as concrete and plastic for soil. They dig their roots in and grow. Plants can even be coaxed to grow out of walls, as long as they are nurtured during the process. This Gift is taught by plant spirits.

System: The Garou must plant seeds in the area to be fertilized. If this is a concrete wall, he must place the seeds in cracks within the surface. He then rolls Charisma + Science (or Herbology) against a difficulty dependent on the toxicity of the area. An abandoned lot might be 5, a typical city building bathed in the smog of passing cars might be 6 or 7, while an oil spill site might be 9.

Central House Gift

Only Dons of the Central House may learn this Gift, for they are the caretakers of the tribal debt and favors pool.

• **Family Debt (Level Five)** — The Garou can call upon the past lives of other Garou to return a favor owed to the Glass Walker tribe, even if the debt was made centuries ago. Using this Gift will cause another Garou with the Past Life Background to become possessed by the ancestor whom the Glass Walker summons. The living Garou must be of the same tribe as the ancestor who is called (a Glass Walker cannot make a Bone Gnawer summon a Silver Fang ancestor). This Gift is taught by any long-lived spirit, such as a turtle or an elephant, and the Glass Walkers often have such spirits witness any business transactions they make with other Garou.

System: The Garou spends one Willpower point and rolls Gnosis against a difficulty of 10 minus the target's Past Life Background rating. If there is no Garou with Past Life present, this Gift will not work; it requires a Garou with deep connections to her ancestors to act as a conduit. If successful, the desired ancestor is summoned and possesses the target. This ancestor will then perform a duty to make up for a favor the Glass Walkers did for him in his lifetime.

The Central House keeps vast records of every debt owed the tribe. It usually requires a committee vote to summon one of their debtors and thus use up the favor owed. However, Dons who learn this Gift are considered to have the power to use it whenever desired, although Dons who abuse it may wind up being voted off the board, so to speak.

The player should be allowed to create the original debt condition and the debtor. "Grom Wyrmfoe of the Silver Fangs owes the Glass Walkers big, because they helped him root out vampires in Moscow in the late 1600s. Well, my character feels it's about time he repaid the favor by helping me kill that damn Gangrel." The Storyteller, however, is the ultimate arbiter of this Gift. It should be used to enhance a story, never to simply power game. If the Storyteller feels the player is asking a greater favor than what was originally given to the ancestor, he is free to have the ancestor deny the call.

Glass Walker characters should also realize that most Garou do not like being puppets for their Past Lives simply at the whim of some damn city Urrah. They will usually try to get revenge at some later date — to do so immediately is to insult the ancestor.

Rites

All Machines Day (Seasonal)

Level Three

See Chapter Two for more information on this rite.

House Bonding Rite (Renown)

Level Two

This ritual sets up a permanent bond between the members of a house. They will, from that point forward, have an innate sense of when their fellow local house members are in trouble. If one member dies, the house members will feel the loss. Garou may only be bonded to one house. This rite is only performed on those who have consistently proven their loyalty to the house; it is a great honor and the recipient receives 2 temporary points of Honor Renown.

Promethean Daze (Seasonal)

Level Two

See Chapter Two for more information on this popular rite.

Reconstitution of the Will (Mystical)

Level Two

This week-long rite usually takes place during seasonal rites, such as Promethean Daze. When completed, all Garou participating in the rite regain their full Willpower points.

Running With the Wyld (Mystical)

Level Two

Called upon at Raves, the rite starts off at a low tone and then escalates into a frenzied pitch. Galliards draw down the power of the Wyld and imbue those assembled with its might. All Garou participating in the rite regain their full Rage points.

Fetishes

Duct Tape of Bonding

Level 1, Gnosis 7

This limitless roll of duct tape can be used, upon activation, to bond together or seal virtually anything. This bonding lasts for one scene. The bonding can be forcibly broken by just about anyone, but barring such willful destruction, the bonding is solid.

To create a Duct Tape of Bonding fetish, a normal roll of duct tape is etched with specific glyphs to identify the user, her house and tribe and the name of the technological or Weaver spirit inhabiting it.

Flight Pack

Level 4, Gnosis 8

Various exhaust ports and snaking tubes sprout from the back of this assembly. When a Garou places this upon his head and shoulders, he can soar high through the sky and even reach Anchorheads when flying within the Penumbra.

The Flight Pack allows the wearer to fly for 10 minutes per success on the activation roll. However, if the Garou spends one Gnosis point while trying to activate the pack, he can then fly to a destination of choice, regardless of time, if the activation was successful. The pack has three flight settings: scenic (4 mph), touring (40 mph), and fast (400 mph).

To create a Flight Pack, one must bind a technology, wind or bird spirit into the fetish.

Information Absorber

Level 2, Gnosis 6

The Information Absorber drains computers and information storage devices of their information. The device is not selective and all information will be drained from the device. This works on books as well, leaving the pages blank. However, equipment protected by another spirit (such as a computer guarded by a Net Spider) will not be affected. This fetish often looks like a remote control unit or computer storage media decorated with trinkets to attract spirits.

Money Tracer

Level 1, Gnosis 6

Resembling a wallet or purse, this fetish can sense the presence of Wyrm taint on money. Once money is placed within the activated fetish, it will direct the Garou to the last Wyrm minion who used the money in service to the Wyrm.

To create a Money Tracer, one must bind a technology or money spirit into the fetish.

Psychotropic Cube

Level 2, Gnosis 7

Often overlooked as a child's toy, this multi-colored cube has been specially crafted to record the sound and a three-dimensional representation of activities in a five foot by five foot area for one hour. The Garou sets the device to activate at a certain time. Once the device has been retrieved, the Garou can replay the events in an empty area of similar size.

Streetlight Changer

Level 1, Gnosis 5

This fetish, usually a small box or tube with a single switch, allows its user to command streetlights to change; it affects all the lights at a given intersection.

To create a Streetlight Changer, one or more of the following spirit types must be bound: technology spirit, electricity elemental or light spirit.

Super Magnet

Level 2, Gnosis 7

A U-shaped device attached to a handle, this fetish produces an electromagnetic field that can erase magnetic media or magnetically lock metal parts together. Someone attempting to break apart this attraction must pit their Strength against the fetish's Gnosis rating in a resisted roll (difficulty 6). This will not work on technology that has been specifically created to be magnetically resistant.

Tie Tack of Persuasion

Level 2, Gnosis 7

Once activated, this tie tack adds two dice to the user's dice pool for any persuasive activities. The fetish's power last for one scene or transaction.

Web Drive Interface

Level 4, Gnosis 6

This fetish, usually a clunky box adorned with a spider and a web-like pattern, connects directly into the CyberRealm and links into the myriad of information sources held within it. A Garou can use it to raise a particular Knowledge by one dot per success on the activation roll (not to exceed five dots total). This extra know-how only lasts for one scene.

Talens

Implant Virus

Gnosis 7

When this talen, usually a plastic bug, is placed upon a piece of machinery and activated, the talen will dissolve and the spirit within it will infest the machinery.

These talens come in various types. Some seek out computer files containing certain key words or phrases and erase those files. Others wait until a certain situation occurs before taking control of the machine's output devices.

To create an Implant Virus, one must bind a Net Spider.

Slagger

Gnosis 6

Most slaggers have a small flame icon drawn on them. When activated, it consumes itself in an intense fire capable of burning through almost anything. The slagger melts virtually everything within a 2 x 3 foot area.

To create a slagger, one must bind a fire elemental.

Totems

Totem of Wisdom
The Monkey King

Background Cost: 7

The Monkey King hatched from a stone egg. Most noted for his wit and ability to evade capture, he has always stood as a symbol of liberty and intellectual advancement.

Traits: The Monkey King grants his children the Gift of Blur of the Milky Eye and Open Seal. Each of his children also has his difficulties for any evasion or escape rolls reduced by two. His children can purchase Abilities with experience points at one point cheaper than the usual cost (the minimum cost is still one).

Ban: Children of the Monkey King should never constrict another's freedom. This does not include Wyrm minions but does include: talens, fetishes, dedicated items, etc.. If spirits freely wish to give their service to a Garou, then the possession of such an item is permissible.

Monkey King children lose Honor renown if they abandon those whom they have befriended or who are within their care (Storyteller's discretion).

Totems of War
Clashing Boom-Boom

Background Cost: 8

Clashing Boom-Boom takes on the form of a stealth bomber and makes her presence known within all machinery of warfare. However, she tends to recklessly fall into the path of the Wyrm, because her limited vision focuses upon destruction alone. She has called upon the Glass Walkers to help rid herself of its corruption.

Traits: Her children each add one to their Firearms and Melee Skills. In addition, their maximum difficulty with weapons is 9, even if it would normally be 10. She requests that her children name all their weaponry and ornament them in some fashion. Garou using the Rite of Binding have -1 to their difficulties when binding spirits into weaponry. She insures that her children's weapons never malfunction or jam.

Ban: Clashing Boom-Boom expects that her powers will only be called upon by the righteous to dispense justice. Those who follow her and call upon her to do otherwise risk having the multitude of her forms turn against them.

O' Mighty Dolla'

Background Cost: 4

O' Mighty Dolla' manifests in any denomination of the little green pieces of paper known as U.S. dollars. Caerns dedicated to him lie within banks, mints and large stockpiles of currency.

Traits: O' Mighty Dolla' can reduce by three the difficulty of any roll that could be influenced by cash changing hands. His Children each gain Resources 2.

Ban: Outside of the United States, O' Mighty Dolla's powers should only be called upon in order to make a profit. His children are asked never to use any other type of currency. He has begun to request that his children abstain from the use of plastic money (credit cards) as well.

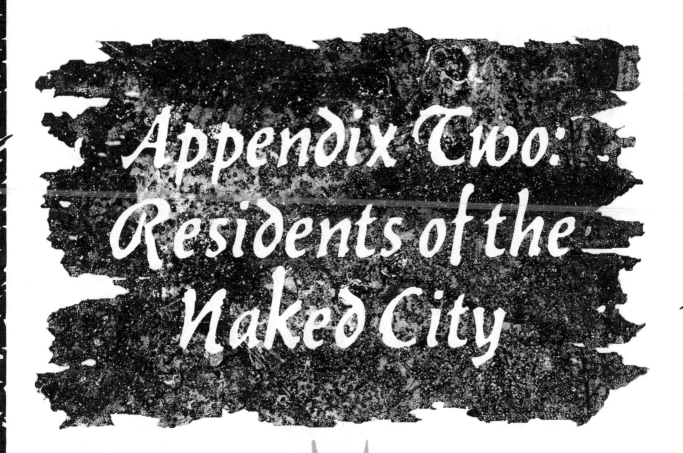

Appendix Two: Residents of the Naked City

But the fused awareness he had shared with Lala was not a dream. They had seen a future and the future was one of promise. It was real. It burned into Amuro's mind. He knew that although only he and Lala had seen it, it did not belong only to them. It was vast. It was universal.

— Yoshiyuki Tomino, *Mobile Suit Gundam, Volume I: Awakening*

Surrounded by the corruption of the Wyrm, we stare down its black throat, past its venomous fangs and laugh at the heinous stench of its breath. Technology is on our side. With the pull of a pin and the flip of a wrist, the beast's stomach explodes with the shock of a concussion grenade. Of course, we could have called upon the wrecking ball above its head to fall....

The City is the battleground. The Machine is our weapon. What are you waiting for? Go get 'em!

Cyberphreak

Quote: *Hey…You know what this is? It's Black Dog Game's bank account PIN and a dupe of their ATM mag strip on a pseudo card. Just remember to spray paint over the camera before you put the card in.*

Prelude: In high school, you jammed as many science and computer classes as possible into your schedule. You managed to talk teachers into letting you stay after school to work with what little technology the school system had to offer.

You started hacking on the net and found out that there was a lot of information and power to be had. You couldn't believe how careless some people were with their programming and how corrupt some people could be.

The Change came on you suddenly, but luckily, members of your tribe tracked you down before you managed to cause too much destruction in suburbia. After all the trouble that went down, it only made sense to leave home with them and go to the big city. Maybe after a couple of years you can figure out a story to tell your dad about the hole in the side of the house and the destruction of his sports car. On second thought, that might not be long enough to let his hot temper cool down about the whole thing.

Concept: You're the little brainy guy that didn't get enough sunlight. You still aren't good at sports, but that doesn't make any difference when you can turn into Crinos form now. You can make a linebacker piss in his pants. Every new technological trick you learn makes you feel great to be alive. More than anything, you love using your knowledge to jam a big wrench down into the cogs of the tyrannical, Wyrm-fetid corporations that abuse technology and destroy nature.

Roleplaying Hints: You're sneaky and proud of it. Don't tip your hand and try to blend in with the normals. Take notes and steal anything that might be useful. Work for a temp service and get jobs at Wyrm-tainted corporations so you can leave viruses in their computer systems and misfile important documents. Bug people's telephones and play the conversations back to just the right people.

Equipment: Home-base computer with mega memory, programs, modem, scanner, video digitizer, printer and universal connections in and out; virus-protection programs; laptop computer for field work, black box (daemon) dialers, electronics tool kit, deadly-virus-on-a-disk in various formats, blank diskettes, power-strip with surge protector, compact car with hatchback.

B. LeBlanc '95

GLASS WALKERS ™

Name: _____
Player: _____
Chronicle: _____

Breed: Homid
Auspice: Ragabash
Camp: Random Interrupts

Pack Name: _____
Pack Totem: _____
Concept: Cyberphreak

Attributes

Physical
Strength _____ ●○○○○
Dexterity _____ ●●○○○
Stamina _____ ●●●○○

Social
Charisma _____ ●●○○○
Manipulation _____ ●●●●○
Appearance _____ ●●○○○

Mental
Perception _____ ●●○○○
Intelligence _____ ●●●●●○
Wits _____ ●●●●○

Abilities

Talents
Alertness _____ ○○○○○
Athletics _____ ○○○○○
Brawl _____ ○○○○○
Dodge _____ ○○○○○
Empathy _____ ○○○○○
Expression _____ ○○○○○
Intimidation _____ ○○○○○
Primal-Urge _____ ○○○○○
Streetwise _____ ●●○○○
Subterfuge _____ ●●●○○

Skills
Animal Ken _____ ○○○○○
Drive _____ ●●○○○
Etiquette _____ ○○○○○
Firearms _____ ●○○○○
Leadership _____ ○○○○○
Melee _____ ○○○○○
Performance _____ ●○○○○
Repair _____ ●●●●○
Stealth _____ ●○○○○
Survival _____ ●○○○○

Knowledges
Computer _____ ●●●●●
Enigmas _____ ●●○○○
Investigation _____ ○○○○○
Law _____ ●○○○○
Linguistics _____ ●●○○○
Medicine _____ ○○○○○
Occult _____ ○○○○○
Politics _____ ●○○○○
Rituals _____ ○○○○○
Science _____ ●●●○○

Advantages

Backgrounds
Contacts _____ ●○○○○
Fetish _____ ●○○○○
Kinfolk _____ ●○○○○
Resources _____ ●●○○○
Totem _____ ●○○○○

Gifts
Persuasion _____
Open Seal _____
Control Simple Machines _____
_____
_____

Gifts
_____
_____
_____
_____
_____

Renown

Glory
○○○○○○○○○○
□□□□□□□□□□

Honor
○○○○○○○○○○
□□□□□□□□□□

Wisdom
●●●○○○○○○○
□□□□□□□□□□

Rank
[ ]

Rage
● ○ ○ ○ ○ ○ ○ ○ ○ ○
□ □ □ □ □ □ □ □ □ □

Gnosis
● ● ● ● ● ○ ○ ○ ○ ○
□ □ □ □ □ □ □ □ □ □

Willpower
● ● ● ● ● ○ ○ ○ ○ ○
□ □ □ □ □ □ □ □ □ □

Health
Bruised		□
Hurt	-1	□
Injured	-1	□
Wounded	-2	□
Mauled	-2	□
Crippled	-5	□
Incapacitated		□

Weakness
WEAVER AFFINITY:
CANNOT REGAIN GNOSIS
IN WILDERNESS

Urban Primitive

Quote: *Spirits of Wires, reach for out me in the night. Let me see through your endless spinning paths and web-like structure. You are within me as I am within you. I am the veins of the city; you are the arteries within me. Awaken and feel our kinship!*

Prelude: Born of two Garou, you were deformed at birth, and trapped in Crinos form until your First Change. Obviously, you could not be taken before the public eye.

Living at the caern wasn't so bad. You were harassed by some, but others always came to your aid and defended you when necessary. You learned more about spirits and the Umbra than any of the others. They were enamored with the physical beauty of technology and had to struggle to look past the glossy covering and meshed wiring within. The insight came easy to you.

Now that you can shapeshift and blend in with human society, you have found how corrupt and pure the City can be. You understand your purpose; you were sent to guide your people's spiritual path. You are the techno-shaman and protector of tomorrow!

Concept: You've learned to connect with the spirituality of the Machine. You know of its Wyrm-tainted side — a huge monstrosity with clashing iron jaws, blaring sirens and spotlight eyes — and of its clean, shining side as well.

You learned long ago that appearances are important to spirits and you dress accordingly to attract their attention. You have become accustomed to other members of your house complaining about your clothing selection and you always snap back with witty remarks or insults. You don't work at containing the Wyld within you as other Glass Walkers do. You work to free that energy from yourself and try to summon more. You have tried to teach yourself how to ride on the very peak of the Wyld without being swept under by its fury.

Roleplaying Hints: Take time to acquaint yourself to new environments. Look for spirit activity and check for possible problems. Take time to free abused spirits. It is your position to guide others to understand the spirituality of the City and the Machine, for much of this has become lost. Garou are spiritual creatures and you have been born a spiritual leader among the Garou. Live up to your birthright.

Metis Disfigurement: Hairless

Equipment: Skin piercings, tattoos, industrial jewelry, torn jeans, used clothing, boots, CD boom box, tool kit, spray paint, large magic markers, duct tape, weird underground magazines, motorcycle.

GLASS WALKERS ™

Name: ⬚⬚⬚   **Breed:** Metis   **Pack Name:**
Player: **Auspice:** Theurge   **Pack Totem:**
Chronicle: **Camp:** Urban Primitive   **Concept:** Techno-Mystic

Attributes

Physical
Strength ●●○○○
Dexterity ●●○○○
Stamina ●●○○○

Social
Charisma ●●○○○
Manipulation ●●●●○
Appearance ●●○○○

Mental
Perception ●●●●○
Intelligence ●●○○○
Wits ●●●●○

Abilities

Talents
Alertness ●●○○○
Athletics ○○○○○
Brawl ●●○○○
Dodge ○○○○○
Empathy ●●○○○
Expression ○○○○○
Intimidation ●●○○○
Primal-Urge ●●●○○
Streetwise ○○○○○
Subterfuge ●●○○○

Skills
Animal Ken ○○○○○
Drive ●○○○○
Etiquette ○○○○○
Firearms ●○○○○
Leadership ○○○○○
Melee ○○○○○
Performance ●○○○○
Repair ●○○○○
Stealth ●○○○○
Survival ○○○○○

Knowledges
Computer ○○○○○
Enigmas ●○○○○
Investigation ○○○○○
Law ●○○○○
Linguistics ○○○○○
Medicine ●●○○○
Occult ●●●○○
Politics ○○○○○
Rituals ●●○○○
Science ●○○○○

Advantages

Backgrounds
Fetish ●○○○○
Kinfolk ●●○○○
Rites ●●●●●●○
Totem ●●●○○
___ ○○○○○

Gifts
Sense Wyrm
Mother's Touch
Control Simple Machines
___
___
___

Gifts
___
___
___
___
___
___

Renown

Glory
○○○○○○○○○○
☐☐☐☐☐☐☐☐☐☐

Honor
○○○○○○○○○○
☐☐☐☐☐☐☐☐☐☐

Wisdom
●●●○○○○○○○
☐☐☐☐☐☐☐☐☐☐

Rank
☐

Rage
●●○○○○○○○○
☐☐☐☐☐☐☐☐☐☐

Gnosis
●●●○○○○○○○
☐☐☐☐☐☐☐☐☐☐

Willpower
●●●●○○○○○○
☐☐☐☐☐☐☐☐☐☐

Health
Bruised		☐
Hurt	-1	☐
Injured	-1	☐
Wounded	-2	☐
Mauled	-2	☐
Crippled	-5	☐
Incapacitated		☐

Weakness
WEAVER AFFINITY:
CANNOT REGAIN GNOSIS
IN WILDERNESS

Capitalist

Quote: *It does seem to be a good deal. The profit margin would be quite high. But I think it's best we check to see how much the Wyrm is involved in this. Its going way too smoothly.*

Prelude: You loved playing Corporate Barons (Black Dog Game Factory, 1957) so much when you where you a kid that you decided you wanted to be a CEO when you grew up. Your parents didn't have a lot of money, but that wasn't going to hold you back. You had the knowledge and looks — and, more importantly, a driving desire to possess a huge bank account.

You went through high school and college with flying colors. You majored in business and business law. Your quest for financial freedom was ensured. Your first business venture was an overnight success. You didn't count on someone trying to forcefully buy you out. They didn't expect for you to turn into an eight foot tall killing machine either.

Concept: You like money and more money. You like the things that you own, but you like the raw power of money more than anything. You like to dress sharp as well as influence other people. You're going to make sure that businesses are run the right way and not as corrupt, worker-raping machines. As a businessperson, you constantly search for deals. Don't ever forget the profit margin even in the midst of battle.

Roleplaying Hints: You dress to show you have money. Hold yourself with an air of superiority, because you can get away with it. Be polite to people, especially those people who are good workers. Show disgust for people who try to get one over on you, your business or the little people.

Always remember to help protect the balance: the balance of trade, the balance of power, the balance of knowledge, etc.. By watching these balances you know how to detect the tipping of commerce's scales. Betting on economic unbalances always produces the greatest yield.

Equipment: Mega Card, black suit, power tie, laptop computer with printer and fax/modem, company car, expense account, cellular phone, penthouse apartment.

GLASS WALKERS™

Name: **Breed:** Homid   **Pack Name:**
Player: **Auspice:** Philodox   **Pack Totem:**
Chronicle: **Camp:** Corporate Wolves   **Concept:** Capitalist

Attributes

Physical
Strength_____ ●●○○○
Dexterity_____ ●●○○○
Stamina_____ ●●○○○

Social
Charisma_____ ●●●○○
Manipulation_____ ●●●●○
Appearance_____ ●●●○○

Mental
Perception_____ ●●○○○
Intelligence_____ ●●●○○
Wits_____ ●●●○○

Abilities

Talents
Alertness_____ ○○○○○
Athletics_____ ○○○○○
Brawl_____ ○○○○○
Dodge_____ ○○○○○
Empathy_____ ○○○○○
Expression_____ ○○○○○
Intimidation_____ ●●○○○
Primal-Urge_____ ○○○○○
Streetwise_____ ○○○○○
Subterfuge_____ ●●●○○

Skills
Animal Ken_____ ○○○○○
Drive_____ ●●○○○
Etiquette_____ ●●○○○
Firearms_____ ●●○○○
Leadership_____ ●●●●○
Melee_____ ○○○○○
Performance_____ ●●●○○
Repair_____ ●○○○○
Stealth_____ ○○○○○
Survival_____ ○○○○○

Knowledges
Computer_____ ●●○○○
Enigmas_____ ○○○○○
Investigation_____ ●●○○○
Law_____ ●●○○○
Linguistics_____ ○○○○○
Medicine_____ ○○○○○
Occult_____ ○○○○○
Politics_____ ●●○○○
Rituals_____ ○○○○○
Science_____ ●○○○○

Advantages

Backgrounds
Allies_____ ●○○○○
Contacts_____ ●●○○○
Kinfolk_____ ●●○○○
Resources_____ ●●●●●
Totem_____ ●●○○○

Gifts
Persuasion
Scent of the True Form
Control Simple Machines
_____
_____
_____

Gifts
_____
_____
_____
_____
_____
_____

Renown

Glory
○○○○○○○○○○
□□□□□□□□□□

Honor
●●●○○○○○○○
□□□□□□□□□□

Wisdom
○○○○○○○○○○
□□□□□□□□□□

Rank
[ ]

Rage
●●●○○○○○○○
□□□□□□□□□□

Gnosis
●●●○○○○○○○
□□□□□□□□□□

Willpower
●●●●●○○○○○
□□□□□□□□□□

Health
Bruised		□
Hurt	-1	□
Injured	-1	□
Wounded	-2	□
Mauled	-2	□
Crippled	-5	□
Incapacitated		□

Weakness
WEAVER AFFINITY:
CANNOT REGAIN GNOSIS
IN WILDERNESS

Heavy Metal Guitarist

Quote: *I hear an echo of her cry through the night / It is our mother — screaming out in pain / I hear your call, my Mother Gai-yah! / Your tears, they fall from the sky with the rain / I know my place / I know it's time / I'll do my best / To save you, Mother Gai-yah!*

Prelude: You've loved music since you can remember. Finally, your parents let you own an electric guitar. You and your friends practiced in the garage for hours on end. You could feel the music in your soul. You learned to use your music to release your tensions and to relieve the tensions of others as well. Somewhere along the way, you had your First Change while playing. You wrecked all the band's equipment. No one is exactly sure what happened, but it was one hell of a show and people are still talking about it. Now you use your music to teach people about the City and the Machine. You try to let them know about the corruption that surrounds them and what they can do to fight against it.

Concept: You try to be quiet. Inside you is a raging force that wants to be constantly released. You try to only allow the "beast" out when you are playing, so it doesn't hurt anyone. Your statements are often very rebellious, but they are meant to wake people up, not to hurt them. Try to remember that — about a day or two later. If the offended party is still around, apologize. If not, then just blow it off. Stick to your guns and don't sell out.

Roleplaying Hints: It is important to you to have a cool look. After all, you are a rocker dude. Practice makes perfect and playing the guitar helps you link into the beat of the City. Sitting around playing your guitar, even when it is unplugged, is enough to bring you satisfaction.

Equipment: Guitar, portable, battery backed-up amplifier, sunglasses, leather jacket, jack boots, boot knife, 9mm pistol, tattoos, condoms, duct tape, fingerless gloves, big hair, ratty old van.

B. LeBlanc '95

lkers

GLASS WALKERS™

Name: **Breed:** Homid   **Pack Name:**
Player: **Auspice:** Galliard   **Pack Totem:**
Chronicle: **Camp:**   **Concept:** Metalhead

Attributes

Physical
Strength ●●○○○
Dexterity ●●●○○
Stamina ●●●○○

Social
Charisma ●●●●○
Manipulation ●●●●○
Appearance ●●●○○

Mental
Perception ●●○○○
Intelligence ●●○○○
Wits ●●○○○

Abilities

Talents
Alertness ○○○○○
Athletics ○○○○○
Brawl ●●○○○
Dodge ○○○○○
Empathy ○○○○○
Expression ●●●●○
Intimidation ●●○○○
Primal-Urge ●●○○○
Streetwise ●●○○○
Subterfuge ●●○○○

Skills
Animal Ken ○○○○○
Drive ●○○○○
Etiquette ○○○○○
Firearms ●●○○○
Leadership ●○○○○
Melee ●○○○○
Performance ●●●●○
Repair ●○○○○
Stealth ○○○○○
Survival ○○○○○

Knowledges
Computer ●○○○○
Enigmas ●○○○○
Investigation ○○○○○
Law ○○○○○
Linguistics ○○○○○
Medicine ○○○○○
Occult ●○○○○
Politics ○○○○○
Rituals ●●○○○
Science ○○○○○

Advantages

Backgrounds
Contacts ●○○○○
Kinfolk ●●○○○
Resources ●●●○○
Rites ●●●●○
  ○○○○○

Gifts
Persuasion
Call of the Wyld
Control Simple Machines

Gifts

Renown

Glory
●●○○○○○○○○
☐☐☐☐☐☐☐☐☐☐

Honor
○○○○○○○○○○
☐☐☐☐☐☐☐☐☐☐

Wisdom
●○○○○○○○○○
☐☐☐☐☐☐☐☐☐☐

Rank
[ ]

Rage
●●●●○○○○○○
☐☐☐☐☐☐☐☐☐☐

Gnosis
●●●○○○○○○○
☐☐☐☐☐☐☐☐☐☐

Willpower
●●●●●○○○○○
☐☐☐☐☐☐☐☐☐☐

Health
Bruised		☐
Hurt	-1	☐
Injured	-1	☐
Wounded	-2	☐
Mauled	-2	☐
Crippled	-5	☐
Incapacitated		☐

Weakness
WEAVER AFFINITY:
CANNOT REGAIN GNOSIS
IN WILDERNESS

Hit Man

Quote: *Tell me who this guy is you want me to kill. Don't worry; the pay you're offering me is good enough. I'm just discriminating on the kinds of jobs I take. I'm sure you've heard that my kind is a superstitious lot.*

Prelude: You loved to sneak around the neighborhood when you were a kid. You liked playing army and hide-and-go-seek. You made complex systems of hidden bridges across the apartment building rooftops. Your parents wanted you to stay inside and study more, but school work was boring to you.

Later, as the Change came, you learned to indulge in the hunt. Once the feeling of tracking prey was in your blood, you wanted to do it more and more. You started searching out evil and tearing it to shreds. Eventually you learned that you could not only use your sneaking and tracking abilities to assassinate Wyrm-minions, but you also make good money doing it, thanks to Mario and his brothers. They brought you into a whole different world. One you never expected. Just around the corner lurks a world of gambling, money laundering and protection rackets.

You hire yourself out to kill people. You try your best to make sure that your target's are Wyrm-fetid. On the other hand, you have taken some jobs because it seemed like the right thing to do.

Concept: You're smooth and levelheaded… yeah, right. You try to do your best to be calm, but it always breaks down into a frenzy of gunfire and dodging bullets. You dress to tone down the look of your killer instincts and to blend in with the surroundings around your "marks." When you aren't after someone, take time to clean your weapons and make sure to plan things out for when the time strikes. You grew up eating spaghetti with "the boys" in Uncle Luigi's restaurant. Now these are real friends. These are the type of friends you can trust to watch your back.

Roleplaying Hints: Laugh everything off. Life's a joke. You know you're going to die sooner or later — probably sooner. Besides, you'll reincarnate anyway, right? Enjoy your life and your money when you aren't on assignment. Frequent night clubs and talk to the "local boys." After all, they're all friends of yours.

Equipment: Sniper rifle with an infrared scope and laser sight, several disposable handguns, extra clips for weapons, silencers and flash-suppresser, combat knife, black leather gloves, sunglasses, disguise kit, soft-soled shoes, well-tailored clothing allowing free movement and concealment of weapons, fake ID, sports car.

GLASS WALKERS ™

Name: **Breed:** Homid   **Pack Name:**
Player: **Auspice:** Ahroun   **Pack Totem:**
Chronicle: **Camp:** Wise Guys   **Concept:** Hit Man

Attributes

Physical
Strength ●●○○○
Dexterity ●●●●●
Stamina ●●●○○

Social
Charisma ●●○○○
Manipulation ●●●●○
Appearance ●●○○○

Mental
Perception ●●○○○
Intelligence ●●○○○
Wits ●●○○○

Abilities

Talents
Alertness ●●○○○
Athletics ●●○○○
Brawl ●●○○○
Dodge ●●○○○
Empathy ○○○○○
Expression ○○○○○
Intimidation ●●○○○
Primal-Urge ○○○○○
Streetwise ●●○○○
Subterfuge ●●○○○

Skills
Animal Ken ○○○○○
Drive ●○○○○
Etiquette ○○○○○
Firearms ●●●●○
Leadership ○○○○○
Melee ●○○○○
Performance ○○○○○
Repair ●○○○○
Stealth ●●○○○
Survival ●○○○○

Knowledges
Computer ○○○○○
Enigmas ○○○○○
Investigation ●○○○○
Law ○○○○○
Linguistics ○○○○○
Medicine ●●○○○
Occult ●○○○○
Politics ○○○○○
Rituals ●○○○○
Science ○○○○○

Advantages

Backgrounds
Allies ●●○○○
Contacts ●○○○○
Kinfolk ●●●○○
Resources ●●○○○
Rites ●○○○○

Gifts
Smell of Man
The Falling Touch
Control Simple Machines
_____
_____
_____

Gifts
_____
_____
_____
_____
_____
_____

Renown

Glory
●●○○○○○○○○
☐☐☐☐☐☐☐☐☐☐

Honor
●○○○○○○○○○
☐☐☐☐☐☐☐☐☐☐

Wisdom
○○○○○○○○○○
☐☐☐☐☐☐☐☐☐☐

Rank
[ ]

Rage
●●●●●●○○○○
☐☐☐☐☐☐☐☐☐☐

Gnosis
●●○○○○○○○○
☐☐☐☐☐☐☐☐☐☐

Willpower
●●●●●●○○○○
☐☐☐☐☐☐☐☐☐☐

Health
Bruised		☐
Hurt	-1	☐
Injured	-1	☐
Wounded	-2	☐
Mauled	-2	☐
Crippled	-5	☐
Incapacitated		☐

Weakness
WEAVER AFFINITY:
CANNOT REGAIN GNOSIS
IN WILDERNESS

Appendix Three: If We Built Statues...

What remains unpredictable... are the sudden and sporadic bursts of large amounts of excess heat. These bursts were what prompted Pons and Fleischmann to make their original claims [about cold fusion] and they have since been seen in other experiments. The bursts in the SRI experiments may run for hours and produce excess heat equaling as much as 300 percent of the input power.

— Jerry E. Bishop, "Cold Fusion," *Popular Science*

Tenderfoot

Long ago in our tribal past, two Garou birthed a metis cub with feet so soft that he could barely walk. They named him Tenderfoot. Tenderfoot had to rely upon the hunting skills of others in order to eat. Young Garou despised him and taunted him relentlessly. Tenderfoot made up for his physical deformity with mental aptitude. He looked into the spirit world and studied humans constantly.

One day, he realized how to solve his problems. Humans had been wearing clothing for sometime and Glass Walkers had begun to do likewise. Taking strips of hide, Tenderfoot covered the bottom of his feet and bound the covering together with sinews. At first, his creations were awkward. The other Garou harangued him relentlessly. However, the humans soon caught onto the idea and began developing it themselves. They, in turn, taught Tenderfoot how to improve upon the initial design. Soon, it was the other Garou who looked stupid as Tenderfoot rose in respect among the humans for his ingenuity in creating the first pair of shoes.

Han "Skin O' Steel" Jankins

Hard work forges the body and molds the soul. The heat of an iron foundry and glowing molten iron team with spirits. Many humans have crafted metal and forged it into forms, but none so well or as spiritual as Skin O' Steel. A great Theurge, though many wanted to call him Ahroun for his size, Skin O' Steel worked in a German iron foundry for most of his life. Children and all manner of Gaia's animals loved his calm and gentle nature. Known best for his construction of techno-fetishes, Skin O' Steel understood the true nature of his job. Gazing into the Penumbra, he called upon spirits to aid his labors and to "calcify" his completed creations.

Unfortunately, Skin O' Steel lived in the dark days of World War II. Forced to work in a Nazi arms factory, he called upon his spirit allies to undermine the Axis war machine. The Nazis had no idea that many of the spirits within in the Penumbral shadow of the iron foundry had "grown up" with

Skin O' Steel. He crafted gasoline tanks that leaked into the Penumbra and increased the density of steel in order to weigh down transportation vehicles. His use of spirits lead the Get of Fenris within the Military Inspector's branch to realize that he was a powerful Glass Walker. Especially excited about the increased density of the steel that he had managed to construct, they began to threaten him. Then they threatened his family and Kinfolk. Lastly, they began the killings. Skin O' Steel had no choice and gave in. The Get of Fenris wanted him to produce machines of war, and so he called upon his spirit's allies' wisdom to formulate a plan.

Early in the cold morning of February 23, 1943, a pack of Get of Fenris dressed in finest SS blacks and a group of top-ranking German scientists assembled to review Skin O' Steel's work. The metals that he had molded and hammered were like nothing they had seen before. As their eyes gleamed bright with the glow of the Urge Wyrm, Skin O' Steel called upon Clashing Boom-Boom. Clashing Boom-Boom pulled an Allied squadron out of its designated flight path and released its cargo of bombs into the iron foundry.

That day, Germany lost many of its top munitions specialists and weapons designers. The Get lost a pack of their hand-picked best. But we, the Glass Walkers, lost the most of all, for we lost a great Theurge.

Xiao Xian, "Machine Kin"

As a child, Xiao Xian wanted to communicate with machines and she treated her favorites like pets. As she grew older, she began to worry about her feelings until her First Change.

Her house realized that she was a powerful Theurge and taught her to communicate with the spirits within machinery. Xiao Xian was greatly disheartened at their limited communication ability. After several years of adjusting to Garou society, she returned to human society and found a job in at Nippon International Robotics (NIR). By talking to the spirits within machinery, she could easily determine how to fix them and rapidly rose through the ranks of skilled repair technicians.

Xiao Xian secretly hoped to expand the intelligence of technological spirits in order to increase the computational ability of physical machinery. Xiao Xian found technological spirits hard to train because a majority of them are Gafflings with a specific purpose and virtually no free will. When working with human scientists, she researched the Glass Walker theories that humanity's link to the Weaver is similar to the way that most Garou link to the Wyld and that humanity has an innate ability to manipulate the structure of the Weaver's web.

Though the major computer companies try to overshadow her work, Xiao Xian has managed to create a computer system with an interactive environment which helps unlock the creativity of its users. She feels that humans innately communicate with machinery on a subconscious level. Even if these computers don't sell as personal computers, the company still stands to gain through their use in industrial robotics and video manipulation.

The CEO of NIR, Johnny Yin, allows Xiao Xian an unlimited budget for research and development. He has had pressure from Ardus Enterprises to stop the manufacturing of the personal computer line. He believes that Xiao Xian's work will lead the world of computing away from the antiquated Ardus hardware that requires constant repairs by Ardus trained employees. Mr. Yin's belief in the system stems from the fact that Tellus Enterprises, one of the world's leading video game producers, is very interested in buying the rights to Xiao Xian's hardware design for use as the "brains" of their updated 128 megabyte video game system.

Frederick "Big Bills" Paul Leo the Fifth

Frederick Paul Leo wasn't overly surprised at the revelation of his Garou nature. He'd felt the call of the planet throughout his life and his anger at many a construction site. His loud mouth about the problems he saw had caused him to get a tanning more than once.

Frederick Paul Leo took on his Garou name unwillingly, yet he has so much money divided within so many different corporations and banks around the world that it would take the Apocalypse to ruin his lifestyle.

Big Bills works hard to focus himself to the primary goal of the Garou—to protect Gaia. He uses his money to do just that. He supplies transportation, food and lodging for less fortunate Garou. He owns a sizable chunk of South American rain forests. He works in political circles to help stiffen the policies of the EPA. On a corporate level, he attempts to buy out corrupt organizations and restructure them into environmentally and socially friendly corporations.

Big Bills was forced into hiding in 1987 when Black Spiral Dancer packs simultaneously attacked several of his mansions. Ventrue vampires, claiming rightful ownership, covertly bought out a large branch of his corporate holdings. Bombs destroyed several of his private limos and sports cars. Rumors pointed to possible assassination attempts by an undercover branch of the United States government, though sources were unable to divulge the reasoning behind such planning. He's still around, though, planning his comeback.

Lost Fringe 4

Sometimes something clicks within a person's mind. They see too much or just inherently feel something deep within themselves that turns them into a rebel once and for all.

When the unidentified government agents attacked his parent's house during his fourth birthday party, Lost Fringe 4's life was turned inside out. No one knows his real name; if he had one, he destroyed it along with every other trace of his human origin. The Fractal Existence, a pack of Random Interrupts, could tell that he was at least Kinfolk and they took him in. Lost Fringe 4 knew about the Wyrm before he was seven and coded his first "practical joke" virus by the time he

was twelve. During a mission to destroy strip mining equipment, the Fractal Existence were ambushed by fomori and Banes. Lost Fringe 4 went berserk, turned into Crinos, and demolished most of the mining site by himself. It wasn't until later that the Garou elders found the link between the small mining company and its parent company Harold & Harold Mining, Inc. The Random Interrupt elders took Lost Fringe 4 into their inner circle and taught him the secrets of the Garou. For the first time in his memory, he felt at peace. Deciding that he'd best serve Gaia by traveling, he scouted out new recruits and gained the aid of many great allies. He managed to find enough ronin Garou to form his own pack by '94.

Computer failures, mechanical malfunction and general mayhem plague the cities that his pack enters. Their tactics involve quick scouting missions, telephone searches, watching local television and infiltrating environmental groups. Once the pack determines their targets, they strike quickly and leave to assault the Wyrm minions of yet another city.

Spooky Tooth

Members of this pack make little effort to hide their Garou natures. Their hit albums of fall 1991 and summer of 1993 have brought them great cult status and a considerable amount of money. Spooky Tooth is known for their hard, metal edge and lyrical rants on politics and the decline of family morals. They warn the world of the impending fate of Gaia in their loud, aggressive style.

The band utilizes the standard, four piece rock and roll arrangement. Luke Pine jams on lead guitar. Roger Wolfe plays rhythm guitar and sings lead vocals. Dennis Kidd runs the band from behind his drum kit. Kay Eight kicked out the bass line until he was killed in a duel with another Garou in Hong Kong a couple of years ago. Wendy Summer has since filled in on bass; she has a different style than Kay Eight did, but she's good in her own right. She's not even a Glass Walker. She's of the Children of Gaia.

Spooky Tooth has been known to turn into Crinos on stage (you may have heard of their Halloween show in '92) and totally destroy their instruments (almost every show at exactly 11:23 P.M.). Once the human audience has been separated from the Garou, Spooky Tooth requests that the Garou go with them to an isolated location for an impromptu Rave. Raging in the moonlight as they play, Spooky Tooth is fully able to perform concerts in Crinos form.

A small house has been formed by their Garou groupies. This house often allies with local houses to raid the known Wyrm holdings. The band itself rarely gets involved due to their position in the media and their importance to the Glass Walkers on a tribal level.

Glass Walkers™

Name:	Breed:	Pack Name:
Player:	Auspice:	Pack Totem:
Chronicle:	Camp:	Concept:

Attributes

Physical
Strength_____ ●0000
Dexterity_____ ●0000
Stamina_____ ●0000

Social
Charisma_____ ●0000
Manipulation_____ ●0000
Appearance_____ ●0000

Mental
Perception_____ ●0000
Intelligence_____ ●0000
Wits_____ ●0000

Abilities

Talents
Alertness_____ 00000
Athletics_____ 00000
Brawl_____ 00000
Dodge_____ 00000
Empathy_____ 00000
Expression_____ 00000
Intimidation_____ 00000
Primal-Urge_____ 00000
Streetwise_____ 00000
Subterfuge_____ 00000

Skills
Animal Ken_____ 00000
Drive_____ 00000
Etiquette_____ 00000
Firearms_____ 00000
Leadership_____ 00000
Melee_____ 00000
Performance_____ 00000
Repair_____ 00000
Stealth_____ 00000
Survival_____ 00000

Knowledges
Computer_____ 00000
Enigmas_____ 00000
Investigation_____ 00000
Law_____ 00000
Linguistics_____ 00000
Medicine_____ 00000
Occult_____ 00000
Politics_____ 00000
Rituals_____ 00000
Science_____ 00000

Advantages

Backgrounds
_____ 00000
_____ 00000
_____ 00000
_____ 00000
_____ 00000

Gifts
_____
_____
_____
_____
_____

Gifts
_____
_____
_____
_____
_____

Renown

Glory
0 0 0 0 0 0 0 0 0 0
□ □ □ □ □ □ □ □ □ □

Honor
0 0 0 0 0 0 0 0 0 0
□ □ □ □ □ □ □ □ □ □

Wisdom
0 0 0 0 0 0 0 0 0 0
□ □ □ □ □ □ □ □ □ □

Rank
[ ]

Rage
0 0 0 0 0 0 0 0 0 0
□ □ □ □ □ □ □ □ □ □

Gnosis
0 0 0 0 0 0 0 0 0 0
□ □ □ □ □ □ □ □ □ □

Willpower
0 0 0 0 0 0 0 0 0 0
□ □ □ □ □ □ □ □ □ □

Health

Bruised		□
Hurt	-1	□
Injured	-1	□
Wounded	-2	□
Mauled	-2	□
Crippled	-5	□
Incapacitated		□

Weakness
WEAVER AFFINITY:
CANNOT REGAIN GNOSIS
IN WILDERNESS

Glass Walkers™

Homid

No Change

Difficulty: 6

Glabro

Strength (+2)_____
Stamina (+2)_____
Appearance (-1)____
Manipulation (-1)__

Difficulty: 7

Crinos

Strength (+4)_____
Dexterity (+1)_____
Stamina (+3)_____
Appearance 0
Manipulation (-3)____

Difficulty: 6

INCITE DELIRIUM
IN HUMANS

Hispo

Strength (+3)_____
Dexterity (+2)_____
Stamina (+3)_____
Manipulation (-3)____

Difficulty: 7

Lupus

Strength (+1)_____
Dexterity (+2)_____
Stamina (+2)_____
Manipulation (-3)____

Difficulty: 6

Other Traits

_____ OOOOO
_____ OOOOO
_____ OOOOO
_____ OOOOO
_____ OOOOO
_____ OOOOO
_____ OOOOO
_____ OOOOO
_____ OOOOO
_____ OOOOO
_____ OOOOO
_____ OOOOO
_____ OOOOO
_____ OOOOO
_____ OOOOO
_____ OOOOO
_____ OOOOO
_____ OOOOO
_____ OOOOO

Fetishes

Item: _____ ☐Dedicated Level ____ Gnosis ____
Power_____

Item: _____ ☐Dedicated Level ____ Gnosis ____
Power_____

Item: _____ ☐Dedicated Level ____ Gnosis ____
Power_____

Item: _____ ☐Dedicated Level ____ Gnosis ____
Power_____

Rites

_____
_____
_____
_____
_____
_____
_____
_____
_____

Combat

Maneuver/Weapon	Roll	Difficulty	Damage	Range	Rate	Clip

Brawling Chart

Maneuver	Roll	Diff	Damage
Bite	Dex + Brawl	5	Strength + 1†
Body Slam	Dex + Brawl	7	Special
Claw	Dex + Brawl	6	Strength + 2†
Grapple	Dex + Brawl	6	Strength
Kick	Dex + Brawl	7	Strength + 1
Punch	Dex + Brawl	6	Strength

† These maneuvers do aggravated damage.

Armor: _____

GLASS WALKERS

Nature: _____   Demeanor: _____

Merits & Flaws

Merit	Type	Cost	Flaw	Type	Bonus
_____	_____	_____	_____	_____	_____
_____	_____	_____	_____	_____	_____
_____	_____	_____	_____	_____	_____
_____	_____	_____	_____	_____	_____
_____	_____	_____	_____	_____	_____

Expanded Background

Allies
_____
_____
_____
_____
_____
_____
_____
_____
_____

Resources
_____
_____
_____
_____
_____
_____
_____
_____
_____

Contacts
_____
_____
_____
_____

Kinfolk
_____
_____
_____
_____

Past Life
_____
_____
_____
_____

Pack Totem
_____
_____
_____
_____

Possessions

Gear (Carried) _____

Equipment (Owned) _____

Sept

Name _____
Caern Location _____
Level _____ Type _____
Totem _____
Leader _____

Experience

TOTAL: [   ]

Gained From: _____
_____

TOTAL SPENT: _____
Spent On: _____
_____

GLASS WALKERS™

History

Prelude

_____
_____
_____
_____
_____
_____
_____
_____
_____
_____
_____

Glass Walker House Membership:_____

Description

Age_____
Hair _____
Eyes_____
Race_____
Nationality_____
Sex_____

	Height	Weight
Homid		
Glabro		
Crinos		
Hispo		
Lupus		

_____
_____
_____
_____
_____
_____

Battle Scars _____
_____
_____

Metis Deformity _____

Visuals

Pack Chart

Character Sketch